Gardeners
Favourite Nurseries

Gardeners' *Favourite* Nurseries

A guide to Britain's best nursery gardens

LESLIE GEDDES-BROWN

First published in 1999 by Columbine Press Limited,
42 Canonbury Square, London N1 2AW
E-mail: dovebooks@aol.com

ISBN 1 902563 01 8

Typeset by Pat Jacobs
Printed in Great Britain by Biddles Limited

Cover photograph by Andrew Lawson

Dedicated to
Anne Hinchliffe

CONTENTS

INTRODUCTION

INTRODUCTION

The idea for this book came to me during a weekend in the South West of England. It seemed the perfect place for a grand tour of nurseries — but how could I discover which were the most worthwhile for bog plants, my particular craze of the moment? Some helpful directory was what I needed. As no such book appeared to exist, it seemed a good idea to create one.

In the hope that other gardeners would agree with me, I started to write to all those who open their gardens through The National Gardens Scheme, whose famous yellow book lists over 3,500 gardens in England and Wales which open to the public for charity. I also wrote to the equivalent scheme in Scotland. Would these enthusiastic gardeners tell me their secrets: the places where they bought their plants?

The response was extraordinary: hundreds, from experts such as Christopher Lloyd and Beth Chatto along with dukes in castles and enthusiasts with postage stamp plots, wrote back, often with their good wishes for the book and the comment that such a publication was needed. It would not only help gardeners everywhere, they said, it would also help small and expert nurseries who prided themselves on the quality of their plants. I had always known that gardeners were generous people, keen to swop plants and experiences — this proved it.

Gardeners' Favourite Nurseries is the result. Here are over 400 nurseries which come with recommendations from the best gardeners of Britain. Along with a short paragraph about what each sells, I have listed the comments from the gardeners who recommended them. These may come without a name because some people preferred to stay anonymous when writing their views which are, of course, their own.

Each nursery which was recommended was asked to provide a catalogue (if one existed) and various details about its operation. Quite a few (especially seedsmen) exist by mail order only and do not welcome personal callers; others are exactly the opposite, finding mail order a nuisance. Virtually all who open to the public are keen to offer customers advice because they care for the future of their plants. These are places which welcome expert plantsmen and beginners alike — as long as visitors respect their working hours. You may get short shrift if you turn up when they're closed.

Both the gardeners and nurseries gave us advice about the book when they wrote: we should include maps showing the nurseries' location. So we did but, of course, these are to be used as a guide only. You'll need a proper road map to find places accurately. It was also suggested that we included a list of specialists and we have done this too. Nurseries asked us to implore customers not to send cash through the post. Please don't. We have listed other ways of paying from credit card to cheque.

Some nurseries were recommended over and over again. Here is our list of the top 10 (actually 14 because several tied.) Each has been awarded our golden bag of compost with its entry. Many others were also chosen again and again.

- Green Farm Plants of Surrey with 33 recommendations
- Beth Chatto Gardens of Essex with 27
- Cotswold Garden Flowers of Worcestershire with 25
- Bluebell Nursery of Derbyshire with 25
- Dingle Nurseries of Powys with 20
- Crûg Farm Plants of Gwynedd with 19
- The Place for Plants of Suffolk with 17
- Elizabeth MacGregor of Kirkcudbright with 16
- Stone House Cottage Nurseries of Worcestershire with 16
- PMA Plant Specialities of Somerset with 15
- Waterwheel Nursery of Gwent with 15
- Merriments Nursery and Gardens of East Sussex with 15
- Cally Gardens of Dumfries and Galloway with 15.
- Apple Court Nursery of Hampshire with 15

I hope you enjoy using this guide as much as I have enjoyed compiling it. Again and again, I had to be forceably torn from the catalogues so they could be properly filed. My grateful thanks to Pat Jacobs, herself a gardener, who has both methodically organised vast masses of data and type-set this book as well as keeping all the deadlines. Also, I would like to give a huge thank-you to all the gardeners who wrote to me with their recommendations: without them this book could not exist.

NURSERIES IN ENGLAND

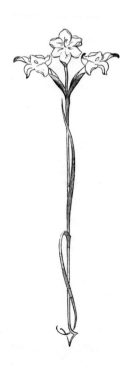

AVON

Blackmore and Langdon A nursery known to anyone who visits Chelsea Flower Show where they have been exhibiting since the show started. Their areas of interest are begonias, delphiniums and phlox. Their experience and interest is immense and they are very keen to pass this on. Ask their advice.

> **Blackmore and Langdon**, Pensford, nr Bristol, Avon BS39 4JL
> **Tel/fax:** 01275 332300
> **Opening hours:** 9.00–17.00 Monday to Friday, 10.00–16.00 Saturday and Sunday.
> **Callers welcome:** yes.
> **Catalogue:** free.
> **Payment:** cash, cheque, major credit/debit cards.
> **Mail order:** yes.
> **Post and packing:** £1.50–£4.50 per order.
> **Delivery:** within a month in season.
> **Availability:** limited supplies of some plants and at certain times of year.
> **Refund/replacement:** yes.
> **Special services:** gift vouchers.

GARDENERS' RECOMMENDATIONS: ✿ *"Have used them over the years for named delphiniums and their stock has been quite excellent."* Mrs Susan Beck. ✿ *"I went there and chatted with the head gardener – pleasant and helpful."* Mrs A Conville. ✿ *"Well organised – fields of delphiniums and phlox a beautiful sight."* Mr and Mrs J Southwell, Sherborne Garden. ✿ *"...excellent plants, service, delivery."* Mrs Craig.

See map page 390.

Chew Valley Trees A fine list of trees which can be chosen at various sizes and prices for the same variety (it's true that smaller plants eventually overtake the larger specimens). They are especially interested in native trees and have plants of the rare black poplar.

> **Chew Valley Trees**, Winford Road, Chew Magna, Bristol, Avon BS40 8QE

Tel: 01275 333752 **Fax:** 01275 333746

Opening hours: 8.00–17.00 Monday to Friday throughout the year, 9.00–16.00 Saturday from 25 September to 27 May.

Callers welcome: yes.

Catalogue: free.

Payment: cash or cheque, possibly credit cards in the future.

Mail order: yes.

Post and packing: normally at cost.

Delivery: agreed at time of order.

Availability: field grown plants by mail order or for collection from November to March. Container plants available for collection all year round.

Refund/replacement: yes.

Special services: woodland design and planting.

GARDENERS' RECOMMENDATIONS: ✿ *"Transformed over last few years. Native trees and hedge plants growing in fields. On Somerset County Council's list of approved suppliers. Used them when planting our spinney."* Mr and Mrs J Southwell, Sherborne Garden.

See map page 390.

Hannays of Bath Plant finders from this nursery have collected seed in the wild from Spain, Lesotho, South Africa and Nepal, while other seed comes from different renowned plant finders like Martyn Rix and John d'Arcy. The plants are therefore rare, choice and limited in quantity. Those recently collected (the catalogue marks each with the initials of the collector) include Alkanna tinctoria from Bulgaria, Iris sintenisii from oak woods on the borders of Bulgaria and Turkey and Rubus paniculatus found at 2,800 feet in Nepal.

Hannays of Bath, Sydney Wharf, Bathwick, Bath, Avon BA2 4ES

Tel: 01225 317577

Opening hours: 10.00–17.00.

Callers welcome: yes.

Catalogue: £1 plus 40p p&p.

Payment: cash or cheque.

Mail order: no.

Availability: supplies can be limited as the nursery is small.

Refund/replacement: yes.

GARDENERS' RECOMMENDATIONS: ✿ *"We find the nursery a pleasure to visit. The owners and/or staff are welcoming and a mine of information, and always seem to have something new and interesting."* Mr and Mrs P Falconer. ✿ *"What I class as a serious nursery ... more display beds were being planted on my last visit – so helpful to see the growth habit of plants released from the confines of pots."* Mrs Jessica Duncan. ✿ *"Always worth visiting, since you can nearly always find uncatalogued items in small quantities."* Mr Tim Longville. ✿ *"The plants are extremely well grown and not expensive compared with garden centres."* Lt Col and Mrs P Mequita. ✿ *"Sheila and Spencer Hannay travel the world in search of rare plant seed. I suspect Spencer Hannay aurally hypnotises visitors with his descriptions. I didn't need a New Zealand yew, but it is there in the garden waiting to be planted."* Diana Yakeley.

See map page 390.

C.S. Lockyer (Fuchsias)

As it says, fuchsia specialists. The tender shrub does come in an amazing range of colours and forms, from frilly doubles to long thin droopy ones such as the species boliviana with blood-red funnels in clusters. Fuchsias are an area with constant new introductions and this firm offers advice and demonstrations about them. The plants, considering their showiness, are extremely good value.

C S Lockyer, Lansbury, 70 Henfield Road, Coalpit Heath, Bristol, Avon BS36 2UZ

Tel/fax: 01454 772219

E-mail: lockyerfuchsias@compuserve.com

Website: http://www. ourworld.compuserve.com/homepages/lockyerfuchsias/

Opening hours: 10.00–13.00, 14.30–17.00 most days (ring first).

Visitors welcome: yes.

Catalogue: Send 4 first class stamps.

Payment: cash or cheque.

Mail order: yes. Minimum order 6 plants.

Post and packing: £4.35 for up to 8 plants.

Delivery: allow 28 days.

Availability: from spring to autumn. Supplies of certain plants may be limited.

Refund/replacement: by arrangement.
Special services: talks and demonstrations.

GARDENERS' RECOMMENDATIONS: *"Long, very inclusive list. A few illustrations which are helpful. Nice people."* Mrs A Conville.

See map page 390.

BEDFORDSHIRE

Bloms Bulbs   It's easy to be put off by this huge catalogue, profusely illustrated, because there's so much on offer. But take it slowly and wonderful things emerge — wild-haired alliums, old-fashioned laced pinks and a deep red calla. Many plants are new introductions and exclusive.

Bloms Bulbs Ltd, Primrose Nurseries, Melchbourne, Bedford, Bedfordshire MK44 1ZZ
Tel: 01234 709099 **Fax:** 01234 709799
Website: http://www.blomsbulbs.co.uk
Opening hours: 9.00–13.00, 14.00–17.00 Monday to Friday.
Visitors welcome: yes.
Catalogue: free.
Payment: cheque, postal order, Visa, Mastercard, bank Giro.
Mail order: yes.
Post and packing: £3.45 for orders up to £50.
Delivery: varies according to order and season.
Availability: limited supplies of certain items.
Refund/replacement: yes.
Special services: gift vouchers.

GARDENERS' RECOMMENDATIONS: *"Used over several years for lily bulbs and the quality has been excellent."* Mrs Susan Beck. *Also recommended by* The Earl Haig.

See map page 393.

BERKSHIRE

Foxgrove Plants Specialist in hardy and unusual plants, Louise Vockins grows everything herself. There are lots of interesting grasses, snowdrops which are developing into a craze, osteospermum and violas, which are doing likewise.

Foxgrove Plants, Foxgrove, Enborne,
nr Newbury, Berkshire RG14 6RE

Tel: 01635 40554

Opening hours: 10.00–17.00 Wednesday
to Sunday. Closed during August.

Visitors welcome: yes.

Catalogue: 50p.

Payment: cash, cheque, postal order.

Mail order: snowdrops only.

Post and packing: £3.

Delivery: allow 28 days.

Availability: supplies can be limited and
some plants are available only at certain
times of year.

Refund/replacement: yes.

GARDENERS' RECOMMENDATIONS: ✿ *"Come and see their stand of Galanthus at the RHS show in Westminster in February. A huge collection. Gold medal winner. Will send by post or bring to next show. Also auriculas and unusual alpines."* Mrs R M Rees.

See map page 390.

Henry Street Garden Centre There are fewer species and old-fashioned roses in this list than there are hybrid teas and patio roses. I prefer it the other way round but, if you are looking for weeping standards or multi-coloured effects, try this nursery.

Henry Street Garden Centre, Swallowfield Road, Arborfield,
Reading, Berkshire RG2 9JY

Tel: 0118 976 1223 **Fax:** 0118 976 1417

Opening hours: 9.00–17.30 Monday to Saturday, 10.00–16.00
Sunday.

Visitors welcome: yes.

Catalogue: free.

Payment: cash, cheque, postal order, major credit cards.

Mail order: yes. Minimum order 1 plant.

Post and packing: £3.50 for 1–3 roses, £5 for 4 and over. £8 for standards.

Delivery: 7–10 days for orders received between mid-October and end February

Availability: mail order from mid-October to end February.

Refund/replacement: plants guaranteed for 12 months.

Special services: pruning demonstrations in early March.

See map page 390.

Meadow House Plants
Harriet Jones opens her garden under the National Gardens Scheme and plants from the garden are often available at the nursery (some are not listed in the catalogue). It's a good list of interesting varieties and she also offers her skills in garden design.

Meadow House Plants, Meadow House, Ashford Hill, Newbury, Berkshire RG19 8BN

Tel/fax: 0118 981 6005

E-mail: harriet@rosejones.freeserve.co.uk

Opening hours: 10.00–12.30 Saturday from April to end July and by appointment.

Visitors welcome: yes.

Catalogue: send 2 first class stamps.

Payment: cash or cheque.

Mail order: no.

Availability: supplies are limited as the nursery is small and plants are only available from April to end October.

Refund/replacement: yes.

Special services: garden design.

GARDENERS' RECOMMENDATIONS: ❀ *"Beautifully kept small private garden with pond and multi-coloured ducks specialising in rockery, alpine and bog plants. Harriet and Tony Jones do all the propagating and many discriminating enthusiasts come and are made welcome."* Mr M J Jurgens.

See map page 390.

Penwood Nurseries "We do everything wrong — but it seems to be working," says the owner of this small but wide-ranging nursery which grows most of its own stock on five or so acres yet sells to personal callers who come from all over the country. They have 20 varieties of birch and oak, 25 of beech and lots of shrubs, herbaceous perennials, old-fashioned roses and alpines. Other plants, such as hybrid tea and floribunda roses they will buy in.

> **Penwood Nurseries**, The Drove, Penwood, Burghclere, nr Newbury, Berkshire RG20 9EW
>
> **Tel:** 01635 254366
>
> **Opening hours:** 9.00–17.00 Monday to Saturday, 10.00–16.00 Sunday.
>
> **Visitors welcome:** yes.
>
> **Catalogue:** none.
>
> **Payment:** cash or cheque.
>
> **Mail order:** no.
>
> **Availability:** limited, the nursery grows up to 5,000 plants in small quantities.
>
> **Refund/replacement:** yes, if satisfied the plant was well treated.

GARDENERS' RECOMMENDATIONS: ✹ *"Very well run mainly tree and shrub nursery with a good range."* ✹ *"Douglas Harris, founder of this family firm, has an unrivalled knowledge of trees, shrubs and herbaceous plants. This knowledge is matched by the scale and quality of specialist species (over 4,000 varieties) available from this well-run and friendly nursery."* Mr and Mrs D Male. ✹ *"Excellent for trees and shrubs and very good value. Owned by Douglas and Margaret Harris. He knows all there is to know about trees and shrubs and has many unusual rarities. We would never go anywhere else!"* Mr and Mrs G A Jones, Meadow House. ✹ *"Specialising in shrubs and ornamental trees their range and stock is unbeatable. They are exceptionally knowledgeable and most of their vast stock is home-produced. Always extremely helpful. Fine, small (private) garden. The Queen was seen there recently."* Mr M J Jurgens

See map page 390.

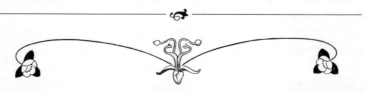

BUCKINGHAMSHIRE

Bernwode Plants A brilliant list which gardeners will refuse to lend. This is a favourite nursery with many top gardeners, who rave about the quality of its plants. The range is vast and well described. An essential catalogue.

> **Bernwode Plants**, Wooton Road, Ludgershall, Buckinghamshire HP18 9RB
>
> **Tel:** 01844 237415 **Fax:** 01844 238920
>
> **E-mail:** email@bernwodeplants.co.uk
>
> **Website:** http://www.bernwodeplants.co.uk
>
> **Opening hours:** 10.00–18.00 Tuesday to Sunday from 1 March to 31 October.
>
> **Visitors welcome:** yes.
>
> **Catalogue:** £2 in UK.
>
> **Payment:** cheque, Visa, Mastercard, Switch, Delta.
>
> **Mail order:** yes.
>
> **Post and packing:** by next-day courier £10 for up to 12 plants, then 35p for each subsequent plant. Apple trees £10 for up to 5, then £1 for each subsequent tree.
>
> **Delivery:** normally within 7–28 days.
>
> **Availability:** supplies can be limited in early spring.
>
> **Refund/replacement:** if justified.
>
> **Special services:** photo display. Database selection of plants for conditions or history. Secure on-line ordering.

GARDENERS' RECOMMENDATIONS: ❀ *"A wide selection of well-grown herbaceous plants, many unusual, and an excellent and scholarly catalogue."* Mr P D Boyd. ❀ *"For unusual variety and ability to grow to order."* Sir Neville and Lady Bowman-Shaw. ❀ *"... list is varied and different. Plants arrived in good condition and established well."* Mrs Danae Johnston. ❀ *"A lovely nursery to visit with a wonderful range of interesting plants and good information and advice available. However, sometimes there are disappointingly large gaps in the plants for sale areas."* Mr Frankie Warren.

See map page 393.

Bressingham Plant Centre A famous name in nurseries. The Blooms of Bressingham have been responsible for new types of planting in the past and continue to maintain a great interest in herbaceous perennials, of which they stock most interesting varieties. They are also a good general nursery and customers find the staff both knowledgeable and helpful.

Bressingham Plant Centre, Dorney Court, Dorney, nr Windsor SL4 6QP

Tel: 01628 669999 Fax: 01628 669693

Opening hours: 9.00–17.30.

Visitors welcome: yes.

Catalogue: none.

Payment: cash, cheque, major credit cards.

Mail order: no.

Availability: supplies can be limited and some plants are available only at certain times of year.

Refund/replacement: yes, 12-month guarantee.

Special services: border planning service, consultation service.

Also at: Elton Hall, Elton, Peterborough PE8 6SH. Tel: 01832 280058 and Bressingham, Diss Norfolk IP22 2AB. Tel: 01379 687464/688133

GARDENERS' RECOMMENDATIONS: ❀ *"A small plant centre in the grounds of Dorney Court. Wonderful herbaceous selection, herbs etc. Excellent staff."* Mr and Mrs B P Stein.

See map page 390.

Buckingham Nurseries and Garden Centre Very good value trees and hedging in a huge list. Ideal for those with large gardens wanting to put in hedges of yew, hornbeam, hawthorn, to create shelter belts and parkland, wildernesses and arboreta. The range goes from common British natives to fancy ornamental trees plus, at the centre itself, a larger choice of unusual plants.

Buckingham Nurseries and Garden Centre, Tingewick Road, Buckingham, Buckinghamshire MK18 4AE

Tel: 01280 813556 **Fax:** 01280 815491

E-mail: enquiries@bucknur.com

Opening hours: summer 8.30–18.00 Monday to Wednesday and Friday, 8.30 -20.00 on Thursday, 10.00–16.00 Sunday; winter 8.30–17.30 Monday to Friday, and occasionally until 20.00 on Thursday, 10.00–16.00 Sunday.

Visitors welcome: yes.

Catalogue: free.

Payment: cash, cheque, Visa, Mastercard, Switch.

Mail order: yes.

Post and packing: £4.95, or £9.95 for express delivery. Local delivery by quotation.

Delivery: depends on season, 2 weeks on average.

Availability: bare-rooted plants supplied between November and March. Pot grown usually available all year round.

Refund/replacement: yes, if returned properly packed within 3 days of receipt.

Special services: advisory service.

GARDENERS' RECOMMENDATIONS: ❀ *"Good for background planting, especially bare-rooted. Good fruit trees."* Mr and Mrs N R Wilson. ❀ *"Recently been refurbished but still small enough to be friendly."* Mrs Liz Whitehall.

See map page 393.

_____

Lower Icknield Farm Nurseries   Holders of the national collection of argyranthemum, which runs to over 50 and are for sale by mail order. Other plants, such as fuchsia, begonias, bedding plants and winter flowering pot plants, are sold direct from the nursery.

Lower Icknield Farm Nurseries, Lower Icknield Way, Great Kimble, Aylesbury, Buckinghamshire HP17 9TX

Tel: 01844 343436, mobile: (9.00–17.30) 0780 397 9993

Opening hours: 9.00–17.30 daily. Closed from Christmas to New Year.

Visitors welcome: definitely.

Catalogue: send 3 first class stamps.

Payment: cheque or postal order.

Mail order: argyranthemums only. Minimum order 10 plants.

Post and packing: included.

Delivery: 10 to 14 days.

Availability: argyranthemums from February to early May.

Refund/replacement: yes.

GARDENERS' RECOMMENDATIONS: *"Patio plants, marguerites and general. Excellent quality."*

See map page 390.

Pasture Farm Plants

Pasture Farm Plants Cleverly, this nursery arranges its plants in colours so you can compare the shades. The small team like unusual perennials, cottage garden plants and white garden plants, all of which are grown in peat-free compost. The varieties are constantly changing.

> **Pasture Farm Plants,** Thame Road, Longwick, nr Princes Risborough, Buckinghamshire HP27 9AX
> **Tel:** 01844 343651
> **Opening hours:** 9.00–18.00 Thursday to Sunday from end March to end October.
> **Visitors welcome:** yes.
> **Catalogue:** none.
> **Payment:** cash or cheque.
> **Mail order:** no.
> **Availability:** the selection of plants is constantly changing.
> **Refund/replacement:** yes.
> **Special services:** farmhouse garden open to customers.

GARDENERS' RECOMMENDATIONS: *"Run by wives of farmers. Excellent quality, modest prices, knowledgeable. Specialises in perennials."* *"Really helpful and knowledgeable staff and most of plants on offer are home grown rather than mass-produced imports."* Mr and Mrs R H Bradbury.

See map page 390.

Potash Nursery Too busy growing plants, says Dennis Richards (in partnership with Jenny Rogers) to get round to a brochure and that's the way it should be. "We sell hardy perennial plants that are specifically selected to have a stunning impact in the garden as we are a design-based nursery." Well worth a visit since design-led planting is now all the rage.

Potash Nursery, Drayton Parslow, Milton Keynes, Buckinghamshire MK17 0JE

Tel: 01296 720578 **Fax:** 01296 720578

Opening hours: 8.00–18.30 Friday to Sunday from April to October.

Visitors welcome: yes.

Catalogue: none.

Payment: cash or cheque.

Mail order: no.

Delivery: plants can be delivered immediately on request subject to availability.

Availability: if plants are not in stock the nursery undertakes to find and supply them.

Refund/replacement: yes.

Special services: professional garden designer will help create complete plantings or schemes.

GARDENERS' RECOMMENDATIONS: ✿ *"Perennials – good sizes."* Dr and Mrs Beric Wright. ✿ *"Really interesting plants for indoor and out. Rare colours of verbascum, excellent pelargoniums. Knowledgeable, helpful and not expensive."* Mr and Mrs H Morley-Fletcher.

See map page 393.

Tendercare This is a big nursery — 15 acres of it — with plants arranged according to size and their growth needs so, if they are under shade in the nursery, that's what they'd like in the garden. The owners are also aware that so much to see may be mind-boggling. Therefore buyers can leave details of what they are trying to achieve and the nursery will send suggestions and a quotation as a basis for a second visit. You can even book an appointment with an expert to guide you round. As the range is huge, from large trees and screening conifers to ferns and grasses, this sounds an excellent basis for those starting a garden. But hardened gardeners will find plenty here too.

Tendercare, Southlands Road, Denham, nr Uxbridge UB9 4HD

Tel: 01895 835544 **Fax:** 01895 835036

E-mail: tendercare@btinternet.com

Opening hours: 8.00–17.00 Monday to Friday, 10.00–16.00 Saturday.

Visitors welcome: yes. Customers requiring advice should ring in advance to make an appointment.

Catalogue: free.

Payment: cash, cheque, all credit/debit cards.

Mail order: no.

Delivery: size of stock dictates that most orders are delivered. Minimum order for free delivery is £500.

Availability: generally all year round, but certain items are seasonal.

Refund/replacement: yes, on stock planted by the Tendercare's planting service.

Special services: planting service.

GARDENERS' RECOMMENDATIONS: *"Very good quality plants."* Maria Carmela, Viscountess Hambleden.

See map page 392.

CAMBRIDGESHIRE

Cambridge Garden Plants Most of the herbaceous perennials, climbers, alpines and herbs sold here are grown on the site. There are plenty of alliums, campanula, euphorbia and pulmonaria — a current favourite of mine. A special service is "lots of gardening advice."

Cambridge Garden Plants, The Lodge, Clayhithe Road, Horningsea, Cambridgeshire CB5 9JD

Tel: 01223 861370

Opening hours: 11.00–17.30 Thursday to Sunday from mid-March to end October.

Visitors welcome: yes.

Catalogue: 80p.

Payment: cash or cheque.

Mail order: no.

Availability: seasonal.

Refund/replacement: yes.

See map page 393.

Honeysome Aquatic Nursery Specialists in plants for ponds, bogs and damp shady areas with a good list of water lilies, free-floating plants and those for the water margins. They also have the essential oxygenating plants to keep water clear of algae and even, for under £3 a dozen, "mixed snails."

> **Honeysome Aquatic Nursery**, The Row, Sutton, nr Ely, Cambridgeshire CB6 2PF
> **Tel:** 01353 778889
> **Opening hours:** by appointment only.
> **Visitors welcome:** yes, by prior appointment.
> **Catalogue:** send 2 first class stamps.
> **Payment:** cheque or postal order.
> **Mail order:** yes.
> **Post and packing:** £5.20 for orders up to £15, £6.50 for orders from £15 to £35, £8.30 thereafter.
> **Delivery:** within 14 days in season.
> **Availability:** plants are despatched from May to early October.
> **Refund/replacement:** yes, if damaged in transit and returned with 2 days of receipt.

GARDENERS' RECOMMENDATIONS: ❀ *"Small but healthy plants very reasonably priced and I have never had any plant unavailable. Friendly and helpful on the phone."* Mr Frankie Warren.

See map page 393.

Monksilver Nursery Good on bulbs and especially snowdrops, for which they have an annual open day; they also like grasses and sedges, wild collected plants, ferns and sedums. The list, however, is wider than this and includes plants so rare they have to be sold by auction.

> **Monksilver Nursery**, Oakington Road, Cottenham, Cambridge, CB4 8TW
> **Tel:** 01954 251555 **Fax:** 01223 502887
> **E-mail:** monksilver@dial.pipex.com
> **Website:** http://www.dialspace.dial.pipex.com/monksilver/
> **Opening hours:** 10.00–16.00 Friday and Saturday from March to June and in October.
> **Visitors welcome:** yes, during opening hours.
> **Catalogue:** send 8 first class stamps.

Payment: cash, cheque, postal order.

Mail order: yes.

Post and packing: £2 per plant for under 5 plants, otherwise £1 per plant.

Delivery: mail order in autumn only.

Availability: rarities are always in limited supply.

Refund/replacement: yes, in accordance with nursery's terms.

Special services: open day mid-September.

GARDENERS' RECOMMENDATIONS: ❀ *"… list is varied and different. Plants arrived in good condition and established well.."* Mrs Danae Johnston. ❀ *"Small garden attached, good range of plants."* Mrs Jane Alhusen. ❀ *"Untidy but Alan Leslie and Joe Sharman have a good knowledge of plants."* Mr Timothy Clark. ❀ *"Was rather disorganised but has come on a lot recently."*

See map page 393.

River Lane Nursery

River Lane Nursery   This is a family-run nursery which prides itself on growing most of what it sells and for making sure that, when bare-rooted plants are bought, the specimens will be taken up no more than a day beforehand. The trees are excellent, there is also a good list of fruit trees and soft fruit, hedging, conifers and smaller items like bulbs and bedding plants.

River Lane Nursery, River Lane, Brampton, Huntingdon, Cambridgeshire PE18 8PU

Tel: 01480 434451   **Fax:** 01480 386762

Opening hours: 9.00–12.30, 14.00–17.00 Monday to Saturday, 10.00–12.30, 14.00–17.00 Sunday.

Visitors welcome: yes.

Catalogue: free.

Payment: cash or cheque.

Mail order: no.

Delivery: only locally.

Availability: large quanity of stock. Bare-root plants October to March only.

Refund/replacement: discretionary.

GARDENERS' RECOMMENDATIONS: ❀ *"Very good trees, bare-rooted and container grown. Also shrubs: fuchsias and clematis."* Mr and Mrs

David Cox. *"Family run. Grow most of what they sell themselves. If you order you know your tree or shrub will be dug the day before, or the very day you want to plant it."* Mr and Mrs P Rushton.

See map page 393.

CHESHIRE

Arley Hall Nursery   Specialises mostly in hardy herbaceous perennials with a tasty list including many pulmonarias, hemerocallis, geraniums and, in the tender perennial area, pelargoniums. The nursery is next door to the gardens of Arley Hall and sells many plants found there.

> **Arley Hall Nursery,** Northwich, Cheshire CW9 6NA
> **Tel:** 01565 777479 **Fax:** 01565 777465
> **Opening hours:** 11.00–17.30 Tuesday to Sunday and bank holiday Mondays from Easter to end September.
> **Visitors welcome:** yes.
> **Catalogue:** £1 or 4 first class stamps.
> **Payment:** cash or cheque.
> **Mail order:** no.
> **Availability:** supplies can be limited and some plants are available only at certain times of year.
> **Refund/replacement:** yes.
> **Special services:** garden advice and design.

GARDENERS' RECOMMENDATIONS: *Arley Hall Nursery is relatively new and varies in quality as to when you go but it is attached to the most glorious gardens and quite often you get things you see growing in the garden. Run by the owners of the Hall. Small, helpful and friendly."* Mr and Mrs J Major.

See map page 395.

Bellhouse Nursery

Bellhouse Nursery   Doreen and Elaine (no surnames for this firm) say their speciality is friendly, happy service. They actually like chatting with customers about the unusual shrubs and herbaceous plants they sell. The list is comprehensive in its area and the firm will pack up an order and take it to the shows it visits.

> **Bellhouse Nursery**, Bellhouse Lane, Moore, nr Warrington, Cheshire WA4 6TR
>
> **Tel:** 01925 740874   **Fax:** 01925 740672
>
> **Opening hours:** 10.00–17.00 Wednesday to Monday from March to October. Closed on Tuesdays and from November to February.
>
> **Visitors welcome:** yes.
>
> **Catalogue:** £1 plus A5 sae.
>
> **Payment:** cash or cheque.
>
> **Mail order:** yes, in spring and autumn.
>
> **Post and packing:** at cost.
>
> **Delivery:** within about a week.
>
> **Availability:** depends on plants ordered.
>
> **Refund/replacement:** yes.

GARDENERS' RECOMMENDATIONS: ✿ *"The ladies at Bellhouse Nursery, Elaine and Doreen are always very helpful and obliging and we find them to be a very knowledgeable duo. They tend to specialise in unusual shrubs and herbaceous perennials and always have an excellent selection."* Mr Richard Horton.

See map page 395.

Caddick's Clematis Nursery

Caddick's Clematis Nursery   A good list of these very fashionable plants, including both the large-flowered and upcoming viticellas. The catalogue also tries to de-mystify the question of when to prune, how to grow and what to do about clematis wilt. If in doubt, you can phone for advice.

> **Caddick's Clematis Nursery**, Lymm Road, Thelwall, Warrington, Cheshire WA13 0UF
>
> **Tel:** 01925 757196
>
> **Opening hours:** 10.00–17.00 Tuesday to Sunday from 1 February to 31 October and on bank holiday Mondays.
>
> **Visitors welcome:** yes.

Catalogue: £1.20.
Payment: cash, cheque, Visa, Mastercard, Switch.
Mail order: yes. Minimum order 2 plants.
Post and packing: from £5.95 for 2 plants.
Delivery: depends on season.
Availability: mail order available from March to May and from September to November.
Refund/replacement: each case judged individually.

GARDENERS' RECOMMENDATIONS: *"Very good plants, service, delivery."* Mrs Craig. *"Good plants well packed. Wide range. Helpful people. Sometimes disappoint by not having quite a few of what you order in stock."* Mr Frankie Warren.

See map page 395.

The Firs Nursery   Not conifers, actually, but hardy perennials of which many are rare or difficult and thus in short supply. The nursery will plan borders and give advice. The selection is not large but interesting.

The Firs Nursery, Chelford Road, Henbury, Macclesfield, Cheshire SK10 3LH
Tel: 01625 426422
Opening hours: 10.00–17.00 Monday, Tuesday, Friday and Saturday, 10.00–19.00 Thursday from March to September.
Visitors welcome: certainly.
Catalogue: send 2 first class stamps.
Payment: cash or cheque.
Mail order: no.
Availability: many plants are rare or unusual and are only produced in limited quantities.
Refund/replacement: yes.
Special services: illustrated lectures. Special opening for horticultural group visits.

GARDENERS' RECOMMENDATIONS: *"Small nursery personally operated. Interesting range of plants – friendly, helpful advice."*

See map page 395.

Fryer's Roses The firm, obviously, are rose specialists but, within that area, concentrate on what are the best and most up-to-date varieties for the garden. They grow over 250 different kinds, especially floribundas and hybrid teas.

> **Fryer's Nurseries Ltd**, Knutsford, Cheshire WA16 0SX
>
> **Tel:** 01565 755455 **Fax:** 01565 653755
>
> **E-mail:** rosesales@fryers-roses.co.uk
>
> **Website:** http://www.fryers-roses.co.uk
>
> **Opening hours:** 9.00–17.30 Monday to Saturday, 10.30–16.30 Sunday.
>
> **Visitors welcome:** yes.
>
> **Catalogue:** free.
>
> **Payment:** cheque, Visa, Mastercard, Access, Switch, Delta.
>
> **Mail order:** yes.
>
> **Post and packing:** £3.95.
>
> **Delivery:** orders received in summer and autumn despatched in rotation during November and early December. Orders received during winter and spring are despatched within a few days, weather permitting.
>
> **Availability:** bare-rooted plants available from October to April. Container roses can be collected from the nursery almost all year round.
>
> **Refund/replacement:** yes.
>
> **Special services:** restaurant.

GARDENERS' RECOMMENDATIONS: ❀ *Recommended by* Mr Clive Richards.

See map page 395.

Lodge Lane Nursery Excellent list of cottage garden plants both in breadth and depth of varieties. The nursery offers a chance to wander round a garden to get ideas, a wild flower meadow recalling the days when fields were colourful and an ancient woodland alive with bird song. A treat for gardeners and anyone who loves the countryside.

> **Lodge Lane Nursery and Gardens**, Bluebell Cottage, Lodge Lane, Dutton, nr Warrington, Cheshire WA4 4HP
>
> **Tel/fax:** 01928 713718
>
> **Opening hours:** nursery 10.00–17.00 Wednesday to Sunday and bank holidays from mid-March to early October. Gardens open from May to mid-September.

Visitors welcome: yes.

Catalogue: send 3 first class stamps.

Payment: cash or cheque.

Mail order: no.

Availability: not all plants are available at any one time. Propagation and growing on is carried out throughout the growing season. Some plants are only available in small quantities.

Refund/replacement: by arrangement.

GARDENERS' RECOMMENDATIONS: *"Very good plants, service, delivery."* Mrs Craig. ⊛ *"Relatively new, good range of herbaceous, all grown on the nursery. Realistic prices. Extremely nice, friendly and knowledgeable owners. Attached garden full of interest and well maintained."* Mr and Mrs M R Everett.

See map page 395.

F Morrey & Son This is a good general nursery with lists for roses, herbaceous plants and good climbers — I spotted some plants quite hard to find like Clematis viticella Huldine and Lady Betty Balfour. Established for a century, it has 90 acres in production.

F Morrey & Son, Forest Road Nursery, Kelsall, Tarporley, Cheshire CW6 0SW

Tel: 01829 751342 **Fax:** 01829 752449

Opening hours: 8.30–17.00.

Visitors welcome: yes.

Catalogue: 20p.

Payment: cash, cheque, Visa, Mastercard, Switch, Delta.

Mail order: no.

Delivery: depends on location.

Availability: bare-rooted plants between October and March.

Refund/replacement: replacement.

Special services: free planning service. "Time, advice and a willingness to solve problems of the gardening sort."

GARDENERS' RECOMMENDATIONS: ⊛ *"An excellent nursery specialising in containerised/bare-rooted trees and shrubs, rhododendron and azalea. Good range. Very friendly, helpful and knowledgeable staff and enthusiastic owner. Large percentage of stock home-grown."* ⊛ *"A genuine old-established family firm growing (in particular) excellent trees and shrubs. A pleasant atmosphere and helpful people." "Good plants, good selection, good value, helpful."* The Hon Christopher McLaren.

See map page 395.

Ness Botanic Gardens

Founded in 1898 by a Liverpool cotton broker, there are now have 62 acres of gardens, greenhouses and experimental areas. They sell plants they propagate from the gardens especially primula, meconopsis, Pieris formosa var forrestii, rhododendron, bamboos and general trees, shrubs etc.

Ness Gardens, University of Liverpool Botanic Gardens, Ness, Neston, South Wirral, Cheshire L64 4AY

Tel: 0151 353 0123 **Fax:** 0151 353 1004

Website: http://www.merseyworldcom/nessgardens/

Opening hours: 9.30–17.00 March to October, 9.30–16.00 November to February.

Visitors welcome: yes.

Catalogue: none.

Payment: cash, cheque, Visa.

Mail order: no.

Availability: supplies can be limited and some plants are available only at certain times of year.

Refund/replacement: yes.

GARDENERS' RECOMMENDATIONS: *"Smallish garden centre, attached to Ness Gardens, but many connoisseur plants available at extremely affordable prices, plus good specimens of a range of good garden plants."* Mr and Mrs E W Dyer.

See map page 395.

Okells Nurseries

This is a plant centre rather than a nursery with, they say, everything from bedding plants to topiary, trees and shrubs. There are also stoneware and terracotta pots.

Okells Nurseries, Duddon Heath, Tarporley, Cheshire CW6 0EP

Tel: 01829 741512 **Fax:** 01829 741587

Opening hours: 9.00–17.00 daily.

Visitors welcome: yes.

Catalogue: free.

Payment: cheque, major credit cards.

Mail order: no.

Availability: all year round.

Refund/replacement: yes.

GARDENERS' RECOMMENDATIONS: *"Tim and Gary Okell started this nursery …it has been a huge success and specialises in heathers."*

See map page 395.

Stonyford Cottage Nursery
A nice perennial list full of plants which are currently highly-sought after — especially salvias but also euphorbias, primulas and pulmonarias.

Stonyford Cottage Nursery, Stonyford Lane, Cuddington, Northwich, Cheshire CW8 2FT

Tel: 01606 888128 **Fax:** 01606 888128

E-mail: sales@stonyford.u-net.com

Opening hours: 10.00–17.30 Tuesday to Sunday and bank holiday Mondays.

Visitors welcome: yes.

Catalogue: send 4 first class stamps.

Payment: cash or cheque.

Mail order: no.

Availability: supplies can be limited.

Refund/replacement: yes.

Special services: garden planning ideas.

GARDENERS' RECOMMENDATIONS:

 "Not sure I should let you in on this one! I'd like to keep it for myself. This is the place I go when I want something rare and special for my own garden. A specialist nursery set amongst its own magnificent NGS garden. I have such rarities as a climbing aconitum, a bi-coloured aconitum and many rare herbaceous plants which were

obtained from Stonyford and now grow happily in my own cottage garden. Extremely knowledgeable owner always on hand to answer questions, discuss new varieties etc." Mrs D Griffiths.

See map page 395.

See also: Dunge Valley Gardens, page 353.

CLEVELAND

Fir Trees Pelargonium Nursery A helpful catalogue from the award-winning nursery which sells luscious pelargoniums, including their own Fir Trees Roseberry Topping and many bred by the late Don Storey.

Fir Trees Pelargonium Nursery, Stokesley, Middlesborough, Cleveland TS9 5LD
Tel/fax: 01642 713066
E-mail: firtre@globalnet.co.uk
Website: http://www.users.globalnet.co.uk/~firtre
Opening hours: 10.00–16.00 daily (weekends by appointment from 1 October to 15 March).
Visitors welcome: yes.
Catalogue: £1 or 4 first class stamps.
Payment: cheque, postal order, Visa, Mastercard, Access.
Mail order: yes.
Post and packing: £6 for up to 5 plants, £3 for 6–14, free thereafter, by next-day carrier.
Delivery: allow up to 6 weeks at peak times, but can be sent immediately if in stock.
Availability: mail order service all year round, however supplies of certain varieties can be limited.
Refund/replacement: if plants are damaged in transit they will be replaced.

GARDENERS' RECOMMENDATIONS: ✪ *"We have enjoyed lovely plants from this nursery."* Susan Bennett and Earl Hyde. ✪ *"They operate a* *very efficient mail order system, telephoning beforehand and packing really well."*

See map page 396.

Town Farm Nursery Plants which are ideal for small gardens are sold here, especially unusual alpines and perennials. The nursery owners will give informal talks about the plants.

Town Farm Nursery, Whitton Village, Stockton on Tees, Cleveland TS21 1LQ

Tel: 01740 631079

Opening hours: 10.00–18.00 Friday to Monday.

Visitors welcome: yes.

Payment: cash or cheque.

Mail order: yes.

Post and packing: £5 plus 10% of order value.

Delivery: 2 weeks, weather permitting.

Availability: supplies can be limited and some plants are available only at certain times of year.

Refund/replacement: yes.

Special services: informal talks with slides in winter.

Note: closing following summer season 2000. The nursery will be relocating and re-opening in 2001.

GARDENERS' RECOMMENDATIONS: ❀ *"Mr Baker's heart is in his alpines but he also has a good range of unusual and interesting herbaceous plants and shrubs. The nursery is in the middle of Mr and Mrs B's private garden, which delightfully demonstrates the beauties of many of the plants they offer. The blessed reverse of the pushy salesman, Mr Baker waits for you to ask – but if you do ask, he is a mine of information and (equally blessed) truthfulness about any of his plants' strengths and weaknesses."* Mr Tim Longville.
❀ *"Outstanding plantsman with a stunning collection of plants both in the garden and for sale. Many are outstanding value. A must for any nursery guide."* Austin Lynch.

See map page 396.

CORNWALL

Bodmin Plant and Herb Nursery The nursery grows about 80 per cent of everything it sells and specialises in herbs, herbaceous perennials and plants for ponds, bogs and damp areas. It has a good list of hardy geraniums and lots of herbs including woad, flax and dyer's chamomile as well as more usual ones. The nursery prides itself on the quality of its plants.

> **Bodmin Plant and Herb Nursery**, Laveddon Mill, Bodmin, Cornwall PL30 5JU
>
> **Tel:** 01208 72837 **Fax:** 01208 76491
>
> **Opening hours:** 9.00–17.00 in winter (GMT), 9.00–18.00 in summer (BST).
>
> **Visitors welcome:** yes.
>
> **Catalogue:** herb and hardy geranium list free to callers, or send 2 first class stamps.
>
> **Payment:** cash, cheque, Visa, Mastercard, Switch, Delta.
>
> **Mail order:** no.
>
> **Availability:** supplies are not usually limited but ring before travelling if a particular plant is required.
>
> **Refund/replacement:** yes.

GARDENERS' RECOMMENDATIONS: ✾ *"A newly re-opened nursery specialising in herb cultivation but stocking an increasingly varied selection of shrubs, perennials, trees and bulbs. Owners well qualified in horticulture and botany and on hand to advise. No garden to visit."* Dr and Mrs M S Stead.

See map page 388.

Bosvigo Plants The famous plantsman's garden has turned to selling what it propagates — mostly rare and unusual herbaceous perennials. They will advise on planting and suggest ideas for difficult areas.

> **Bosvigo Plants**, Bosvigo House, Bosvigo Lane, Truro, Cornwall TR1 3NH
>
> **Tel/fax:** 01872 275774

Opening hours: 11.00–18.00 Thursday to Saturday from March to end September.

Visitors welcome: yes.

Catalogue: send 4 second class stamps.

Payment: cash or cheque.

Mail order: no.

Availability: plants can sell out. Certain items are not ready until late in the year.

Refund/replacement: yes.

GARDENERS' RECOMMENDATIONS: ✤ *"Very wide range of unusual perennials, most of which can be seen in their full glory in Wendy Perry's garden. She is usually on hand to advise on suitable positions and associations. My personal favourite (I spend a lot of money here!)"* Dr and Mrs M S Stead. ✤ *"Always interesting new plants. Well grown and potted. Sensible helpful catalogue."* Mrs A Conville. ✤ *"… list is varied and different. Plants arrived in good condition and established well. Excellent garden."* Mrs Danae Johnston. ✤ *"Every time I go something new catches the eye."* Miss J Hall. ✤*Also recommended by* Mr John Carter, Rowden Gardens.

See map page 388.

Jennifer Bousfield at Bregover Plants

Jennifer's nursery and cottage garden are high up on the edge of Bodmin Moor in Cornwall where the rainfall is high, frost is common and there's very little sun in winter. Summer is very hot. If your conditions are similar, then her choice of plants will also suit your garden. She sells hardy plants for the cottage garden, for woodland, waterside and wild gardens along with others ideal for the herbaceous border. Many are either unusual or older varieties. You can see plants growing in her own garden and she can offer tons of advice on how to deal with them.

Jennifer Bousfield at Bregover Plants, Middlewood, nr Launceston, Cornwall PL15 7NN

Tel: 01566 782661

Opening hours: 11.00–17.00 Wednesday to Friday from mid-March to mid-October. Weekends and winter months by appointment.

Visitors welcome: yes. Advisable to telephone first if specific plants required.

Catalogue: send 2 first class stamps.

Payment: cash or cheque.

Mail order: yes, for most items.

Post and packing: £2.50 plus 30p per plant.

Delivery: plants despatched from October to December and February to early April, normally within 3 weeks of receiving payment, weather permitting.

Availability: size of nursery restricts stock and certain plants are best sent in spring.

Refund/replacement: no liability accepted for winter losses or for plants, such as auriculas, requiring specialist care.

Special services: most plants can be seen growing in the cottage garden.

GARDENERS' RECOMMENDATIONS: ✤ *"Hardy plants for the herbaceous border, cottage garden, woodland, waterside and wild garden. A delightfully informal garden particularly good for moisture loving plants beside streams."* Dr and Mrs M S Stead. ✤*Also recommended by* Mr John Carter, Rowden Gardens.

See map page 388.

Burncoose Nurseries Anyone who has been to Chelsea will recognise the name of the nursery which has a splendid site in the marquee. Recently it won a silver gilt medal for its trees and shrubs and a silver for hydrangeas. It won 21 further awards — most of them golds — at other shows including one for botanic interest at a show in Rome. It has a good general list but, being in Cornwall, is able to offer slightly tender plants too. The nursery has a 30-acre woodland garden attached.

Burncoose Nurseries, Gwennap, Redruth, Cornwall TR16 6BJ

Tel: 01209 861112/860316 **Fax:** 01209 860011

E-mail: burncoose@eclipse.co.uk

Website: http://www.eclipse.co.uk/burncoose

Opening hours: 8.30–17.00 Monday to Saturday. 11.00–17.00 Sunday.

Visitors welcome: yes.

Catalogue: £1.50.

Payment: cheque, Visa, Access, Switch.

Mail order: yes.

Post and packing: from £7.50 for orders under £20 to £26 for orders over £100. 15% for orders over £200.

Delivery: allow 3-5 weeks.

Availability: all year round, with a few exceptions.

Refund/replacement: yes, in accordance with normal terms of business if reasonable cause for complaint.

Special services: orders can be collected from shows.

GARDENERS' RECOMMENDATIONS: ✾ *"Wonderful range of exotic plants – encourages us to 'feel the boundaries' of what we can grow in the Midlands."* Mr and Mrs E W Dyer. ✾ *"Burncoose are excellent for trees and shrubs, including tender ones. They always win gold medals at the RHS shows."* Ernst and Janet Sondheimer. ✾ *"Nice big plants well grown. Not always very well packed. Rather expensive especially the postage. Pleasant nursery and gardens to visit."* ✾ *"Excellent service with a wide range of excellent plants."* R E Dee, Head Gardener, Heligan Gardens.

See map page 388.

Cross Common Nursery A touch of the exotics here: a range of palms, agaves, tree ferns, osteospermums and other startling plants to give a sub-tropical touch to your garden. The nursery specialises in plants which cope with exposed gardens by the sea.

Cross Common Nursery, The Lizard, Helston, Cornwall TR12 7PD

Tel/fax: 01326 290722

Opening hours: 9.30–17.30 daily from Easter to 1 September, 9.30–17.00 Monday to Saturday during September and October. By appointment at other times.

Visitors welcome: yes.

Catalogue: send 3 second class stamps.

Payment: cheque.

Mail order: yes (rooted cuttings).

Post and packing: from £1.50 by post. From £13.99 by 24-hour carrier.

Delivery: customers advised on receipt of order.

Availability: supplies can be limited and some plants are available only at certain times of year.

Refund/replacement: yes, if notified within 7 days of receipt.

GARDENERS' RECOMMENDATIONS: ✤ *"Small but offers an outstanding variety of shrubs etc. Mr Triggs' knowledge is wide and his choice of plants unusual. He appears to be able to supply virtually any plant you ask for, however rare. I save my purchasing until I visit the Lizard twice a year! His prices are very reasonable."* Mr and Mrs P Curtis.

See map page 388.

The Duchy of Cornwall Nurseries

With 16 acres of grounds surrounded by its own woodland, the nursery has the widest range of hardy garden plants in the county — some 4,000 varieties. As well as that, the firm is keen to maintain a diverse wildlife and offers a woodland walk to a natural pond. Prince Charles keeps well in touch with the nursery and can be seen, surrounded by its staff, in the helpful catalogue.

> **Duchy of Cornwall Nurseries**, Cott Road, Lostwithiel, Cornwall PL22 0HW
>
> **Tel:** 01208 872668 **Fax:** 01208 872835
>
> **E-mail:** nursery@duchyofcornwall.gov.uk
>
> **Opening hours:** 9.00–17.00 Monday to Saturday, 10.00–17.00 Sunday.
>
> **Visitors welcome:** yes.
>
> **Catalogue:** £1.50.
>
> **Payment:** cash, cheque, major credit/debit cards.
>
> **Mail order:** yes.
>
> **Post and packing:** £9 for up to 10 plants, by quotation thereafter.
>
> **Delivery:** 2 weeks on average.
>
> **Availability:** supplies can be limited and some plants are available only at certain times of year.
>
> **Refund/replacement:** yes.

GARDENERS' RECOMMENDATIONS: ✤ *"Well rooted plants, not forced to bloom, a wide and interesting selection. Helpful and knowledgeable staff. I have never lost a plant which came from the Duchy of Cornwall Nursery."* ✤ *"Tucked away far from anywhere, it seems – a long journey for us North Devonians, and a trailer would be needed if on holiday! First established in the 70s for supplying the Duchy's woodlands, it is a large site surrounded by woodlands with a vast range* *of very good plants."* Mrs Jessica Duncan. *Also recommended by:* Mr and Mrs R Hubbard, Hill House Nursery *and* Dr Smart, Marwood Hill Nursery.

See map page 388.

Fir Tree Farm Nursery

Fir Tree Farm Nursery No, the nursery doesn't specialise in firs but in perennials and clematis. The catalogue is absolutely packed with ideas and there are masses of anemones, irises, poppies and salvias. Very addictive.

Fir Tree Farm Nursery, Tresahor, Constantine, Falmouth, Cornwall TR11 5PL

Tel/fax: 01326 340593 (ring first for fax)

E-mail: ftfnur@aol.com

Website: http://www.members.aol.com/ftfnur

Opening hours: 10.00–17.00 Thursday to Sunday from 1 March to 30 September.

Visitors welcome: yes.

Catalogue: send 6 first class stamps.

Payment: cash, cheque, major credit cards.

Mail order: yes. Minimum order £25.

Post and packing: £5 by parcel post, £15 by carrier.

Delivery: allow 4 weeks.

Availability: some plants are in limited supply.

Refund/replacement: yes, in case of reasonable complaint.

Special services: free landscaping and planting advice.

GARDENERS' RECOMMENDATIONS: *"A very wide selection of unusual perennials and the biggest variety of clematis available in the county, over 80 different types. Well worth a detour."*

See map page 388.

Lower Kenneggy Nurseries

Lower Kenneggy Nurseries Sited near Penzance, the nursery has plenty of plants which thrive on the coast. They have a good range from Australia and Tasmania, New Zealand, South Africa and South America as well as stocking Mediterranean species.

Lower Kenneggy Nurseries, Rosudgeon, Penzance, Cornwall
TR20 9AR

Tel: 01736 762959

Opening hours: 10.00–17.00 daily except Mondays from April to September.

Visitors welcome: yes.

Catalogue: none.

Payment: cash or cheque.

Mail order: no.

Availability: range of plants is continually changing.

Refund/replacement: yes.

GARDENERS' RECOMMENDATIONS: ✼ *"This is a small seaside nursery specialising in interesting and unusual plants for mild and windy coastal gardens. Friendly and knowledgeable owner always willing to give advice. A good eye for new and usable plants."*

See map page 388.

Trevena Cross Garden Centre   Specialities here are plants from the southern hemisphere including banksia, hakeas, leucadendrons, proteas and telopeas — many are happy planted by the coast but few like it cold. Otherwise the nursery has a good aquatic centre and the only sub-tropical tearooms in the south-west. Tropical looking plants are very much the rage and this nursery can offer excellent plants — and advice.

Trevena Cross Garden Centre, Breage, Helston, Cornwall
TR13 9PS

Tel: 01736 763880 **Fax:** 01736 762828

Opening hours: 9.00–17.00 Monday to Saturday, 10.30–16.30 Sunday.

Visitors welcome: yes.

Catalogue: free (send A5 sae).

Payment: cheque, Visa, Access, Switch.

Mail order: yes.

Post and packing: from £13 by Interlink next-day delivery.

Delivery: up to 7 days.

Availability: 90-95% of plants grown on site. Smaller plants can be sent at a reduced price if catalogue-priced plants are sold out .

Refund/replacement: yes.

GARDENERS' RECOMMENDATIONS: ⊛ *"Not the usual mass produced popular shrubs, but many rarities mostly propagated on own premises."* ⊛ *"A good general garden centre with wide range of southern hemisphere rare and exotic plants."*

See map page 388.

Trewithen Nurseries

As our winters get milder and summers warmer, Britain is getting interested in plants which once could only be grown in the South West. Trewithen has good phormiums, magnolias and a big selection of rhododendron and azaleas needing, of course, an acid soil.

Trewithen Nurseries, Grampound, Truro, Cornwall TR2 4DD

Tel: 01726 883647/882764 **Fax:** 01726 882301

Opening hours: 10.00–16.30 from 1 March to 30 September. 10.00–15.00 from 1 October to end February.

Visitors welcome: yes.

Catalogue: £1.25.

Payment: cash, cheque, major credit cards.

Mail order: no.

Delivery: wholesale orders – delivery for orders over £200 free within 30 mile radius, 15p per mile between 30 and 60 miles, 20p per mile over 60 miles.

Availability: not limited.

Refund/replacement: yes, where appropriate.

GARDENERS' RECOMMENDATIONS: ✸ *"Impossible to leave without the boot full of huge rhodos, azaleas, camellias at very good prices for large plants."* ✸ *"Excellent, good value, interesting range, attached to one of Cornwall's finest historic gardens."* ✸ *"A good selection of plants, particularly camellias and very competitively priced."* Mr G J and Lady Mary Holborow. *Also recommended by* Dr Smart, Marwood Hill Nursery.

See map page 388.

See also: Pine Lodge Garden Nursery, page 360.

COUNTY DURHAM

Beamish Clematis Nursery   The list has 350 varieties of clematis with plenty of viticellas, orientalis and texensis as well as the large flowered hybrids and herbaceous clematis but, like many nurseries, they have diversified over the years. The list now includes roses, shrubs, trees and grasses and bamboo, including the hard-to-find Chusquea couleou.

> **Beamish Clematis Nursery**, Burntwood Cottage, Stoney Lane, Beamish, County Durham DH9 0SJ
> **Tel/fax:** 0191 370 0202
> **Opening hours:** 9.00–17.00 daily. Closed December and January.
> **Visitors welcome:** yes, customers are encouraged to visit the nursery.
> **Catalogue:** send 3 first class stamps.
> **Payment:** cash or cheque.
> **Mail order:** yes. Minimum order £50.
> **Post and packing:** at cost.
> **Delivery:** 3 days.
> **Availability:** supplies of rare plants can be limited. Advisable to telephone before visiting.
> **Refund/replacement:** by arrangement – they have never had a dissatisfied customer.

Special services: plant tracing service, containers planted (not bedding), planting schemes.

GARDENERS' RECOMMENDATIONS: *"Excellent selection of clematis, friendly personal service, vast knowledge, first class plants. Small, owner-run, lots of advice."* Austin Lynch.

See map page 396.

J Beveridge Nurseries   The firm has been going since 1910 when James Beveridge set up in County Durham. His grandsons now run the nurseries and make a point of their friendly and personal service. "James Beveridge would hardly recognise the place," they say now. "He would, however, be pleased to see that we still use traditional techniques such as the steam sterilising of soil to produce our own composts, hardening off plants properly in cold frames and over-wintering of hardy stock on our open hillside." The stock is wide ranging and, gathering by this treatment, extremely hardy.

> **J Beveridge**, The Nurseries, Ebchester, County Durham DH8 0SX
> **Tel:** 01207 560228 **Fax:** 01207 563429
> **Opening hours:** 8.00–18.00 Monday to Friday, 8.00–16.30 at weekends.
> **Visitors welcome:** very much so.
> **Catalogue:** none.
> **Payment:** cash or cheque.
> **Mail order:** no.
> **Availability:** certain items are seasonal, however a great variety of plants is available throughout the year.
> **Refund/replacement:** yes.

GARDENERS' RECOMMENDATIONS: *"...thoroughly recommended for growing their own hardy stock, suitable for planting here in the north of England. ...willing to give advice and charging sensible prices."* Mrs I Bonas, county organiser for the National Gardens Scheme.

See map page 397.

Eggleston Hall Gardens

Eggleston Hall Gardens The Hall's gardens were famous over a hundred years ago and recently the walled gardens have been revived so that many of the plants in the catalogue can be seen in full maturity. The nursery offers an excellent general list, help with landscaping, expert guidance for plant buyers.

> **Eggleston Hall Gardens**, Barnard Castle, County Durham DL12 0AG
>
> **Tel:** 01833 650403 **Fax/Answerphone:** 01833 650378
>
> **Opening hours:** 10.00–17.00 daily.
>
> **Visitors welcome:** yes.
>
> **Catalogue:** £1.50.
>
> **Payment:** cash, cheque, major credit cards.
>
> **Mail order:** no.
>
> **Availability:** some rare plants are in short supply and only available at certain times of year.
>
> **Refund/replacement:** yes.

GARDENERS' RECOMMENDATIONS: ✤ *"Excellent selection of plants, usual and unusual. They will get hold of special things where possible."* ✤ *"First class selection of plants, personal service, knowledgeable gardener, delightful gardens, many unusual plants. A true garden/nursery. Excellent value for money."* Austin Lynch. ✤ *"Good with a fairly extensive range."* Mr C Wyvill.

See map page 397.

Elmridge Nurseries

Elmridge Nurseries A general nursery, selling shrubs, trees, herbaceous and alpine perennials, hedging, bedding, plants for water and glasshouse and fruit trees.

> **Elmridge Nurseries**, Coniscliffe Road, Darlington, County Durham DL3 8DH
>
> **Tel:** 01325 462710 **Fax:** 01325 363550
>
> **Opening hours:** 8.30–17.30 Monday to Saturday, 10.30–16.30 Sunday.
>
> **Visitors welcome:** yes.
>
> **Catalogue:** free.
>
> **Payment:** cash, cheque, major credit cards.
>
> **Mail order:** no.
>
> **Delivery:** free local delivery within 2 days.

Availability: supplies can be limited and some plants are available only at certain times of year.

Refund/replacement: yes.

Special services: plant finding service.

GARDENERS' RECOMMENDATIONS: *"As county organiser for the National Gardens Scheme for 23 years, I know the nursery very well. They are thoroughly recommended for growing their own hardy stock, suitable for planting here in the north of England."* Mrs I Bonas.

See map page 396.

New Row Farm Nurseries   This is a wholesale nursery only which does welcome personal callers by appointment. It grows its own plants in a climate it describes as "robust" and has a wide choice of the more usual varieties. Because this is a wholesale house, expect less feather-bedding than normal.

New Row Farm Nurseries, Tow Law, Bishop Auckland, County Durham DL13 4PH

Tel: 01388 527698 **Fax:** 01388 528364

E-mail: norman.ridley@virgin.net

Opening hours: 8.00–16.30 Monday to Thursday, 8.00–15.30 Friday. Closed weekends and bank holidays.

Visitors welcome: yes.

Catalogue: none.

Payment: cash or cheque.

Mail order: no.

Availability: supplies can be limited and some plants are available only at certain times of year.

Refund/replacement: yes.

GARDENERS' RECOMMENDATIONS: *"As county organiser for the National Gardens Scheme for 23 years, I know this nursery very well and have used them personally."* Mrs I Bonas.

See map page 397.

CUMBRIA

Mr T H Barker and Son A good clematis nursery with a wide selection of both species and hybrids which all have helpful entries in the catalogue. There is also a short list of other climbers. Help in choosing plants is available.

> **Mr T H Barker and Son**, Baines Paddock, Haverthwaite, Ulverston, Cumbria LA12 8PF
>
> **Tel:** 01539 558236
>
> **E-mail:** rachel@thbarker.demon.co.uk
>
> **Website:** http://www.saska.demon.co.uk/clematis.htm
>
> **Opening hours:** 9.30–17.30. Closed Tuesday mornings and December/January.
>
> **Visitors welcome:** yes.
>
> **Catalogue:** £1.
>
> **Payment:** cheque on receipt of invoice.
>
> **Mail order:** yes. Minimum order 2 plants.
>
> **Post and packing:** £6.75.
>
> **Delivery:** 3 days.
>
> **Availability:** depends on demand. Plants normally available from spring to late autumn.
>
> **Refund/replacement:** yes.

GARDENERS' RECOMMENDATIONS: ✿ *"Excellent range of clematis propagated on site, also selection of cottage garden plants."* Mrs V G Darby.

See map page 397.

Chiltern Seeds A huge catalogue stuffed with plants you never dreamed you could grow from seed: cedars, for example, roses and tree ferns. It's extremely exciting to think what can turn up from a cheap packet of seeds — groves of olive trees, whole vegetable gardens, conservatories scented with plumbago and datura and posies of Japanese cutting flowers. This catalogue has them all. There are all the expected ones, as well.

Chiltern Seeds, Bortree Stile, Ulverston, Cumbria LA12 7PB
Tel: 01229 581137 **Fax:** 01229 584549
E-mail: info@chilternseeds.co.uk
Website: http://www.chilternseeds.co.uk
Opening hours: normal office hours Monday to Friday.
Visitors welcome: yes, to collect an order. No nursery, garden centre or other facilities for the general public.
Catalogue: send 50p in stamps.
Payment: cheque, postal order, Transcash, Switch, major credit cards.
Mail order: yes.
Post and packing: 60p for orders up to £15 in UK, free thereafter.
Delivery: normally 1 week, but longer during busy period (January to April).
Availability: all year round.
Refund/replacement: replacement.
Special services: gift vouchers and gift seeds.

GARDENERS' RECOMMENDATIONS: ☸ *"A delightful catalogue which will make you laugh out loud! Superb range of seeds. I always ask for seeds to be sent in packets with instructions because I find the unmarked packets usually sent, even when used in conjunction with their good sowing guide, rather long-winded and tricky."* Mr Frankie Warren. *"Erotic reading for the gardener."* Simone Nelson.

See map page 397.

D W Hickson and Sons   The firm specialises in herbaceous perennials with special interest in plants which have interesting flowers and foliage: irises, daylilies, geraniums and hostas. All, of course, are also extremely fashionable in the garden. The plants they sell are large and well established.

D W Hickson and Sons, Garden House Nursery, Dalston, Carlisle, Cumbria CA5 7LL
Tel: 01228 710297
Opening hours: 9.00–17.00 daily from March to October.
Visitors welcome: yes.
Catalogue: none.
Payment: cash or cheque.
Mail order: no.

Availability: greatest variety from May to July.
Refund/replacement: yes.

GARDENERS' RECOMMENDATIONS: ❀ *"It's not a beautiful nursery but it is so inexpensive and carries a huge stock of perennials. It is my mainstay."* Mr and Mrs R L Jefferson.

See map page 397.

Larch Cottage Nurseries   Known for the rare and unusual cottage garden plants which are displayed in pond gardens, Japanese gardens and a monastic herb garden — so there's lots of inspiration for gardeners. The firm will also design similar gardens for customers. There are extensive lists of herbaceous plants with many varieties on offer plus ferns, bamboos and grasses.

Larch Cottage Nurseries, Melkinthorpe, Penrith, Cumbria CA10 2DR
Tel: 01931 712404 **Fax:** 01931 712727
Opening hours: daily 10.00–19.00 or dusk in winter. Restaurant open from 10.00–17.00.
Visitors welcome: yes.
Catalogue: £1.50.
Payment: cheque, major credit cards.
Mail order: yes.
Post and packing: £10.
Delivery: usually next day depending on availability.
Availability: most items in plentiful supply. Rare plants are limited due to slow propagation.
Refund/replacement: by arrangement.
Special services: landscaping service in Cumbria.

GARDENERS' RECOMMENDATIONS: ❀ *"Some rare and unusual plants in most unusual and creative surroundings boasting a medieval herb garden and interesting architecture."* Mr and Mrs M S Hardy-Bishop. ❀ *"I wish this nursery was much nearer. It's a real experience to visit! …much enthusiasm from the young owners and such a variety of plants etc. Plus a superb coffee shop with home baking."* Mr and Mrs H Lock. ❀ *"A vast array of perennials, some rare and choice. Unusual shrubs, 100 of the best roses, beautiful layout with pond and gardens and delicious coffee and food. A fantastic combination.*

Husband and wife team. She = plantswoman, he landscapes." Mr and Mrs R L Jefferson.

See map page 397.

Muncaster Plants

Adam and Sue Clark specialise in rhododendrons and azaleas but are increasingly selling plants from China and the Himalayas, including sorbus and primulas grown from seed collected in the wild. They will send details on request. They also offer cultural and landscaping advice.

Muncaster Plants, Muncaster Castle, Ravenglass, Cumbria CA18 1RJ
Tel: 01229 717357 **Fax:** 01229 717818
E-mail: acrhodos@globalnet.co.uk
Website: http://www.users.globalnet.co.uk/~acrhodos
Opening hours: 10.00–17.00 from April to October and at other times by appointment.
Visitors welcome: yes, preferably by appointment.
Catalogue: send 2 first class stamps.
Payment: mail order – cheque, bank transfer. Personal callers – cheque, major credit cards.
Mail order: yes. Minimum order £20.
Post and packing: at cost.
Delivery: by arrangement depending on time of year.
Availability: certain rhododendrons are always in short supply.
Refund/replacement: by arrangement.
Special services: landscaping, planting and cultural advice.

GARDENERS' RECOMMENDATIONS: ❁ *"Specialist and reliable."* Mr Bruce Archibold, former chairman RHS Rhododendron, Camellia and Magnolia Group.

See map page 397.

Next Ness Nurseries

Sells hardy perennials, shrubs, roses and climbers along with bonsai.

Next Ness Nurseries, Glenvilla, Next Ness, Ulverston, Cumbria LA12 7QW

Tel: 01229 583622

Opening hours: 9.00–18.00 daily except Wednesday. Closed at Christmas, during January and the first 2 weeks of August.

Visitors welcome: yes.

Catalogue: none.

Payment: cash or cheque.

Mail order: no.

Availability: supplies can be limited and some plants are available only at certain times of year.

Refund/replacement: depending on circumstances.

GARDENERS' RECOMMENDATIONS: ✱ *"Wide range of good low cost plants."* Mr and Mrs R McBurnie. ✱ *"Run by a couple who are really knowledgeable, especially about water plants."* Mrs J Barratt.

See map page 397.

Weasdale Nurseries

Weasdale Nurseries This is a good list of large and small trees, those suitable for bonsai, and the bigger shrubs. The catalogue is very helpful on planting, size and general shape — and the firm is happy to take in wedding lists for couples with gardening ambitions.

Weasdale Nurseries, Newbiggin-on-Lune, Kirkby Stephen, Cumbria CA17 4LX

Tel: 01539 623246 **Fax:** 01539 623277

E-mail: sales@weasdale.com

Website: http://www. weasdale.com

Opening hours: 8.00–13.00, 14.00–18.00 Monday to Friday.

Visitors welcome: preferably by appointment.

Catalogue: £1 paid by cheque, postal order or in stamps, or £1.50 by credit card.

Payment: cash, cheque, postal order, Visa, Mastercard, Switch.

Mail order: yes.

Post and packing: hedging and forest trees £10 plus VAT, specimens £15 plus VAT or 10% of order value if greater.

Delivery: up to 2 months before Christmas, otherwise 10–14 days.

Availability: despatched between mid-November and late March to late April.

Refund/replacement: depending on circumstances.

Special services: wedding lists, memorial plaque engraving service.

Gardeners' Recommendations: *"A good traditional specialist tree nursery. In a startlingly bleak (and out of the way) spot, anything which he offers can be guaranteed to be well grown and bone hardy. The range isn't huge and it isn't experimental (in his climate experiment makes no sense) but, equally, it contains no rubbish."* Mr Tim Longville.

See map page 397.

Derbyshire

Bluebell Nursery Suzette and Robert Vernon have decided to give Chelsea a miss to spend more time in their own garden and arboretum. The last was started in 1992 in a six-acre pony paddock but now holds more than 2,000 native trees and it shows what can be achieved in a few years from scratch. They have an excellent list of trees and shrubs with an exceptional collection of oaks — one of which, the Valonia oak, already has acorns at five years old. A prime nursery for those interested in trees.

Bluebell Nursery, Annwell Lane, Smisby, nr Ashby de la Zouch, LE65 2TA

Tel: 01530 413700 **Fax:** 01530 417600

E-mail: castell@bigfoot.com

Website: http://www.bluebellnursery.com

Opening hours: March to October 9.00–17.00, 10.30–16.30 on Sundays. November to February 9.00–16.00, closed on Sundays. Closed between 25 December and 4 January.

Visitors welcome: yes.

Catalogue: £1 plus 2 first class stamps.

Payment: cheque, Visa, Access, Switch.

Mail order: yes.

Post and packing: £5.50 for first plant, £1.30 per plant thereafter in most of mainland UK.

Delivery: 4-day carrier service. Overnight by arrangement.

Availability: many species grown in small numbers and a waiting list operates for a few difficult plants.

Refund/replacement: yes, if notified within 12 months.

Special services: Guided tours of garden and arboretum by arrangement. Occasional lectures.

GARDENERS' RECOMMENDATIONS: ✿ *"Owners are informative and very helpful. Prices not cheap but very worth the money. The new Bluebell garden is imaginatively laid out and will, in time, be outstanding."* Col and Mrs J G T Polley. ✿ *"This nursery has a spectacular range of rare trees and shrubs, a fascinating arboretum on site and the staff could not be more helpful."* Rob Hubble and Stella Tracey. ✿ *"Wonderful shrubs and trees, so unusual."* Mrs Rosemary Hannay. ✿ *"A small nursery for real enthusiasts; full of interesting and unusual finds, and an owner who knows his plants and the local growing conditions."* Rod and Penny Smith. ✿ *"This is one of my favourite nurseries. The catalogue is a mine of information and temptations. We have bought some wonderful healthy unusual trees, shrubs and climbers."* ✿ *"They are helpful with advice and will help identify unknown specimens in existing gardens. They have made an arboretum themselves around the nursery in very adverse conditions, open to the wind and in waterlogged clay."* ✿ *"Trees and shrubs to die for."* Simone Nelson.

See map page 393.

Dam Farm House Gardens

A nursery with no catalogue but which specialises in roses, shrubs, perennials and alpines. The owner, Mrs J M Player, will help with advice.

Dam Farm House Gardens, Dam Farm House, Yeldersley Lane, Ednaston, Derbyshire DE6 3BA

Tel: 01335 360291

Opening hours: by appointment from 1 April to 31 October.

Visitors welcome: yes, by appointment.

Catalogue: none.

Payment: cash or cheque.

Mail order: no.

Availability: supplies can be limited and some plants are available only at certain times of year.

Refund/replacement: no.

See map page 393.

DHE Plants The nursery specialises in alpine and rock garden plants with about 900 varieties on offer. They will send out lists of erodium, heliathemum and saxifrages.

> **DHE Plants**, Rose Lea, Darley House Estate, Matlock, Derbyshire DE4 2QH. Nursery stock at Robert Young Floral Centre, Bakewell Road, Matlock.
>
> **Tel:** 01629 732512
>
> **Opening hours:** 10.00–16.30 (or dusk if earlier) daily.
>
> **Visitors welcome:** yes, but please telephone in advance.
>
> **Catalogue:** send 2 first class stamps.
>
> **Payment:** cash or cheque.
>
> **Mail order:** yes, from October to April only.
>
> **Post and packing:** at cost.
>
> **Delivery:** by arrangement.
>
> **Availability:** supplies can be limited and some plants are available only at certain times of year.
>
> **Refund/replacement:** yes.

GARDENERS' RECOMMENDATIONS: ❀ *"Good source of home-grown plants."*

See map page 396.

Fir Croft Alpine Plant Centre A huge range of alpines — over 3,000 varieties — including saxifrage (400 of them), sempervivum (a massive 650) and primulas (300) displayed on raised beds (excellent for gardeners in wheel chairs.) A professional botanist is available to give advice.

> **Fir Croft Alpine Plant Centre**, Froggatt Road, Calver, Derbyshire S32 3ZD
>
> **Opening hours:** 10.00–17.00 on Saturday and Monday, 13.00–17.00 on Sunday.
>
> **Visitors welcome:** yes.
>
> **Catalogue:** send 2 second class stamps for sempervivum list.
>
> **Payment:** cash or cheque.
>
> **Mail order:** no.
>
> **Availability:** 3,000+ varieties are grown on a rotational basis so stock is constantly changing.
>
> **Refund/replacement:** by arrangement (never arisen).
>
> **Special services:** show garden open for NGS.

GARDENERS' RECOMMENDATIONS: *"One of the largest selections in Britain. Over 3,000 varieties displayed on stone-built raised beds. Top quality plants at extremely low prices. Sales area surrounded by display garden. Listed in Good Gardens Guide. Situated in the middle of the superb Peak District national park"* *"Excellent specialists in alpine plants."* Mr and Mrs R Porter. *"Super alpine collection."* Mr and Mrs David Ketley, Dunge Valley Gardens.

See map page 396.

Handley Rose Nurseries

This is a small nursery with an emphasis on roses (though clematis, shrubs, alpines and flowers are also available). They will give advice on all aspects of rose-growing.

> **Handley Rose Nurseries**, Lightwood Road, Marsh Lane, Sheffield, S21 5RG
> **Tel:** 01246 432921
> **Opening hours:** 9.00–19.00
> **Visitors welcome:** yes.
> **Catalogue:** free list.
> **Payment:** cash or cheque.
> **Mail order:** yes.
> **Post and packing:** £4.
> **Delivery:** allow 2 weeks in season.
> **Availability:** orders are posted between November and March. Plants can be collected at any time except Wednesdays.
> **Refund/replacement:** yes.
> **Special services:** personal attention and advice on all aspects of rose growing.

GARDENERS' RECOMMENDATIONS: *"Good collection of roses, well grown, will source rare material, friendly, knowledgeable."* Mr David Kesteven, Head Gardener, Renishaw Hall.

See map page 396.

Peter Grayson (Sweet Peas)

The firm, unusually, sells only by mail order and is not open to the public. Nor does it sell plants — seeds only, which makes perfectly good sense since sweet peas are generally not difficult to raise. Mr. Grayson boasts that this is the largest list of sweet peas in the world. The catalogue is helpful, with some illustrations and dates of introduction, along with a book giving further details on how to grow them. A must for the sweet pea lover like me. There is also a small seed collection of cottage garden plants such as hollyhocks and nasturtiums.

Peter Grayson (Sweet Peas),
34 Glenthorne Close, Brampton,
Chesterfield, Derbyshire S40 3AR

Tel/fax: 01246 278503

Visitors welcome: no,
not open to the public –
mail order only.

Catalogue: free.

Payment: cheque or
postal order.

Mail order: yes.

Post and packing:
50p for orders under
£10, free thereafter.

Delivery: normally by return.

Refund/replacement: money back guarantee.

GARDENERS' RECOMMENDATIONS: ✤ *"A sweet pea specialist. Lovely fragrant old-fashioned varieties."*

Tissington Nursery Derek and Sue Watkins grow choice and unusual shrubs and herbaceous perennials in small numbers. They also have climbers and a few conservatory plants. It's a good idea to ask what they have, and when, before calling.

Tissington Nursery, Tissington Village, nr Ashbourne, Derbyshire
DE6 1RA

Tel: 01335 390650 **Fax:** 01335 390693

Opening hours: 10.00–18.00 Wednesday to Sunday from March
to September.

Visitors welcome: yes.

Catalogue: send 3 first class stamps.

Payment: cash, cheque, Visa, Mastercard.

Mail order: no.

Availability: plants are produced in small batches which
become ready at certain times throughout the year.

Refund/replacement: yes.

GARDENERS' RECOMMENDATIONS: ⊕ *"Good range of plants, helpful owners. Situated in the centre of beautiful Tissington village. Excellent tea rooms close by."* Mr and Mrs Spencer.

See map page 395.

See also: Lea Gardens, page 356.

DEVON

Shirley Reynolds at Axe Valley Penstemons Mrs Reynolds holds the NCCPG national collection of penstemons and offers a list of over 100 cultivars and 30 species. She hopes eventually to offer these by mail order and can give very helpful advice on their propagation.

> **Shirley Reynolds at Axe Valley Penstemons,** Blue Firs, Wessiters Drive, Seaton, Devon EX12 2PJ
>
> **Tel:** 01297 625342 **Fax:** 01297 64085
>
> **E-mail:** sher.bluefirs@btinternet.com
>
> **Opening hours:** 14.00–17.00 Thursday from mid-May to mid-September or by appointment.
>
> **Visitors welcome:** yes.
>
> **Catalogue:** free.
>
> **Payment:** cash or cheque.
>
> **Mail order:** no.
>
> **Availability:** good selection from mid-May to mid-September.
>
> **Refund/replacement:** replacement.

GARDENERS' RECOMMENDATIONS: ⊕ *Recommended by* Mrs Dorothy Anderson.

See map page 389.

Ann and Roger Bowden Hostas The National Collection of hybrid hostas is kept at this nursery and at present runs to 750 varieties, about 300 of which are in the catalogue (others may also be available.) What a hosta can do with its leaves is extraordinary: yellow and white margined, or the colours reversed, leaves may be deeply ribbed, crinkled or velvety. Other shades include a soft greeny-blue and a vibrant green. The catalogue is helpfully illustrated in full colour.

Ann and Roger Bowden Hostas, Sticklepath, Okehampton, Devon EX20 2NL

Tel: 01837 840481 **Fax:** 01837 840482

E-mail: bowdenhostas@eclipse.co.uk

Opening hours: by appointment only.

Visitors welcome: yes, by appointment.

Catalogue: send 3 first class stamps.

Payment: cash, cheque, major credit cards.

Mail order: yes.

Post and packing: £2 to £5 for orders up to £40. Free thereafter.

Delivery: normally 2-4 weeks, possibly longer from May to July.

Availability: all year round.

Refund/replacement: yes, if warranted.

GARDENERS' RECOMMENDATIONS: ❀ *"Quite wonderful collection of hostas – excellent quality plants."* Mrs Susan Beck. ❀ *"… list is varied and different. Plants arrived in good condition and established well. Has a good garden."* Mrs Danae Johnston. ❀ *"Well displayed and labelled and attractive garden across the road."* Mr and Mrs J Southwell, Sherborne Garden. ❀ *"An excellent specialist nursery – wonderful hostas and a first rate catalogue."* Mrs P Clarke.

See map page 389.

———————————— 🐇 ————————————

Burnham Nurseries Orchids are a subject to themselves, with devoted admirers by the dozen. This nursery sells nothing but orchids along with books on the subject, collections for beginners, the impatient and for those with large warm rooms. It's an excellent list, well illustrated — but better still visit the nursery where there's a constantly changing exhibition of the plants.

Burnham Nurseries, Forches Cross, Newton Abbot, Devon
TQ11 6PZ
Tel: 01626 352233 **Fax:** 01626 362167
E-mail: burnhamorchids@eclipse.co.uk
Website: http://www.eclipse.co.uk/burnhamorchids
Opening hours: 10.00–16.00 daily.
Visitors welcome: yes.
Catalogue: free.
Payment: cheque, major credit cards, Switch.
Mail order: yes.
Post and packing: £8 for next day delivery.
Delivery: 24 hours.
Availability: all year round.
Refund/replacement: yes.
Special services: free workshops at the nursery.

GARDENERS' RECOMMENDATIONS: ✾ *"Specialist and reliable."* Mr
Bruce Archibold, former chairman RHS Rhododendron, Camellia
and Magnolia Group.

See map page 388.

Burrow Farm Garden

Burrow Farm Garden The nursery sells plants propagated from
a six-acre garden nearby. They specialist in moisture and shade-loving
plants and shrubs with interesting foliage.

Burrow Farm Garden, Dalwood, Axminster, Devon EX13 7ET
Tel: 01404 831285 **Fax:** 01404 831844
Opening hours: 10.00–19.00 daily from 1 April to 30 September.
Visitors welcome: yes.
Catalogue: none.
Payment: cash or cheque.
Mail order: no.
Availability: supplies can be limited and some plants are
available only at certain times of year.

Refund/replacement: yes.

Special services: Design and landscaping service, plants displayed in adjoining 6-acre garden.

GARDENERS' RECOMMENDATIONS: *"Very good interesting plants."* Mrs N Bitschi.

See map page 389.

Cottage Garden Plants and Herbs

Cottage Garden Plants and Herbs Here you can find all the cottager's favourite plants, simple and colourful herbaceous perennials, pretty and useful herbs and a good selection of hardy geraniums. Cottage plants are ideal for new gardeners since they are generally easy to grow.

Cottage Garden Plants and Herbs, North Lodge, Canonteign, Christow, Devon EX6 7NS

Tel: 01647 252950

Opening hours: 10.00–17.00 weekends and bank holidays.

Visitors welcome: yes, by appointment.

Catalogue: none.

Payment: cash or cheque.

Mail order: no.

Availability: Easter to end October.

Refund/replacement: replacement.

GARDENERS' RECOMMENDATIONS: *Recommended by* Mrs Dorothy Anderson.

See map page 389.

Cuckoo Nursery A nursery with hardy outdoor grown cottage garden plants, especially unusual perennials plus climbers, shrubs and conifers. There is also a collection of exotic and unusual conservatory and house plants.

Cuckoo Nursery, Homestead, Wagland Farm, Halwell, Totnes, Devon TQ9 7LB

Tel: 01548 821610

Opening hours: 10.00-18.00, preferably by appointment.

Visitors welcome: yes.
Catalogue: none, but free plant list available.
Payment: cash or cheque.
Mail order: no.
Availability: stock is constantly changing throughout the year.
Refund/replacement: yes.
Special services: delivery can be arranged.

GARDENERS' RECOMMENDATIONS: *"An enormous choice of well grown plants at sensible prices, many quite unusual. Nice people, very knowledgeable."* Mrs Anne Hockaday.

See map page 388.

Devon Violet Nursery   Holders of the national collection of Viola odorata along with hybrid and Parma violets in up to 130 varieties (far more than in the tasteful violet-coloured list.)

Devon Violet Nursery, Rattery, South Brent, Devon TQ10 9LG
Tel: 01364 643033
E-mail: devon.violets@virgin.net
Website: http://www.sweetviolets.co.uk
Opening hours: 10.00–17.00 October to June. Advisable to telephone first.
Visitors welcome: yes.
Catalogue: free.
Payment: cheque, Visa shortly.
Mail order: yes. Minimum order 6 plants.
Post and packing: £3.50 for up to 15 plants, £5 for 15-25 plants in UK.
Delivery: next day in UK. Approx 7 days in Europe.
Availability: plants despatched between October and 1 June.
Refund/replacement: yes.
Special services: cut violet flowers can be supplied.

See map page 388.

Dulford Nurseries   David and Mary Barrow's nursery is full of interesting trees, both broadleaf, conifer and fruit. There are 26 different beeches, 17 birches and the native, but rare, black poplar. They also supply bare-rooted hedging plants and will plant and fence the trees or hedges.

Dulford Nurseries, Dulford, Cullompton, Devon EX15 2DG
Tel: 01884 266361 **Fax:** 01884 266663
Opening hours: 07.30–16.30 Monday to Friday.
Visitors welcome: yes, by appointment. Customers will have personal attention.
Catalogue: free.
Payment: cash or cheque.
Mail order: own transport or carrier service for smaller trees/ shrubs.
Post and packing: by own transport at cost when possible, or by carrier from £13 for up to 10 kg.
Delivery: allow up to 3 weeks.
Availability: bare-rooted trees from November to March inclusive. Containerised trees and shrubs available all year.
Refund/replacement: replacement within first year of planting in case of genuine failure.
Special services: planting, park fencing, garden care, local landscaping.

GARDENERS' RECOMMENDATIONS: ✤ *"Excellent selection of trees and some shrubs. Many propagated at the nursery. Good quality plants."* Mr and Mrs Gueterbock.

See map page 389.

Endsleigh Gardens A charming nursery which specialises in Japanese maples, grafted wisterias and an excellent range of West Country apple and cherry trees such as Cornish Gillyflower and Early Bower apples and and Burcombe and Bullion cherries. They offer a grafting service.

Endsleigh Gardens Nurseries, Milton Abbot, Tavistock, Devon PL19 0PG
Tel: 01822 870235 **Fax:** 01822 870513
Opening hours: 8.00–17.00 Monday to Saturday, 14.00–17.00 Sunday. Closed on Sunday in December and January.
Visitors welcome: yes.
Catalogue: send 2 first class stamps.
Payment: cheque, major credit cards.

Mail order: yes. Minimum order £8 plus p&p.
Post and packing: at cost.
Delivery: overnight or by Parcel Force.
Availability: supplies are not normally limited.
Refund/replacement: yes.

GARDENERS' RECOMMENDATIONS: ❁ *"Quality plants, with many unusual."* Mr and Mrs K R Willcock. ❁ *"A real nursery, propagating a wide range of hardy stock, including a fine selection of uncommon trees. Good planting size and reasonable prices. No mass production or hype, and people who know what they are talking about – of great interest to us as retired nurserymen!"* Mr and Mrs G Goatcher. ❁*Also recommended by* Mr John Carter, Rowden Gardens.

See map page 388.

Fairhaven Nursery I'm not entirely sure how this list is chosen — there are conifers, ferns, trees shrubs and herbaceous plants. I suspect that what is offered is purely personal choice because there are good selections of, say, lavender and cornus.

Fairhaven Nursery, Chittlehampton, Umberleigh, Devon EX37 9QT
Tel: 01769 540528
Opening hours: open most days, but best to ring first to avoid disappointment.
Visitors welcome: yes.
Catalogue: send 2 first class stamps.
Payment: cash or cheque.
Mail order: yes.
Post and packing: at cost.
Delivery: by return if in stock, otherwise as and when available.
Availability: supplies can be limited and some plants are available only at certain times of year.
Refund/replacement: yes.

GARDENERS' RECOMMENDATIONS: ❁ *"Nice selection. Well grown."* Mr and Mrs J Greenaway.

See map page 389.

Fast Rabbit Farm The owners bought the farm in 1987 and started to make a garden in 1991, landscaping the hillsides with excavators. They now sell the plants they grow, as do many smaller nurseries. These include woodland and waterside plants like magnolias, rhododendrons, camellias and primulas. They take seed from botanical expeditions and propagate from cuttings in their greenhouses.

> **Fast Rabbit Farm**, Ash Cross, Dartmouth, Devon TQ6 0LR
> **Tel:** 01803 712437
> **Opening hours:** 9.00–17.00.
> **Visitors welcome:** yes.
> **Catalogue:** none.
> **Payment:** cash or cheque.
> **Mail order:** no.
> **Refund/replacement:** yes.

GARDENERS' RECOMMENDATIONS: ✿ *Recommended by* Mrs Dorothy Anderson.

See map page 388.

Feebers Hardy Plants The nursery is sited in a valley bottom without drainage (where is the water to go to?) on heavy, wet clay soil — the sort that is yellow three inches down. So the plants grown here are all suitable for such appalling conditions. There are perennials, annuals, shrubs and climbers. The owner, the great niece of Amos Perry, is also beginning to grow the plants he propagated with the help of Capel Manor.

> **Feebers Hardy Plants**, 1 Feebers Cottage, Westwood, Broadclyst, Devon EX5 3DQ
> **Tel:** 01404 822118
> **Opening hours:** normally 10.00–17.00 on Thursday and 14.00–18.00 on Saturday from March to July and September to end October or by appointment.
> **Visitors welcome:** by appointment only.
> **Catalogue:** send 2 first class stamps.
> **Payment:** cash or cheque.
> **Mail order:** a limited range.
> **Post and packing:** by arrangement and depending on plants.
> **Delivery:** seasonal.

Availability: plants propagated in small quantities only.
Refund/replacement: yes, if justified.

GARDENERS' RECOMMENDATIONS: ❀ *"Broad selection of hardy plants."* Mrs N Bitschi. ❀ *"Owners, Mike and Edna Squires are past Chairman and Secretary respectively of the Devon Group of the NCCPG. A wide range of plants particularly suited to growing in heavy clay soil."* Roger Stuckey, Chairman of Exeter Group of the Alpine Garden Society.

See map page 389.

Fillan's Plants

The nursery specialises in two different kinds of plants: one is woody plants — hydrangea, deutzia, magnolia, philadelphus — of which they have a vast range along with bog plants, ferns and herbaceous plants which like a woodland setting. The second is a fancy for big-leaved exotics such as cannas, bananas and palms to create the modern, tropical garden.

Fillan's Plants, Pound House Nursery, Buckland Monachorum, nr Yelverton, Devon PL20 7LJ
Tel: 01822 855050 **Fax:** 01822 614351
Opening hours: by appointment only.
Visitors welcome: yes, by appointment.
Catalogue: send 3 first class stamps.
Payment: cheque.
Mail order: yes.
Post and packing: £10 in UK.
Delivery: by arrangement.
Availability: supplies can be limited.
Refund/replacement: yes.

GARDENERS' RECOMMENDATIONS: ❀ *"This is a nursery run by a very knowledgeable plantsman (Mark Fillan), who has a great love of plants and propagates a wide variety of material, often from collectors or botanical interchange. Mainly shrubs, but some herbaceous things, and all carefully chosen for garden merit. Good on magnolia, hydrangeas, paeonies."* Mr Michael Stone. ❀ *"Very good for woody plants difficult to find elsewhere."* ❀ *"Introducers of botanical novelties."* Mr and Mrs J F Phillips. ❀ *"Excellent selection of ferns and hydrangeas."* Mr and Mrs R H J Clemo.

"An excellent source of magnolias and, I believe, ferns." Mr and Mrs D R A Quicke.

See map page 388.

The Garden House

Like many nurseries, this one started as a garden propagating its own plants. Now they sell them too. The specialities, therefore, are the unusual plants they love.

> **The Garden House**, Buckland Monachorum, nr Yelverton, Devon PL20 7LQ
> **Tel:** 01822 854769 **Fax:** 01822 855358
> **Opening hours:** 10.30–17.00 daily from March to end October.
> **Visitors welcome:** yes.
> **Catalogue:** none.
> **Payment:** cash, cheque, major credit cards.
> **Mail order:** no.
> **Availability:** supplies can be limited and some plants are available only at certain times of year.
> **Refund/replacement:** usually.

GARDENERS' RECOMMENDATIONS: *"While this is a well known garden in its own right, affiliated nowadays to the RHS, it has always had a nursery alongside, which sells material propagated from the garden itself. There have always been unusual things, and selected varieties of herbaceous plants, with some shrubs as well. Obviously worth the journey for the garden anyway, and usually difficult to escape without a plant or two in the boot."* Mr Michael Stone. *"This is a most exciting nursery. When I started gardening most of my plants came from them. It still is a red letter day when we go."* Miss J Hall. *"Lovely display garden and many unusual plants available at the nursery at sensible prices."* Mr and Mrs E W Dyer.

See map page 388.

Glebe Cottage Plants

I wish I could tell you more about this nursery, which has been recommended by several gardeners — but they don't seem to respond either to letters or repeated telephone calls. We include them because they obviously strike a chord with gardeners and because Carol Klein is not only well known but created a fine garden at Chelsea in 1999.

Glebe Cottage Plants, Pixie Lane, Warkleigh, Umberleigh, Devon EX37 9DH

Tel/fax: 01769 540554

Opening hours: by appointment.

Callers welcome: by appointment only.

Catalogue: £1.50

Payment: cash or cheque.

Mail order: no.

Refund/replacement: by arrangement.

GARDENERS' RECOMMENDATIONS: ✿ *"Carol was selling in the Barnstaple Pannier Market when we came to Devon in 1985. TV fame hasn't changed her a bit and she is still as deeply committed to her plants as ever! Quite a bit of my stock came from her stall and nursery in the early days. It is essential to phone before visiting the nursery (if you can actually make contact nowadays!) The garden is a quart in a pint pot, packed with inspirational planting associations."* Mrs Jessica Duncan. ✿ *"Excellent."* Mrs N Bitschi. ✿ *"I buy from Carol Klein when she attends shows in London and enjoy her passion for 'natural' plants, though they don't always do well in my soil and conditions."* Susan Bennett.

See map page 389.

Greenlands Nursery Mrs. Anderson runs a small nursery with interesting and unusual herbaceous perennials and a few shrubs — some are in short supply. She opens her garden under the NGS scheme where you can see the plants in maturity.

Mrs D E Anderson at Greenlands Nursery, Ash Thomas, Tiverton, Devon EX16 4NP

Tel/fax: 01884 821257 (ring first for fax)

Opening hours: by appointment.

Visitors welcome: yes.

Catalogue: none.

Payment: cash or cheque.

Mail order: no.

Availability: supplies can be limited.
Refund/replacement: yes.
Special services: teas on NGS open days.

GARDENERS' RECOMMENDATIONS: ✽ *"For alpines and herbaceous."* Mrs N Bitschi.

See map page 389.

Greenway Gardens Nursery

Greenway Gardens Nursery   The nursery is positioned within two walled gardens in the private gardens of Greenway House in the Dart Valley. The nursery grows its own stock — anything from birches raised from seed, some collected from Yunnan to rhododendrons grown from seeds from Greenway itself. A most interesting list.

Greenway Gardens, Churston Ferrers, Brixham, Devon TQ5 0ES
Tel: 01803 842382   **Fax:** 01803 842383
Opening hours: 14.00–17.00 (16.30 from November to March) Monday to Friday excluding bank holidays. 10.00–12.00 Saturday.
Visitors welcome: yes.
Catalogue: send 3 first class stamps.
Payment: cash or cheque.
Mail order: yes.
Post and packing: £14.09 for 10 kg, 36p per kg thereafter by Interlink, plus packing £2.70 per large box (4-5 pots).
Delivery: next day by arrangement.
Availability: as the nursery is small supplies can be limited.
Refund/replacement: by arrangement (they have never had a dissatisfied customer).

GARDENERS' RECOMMENDATIONS: ✽ *"Plants from around the world – quite unusual."* Mr and Mrs R H J Clemo. ✽ *"Greenway is Agatha Christie's old garden and the family still owns it. The gardens are splendid and the nursery offers a tantalising range of rare shrubs, particularly South American ones on the outer edges of hardiness. Their prices are very reasonable too."* Mr Tim Longville. ✽ *"Very interesting plants, well grown. Helpful and friendly advice from Roger Clark and his staff."* Dr J A Marston.

See map page 388.

Hidden Valley Nursery

Hidden Valley Nursery Linda and Peter Lindley specialise in hardy perennials with good geraniums, lamiums and epimediums among others.

Hidden Valley Nursery, Umberleigh, Devon EX37 9BU

Tel: 01769 560567, mobile: 07899 056168
Fax: 01769 560567 between 11 pm and 7 am.

E-mail: hiddenvalley@email.com

Website: http://www.melnet.clara.net/hiddenvalley.htm

Opening hours: by appointment.

Visitors welcome: yes, by appointment.

Catalogue: Send 2 first class stamps.

Payment: cash or cheque.

Mail order: yes, in March only.

Post and packing: from £7.95 for orders up to £10, £8.95 for orders up to £20, £9.95 thereafter.

Delivery: 14 to 28 days.

Availability: supplies can be limited and some plants are available only at certain times of year.

Refund/replacement: yes.

GARDENERS' RECOMMENDATIONS: ❀ *"Excellent quality, nice people, good mail order. Interesting and unusual herbaceous."* ❀ *"Good strong and large plants, well delivered, some unusual plants available."* Mr Mark Robson.

See map page 389.

Hill House Nurseries

Hill House Nurseries Attached to the Victorian Hill House, the nursery has more than 18,000 square feet of glasshouses open to the public. The owners aim for a huge selection of usual and unusual plants of the best quality and at the lowest prices. The list they sent me certainly bears this out.

Hill House Nurseries, Landscove, nr Ashburton, Devon TQ13 7LY

Tel/fax: 01803 762273

Opening hours: 11.00–17.00 daily.

Visitors welcome: yes.

Catalogue: none.

Payment: cheque, Visa, Mastercard, Switch.

Mail order: no.

Availability: most plants are available all year round.
Refund/replacement: yes.
Special services: tea room open from March to October.

GARDENERS' RECOMMENDATIONS: ❀ *"Always very helpful. Grow most of their stock on site. Many unusual plants."* Mrs Anne Hockaday. ❀ *"All plants home grown. Some rare and exotic. Most helpful owners."* Misses E and A Hebditch. ❀ *"Hill House Nursery has a good garden and you can get a cup of tea, but once inside you will find all sorts of treasures especially in the green houses. Prices here are very good."* W D Witherick and M Wilkinson. *"Always extremely helpful. Interesting garden alongside."* Mr and Mrs I Callan.

See map page 388.

International Animal Rescue and Animal Tracks I'm not entirely clear why an animal rescue charity should sell plants — but it does and money from sales go to support animal rescue. The list is mostly of alpine and rockery plants and perennials but there are also some shrubs, succulents and grasses.

International Animal Rescue, Animal Tracks, Ash Mill,
South Moulton, Devon EX36 4QW
Tel: 01769 550277 **Fax:** 01769 550917
E-mail: i.a.r@eclipse.co.uk
Website: http://www.iar.org.uk
Opening hours: 10.00–17.30 daily from 1 March to 31 October.
Visitors welcome: yes.
Catalogue: free.
Payment: cash or cheque.
Mail order: no.
Availability: supplies can be limited during winter months.
Refund/replacement: yes.

GARDENERS' RECOMMENDATIONS: ❀ *"I always buy from their stall at the various plant fairs. Lovely well-grown plants, usually something new to me."* Mrs Jessica Duncan.

See map page 389.

Kenwith Nursery The specialist in dwarf and rare conifers, the nursery has a huge, comprehensive list of plants which will fit into a single trough garden or create an entire Japanese planting. Juniperus horizontalis Neumann must be one of the smallest, slowest growing fir trees ever, while Cryptomeria japonica Tenzan will only reach 8cm high in 10 years. Otherwise, there are monkey puzzles, Lebanon cedars and 10 different yews.

Kenwith Nursery, Blinsham, nr Torrington, Beaford, Winkleigh, Devon EX19 8NT

Tel: 01805 603274 **Fax:** 01805 603663

Opening hours: 10.00–16.30 daily from March to November and from Wednesday to Saturday in winter.

Visitors welcome: yes.

Catalogue: send 3 first class stamps.

Payment: cash, cheque, Visa.

Mail order: yes. Minimum order £10 plus postage.

Post and packing: £5 by post of £15 for next day delivery.

Delivery: allow 4 days.

Availability: plants are normally available from September until sold out.

Refund/replacement: no, "although a sympathetic ear will be given."

GARDENERS' RECOMMENDATIONS: ✸ *Excellent quality. Dare not visit – instant bankruptcy.*"

See map page 388.

Knightshayes Nursery The range of 2,500 plants can be seen growing in the 30 acres of display gardens. The stock — bulbs, herbaceous perennials, trees and shrubs, alpines and seeds — is propagated from the gardens and there's always friendly help and advice from the experts there.

Knightshayes Nursery, Tiverton, Devon EX16 7RG

Tel/fax: 01884 253264

E-mail: dknmhx@smtp.ntrust.org.uk

Opening hours: 10.30–17.30 daily from April to October inclusive.

Visitors welcome: yes, during opening hours.

Catalogue: none.

Payment: cash, cheque, Visa, American Express, Switch.

Mail order: no.
Availability: supplies can be limited and some plants are available only at certain times of year.
Refund/replacement: yes.

GARDENERS' RECOMMENDATIONS: ❁ *"Here you find the plants no-one else has and that you have always wanted …mostly grown on premises always with something new and exciting to try. Lots of expertise available."* ❁ *"Interesting shrubs particularly."* Mrs Jessica Duncan.

See map page 389.

Lydford Alpines

Alpines are very satisfactory plants for small gardens or less active gardeners. This nursery loves rock gardens and trough gardens, beds of tufa and scree. The catalogue is brief and, apparently, doesn't list everything they grow.

Lydford Alpines, 2 Southern Cottages, Lydford, Okehampton, Devon EX20 4BL
Tel: 01822 820398
Opening hours: 11.00–17.00 Tuesday and Thursday from April to October. By appointment at other times.
Visitors welcome: yes.
Catalogue: send 3 first class stamps.
Payment: cheque.
Mail order: saxifrages only. Minimum order £10.
Post and packing: £5.90 for 1-5 plants, £6.90 for 6–12, £7.90 for 13–18.
Delivery: allow 1 week.
Availability: mail order from November to March only.
Refund/replacement: by arrangement.
Special services: illustrated talks on alpines, within 40 miles of the nursery.

GARDENERS' RECOMMENDATIONS: ❁ *"Easily the best specialist alpine nursery in Devon – nursery in a display garden. Owners are extremely knowledgeable about all aspects of growing alpines – endless advice if required."* Rob Hubble and Stella Tracey.
❁ *"A good range of interesting and more unusual specialist rock plants with an excellent display garden on the edge of Dartmoor. Committee members of the Exeter Group of the Alpine Garden*

Society." Roger Stuckey, Chairman of Exeter Group of the Alpine Garden Society

See map page 388.

---

cs

Marwood Hill Gardens

The gardens to which this nursery is attached cover over 18 acres and have been made from pastureland over the last 30 years. Some of its plants have won RHS awards of merit and many are grown for specific sites such as bog areas, walled gardens and windy hillsides.

Marwood Hill, nr Barnstaple, Devon EX31 4EB
Tel: 01271 342528
Opening hours: 11.00–17.00 daily.
Visitors welcome: yes.
Catalogue: send 5 second class stamps.
Payment: cash or cheque.
Mail order: no.
Availability: all plants are propagated at the gardens so some may be sold out at times.
Refund/replacement: yes.

GARDENERS' RECOMMENDATIONS: ✿ *"Dr Smart must be one of the most knowledgeable (and energetic!) gardeners in the country today, with acres of meandering planting alongside the lake and stream and more recently covering the adjacent hillside. His wife is an expert plantswoman in her own right, so Marwood is now doubly blessed. Walking through the garden is like turning the pages of a horticultural encyclopaedia. A day really should be set aside to do the garden justice."* Mrs Jessica Duncan. ✿ *"Interesting plants, mostly not expensive, very good for ground cover and herbaceous and mostly grown on premises."* ✿ *"Rare shrubs and trees, particularly those for the milder parts of the country. Amazing garden. Inspirational in every possible way."* Mr Tim Longville. *"Gorgeous garden/lakes/plant sale."* Mrs N Bitschi.

See map page 388.

---

cs

Meadow Cottage Plants Hardy perennials are the speciality here and, within that, hardy geraniums. There is a fine list of these along with astilbe, penstemon and sidalcea plus a few bamboos.

> **Meadow Cottage Plants**, Pitt Hill, Ivybridge, Devon PL21 0JJ
> **Tel:** 01752 894532
> **Opening hours:** by appointment only.
> **Visitors welcome:** yes, by appointment.
> **Catalogue:** send 2 second class stamps.
> **Payment:** cash or cheque.
> **Mail order:** no.
> **Availability:** some rare plants are in short supply.
> **Refund/replacement:** yes.

GARDENERS' RECOMMENDATIONS: ❀ *Recommended by* Mrs Dorothy Anderson.

See map page 388.

Nicky's Rock Garden Nursery Plants are collected from seed sources such as the Alpine Garden Society and the North American Rock Garden Society as well as propagated from the owners' own garden. They will give advice on planting up rock gardens, troughs and alpine areas.

> **Nicky's Rock Garden Nursery**, Hillcrest, Broadhayes
> Stockland, Honiton, Devon EX14 9EH
> **Tel:** 01404 881213
> **Opening hours:** 9.00 to dusk.
> **Visitors welcome:** yes, phone call in advance appreciated.
> **Catalogue:** 40p at the nursery, or 3 first class stamps by post.
> **Payment:** cash or cheque.
> **Mail order:** no.
> **Availability:** small stocks of most plants, though plants from seed are more numerous.
> **Refund/replacement:** yes.

GARDENERS' RECOMMENDATIONS: ❀ *"…unusual, well-produced plants at reasonable prices. The owners are always generous with their plant knowledge."* ❀ *"A good range of alpine plants, as well as shrubs and herbaceous plants, with an impressive display garden. The owners are show secretaries for the Alpine Garden Society and organise the South West Alpine Show."* Roger Stuckey, Chairman of Exeter Group of the Alpine Garden Society.

See map page 389.

Otter Nurseries Ltd   Taking advantage of their site in the south west of England, this nursery is able to grow most of its own plants and to try out unusual varieties. They have over 50 varieties of hydrangea, 16 ceanothus and eleven escallonias. There's a big restaurant and lots of parking.

> **Otter Nurseries Ltd**, Gosford Road, Ottery St. Mary, Devon EX11 1LZ
>
> **Tel:** 01404 815815   **Fax:** 01404 815816
>
> **Opening hours:** 9.00–17.30 Monday to Saturday, 10.30–16.30 Sunday.
>
> **Visitors welcome:** yes.
>
> **Catalogue:** none.
>
> **Payment:** cash, cheque, major credit cards.
>
> **Mail order:** no, but delivery sometimes possible.
>
> **Delivery:** within 7 days.
>
> **Availability:** normally all year round.
>
> **Refund/replacement:** 2-year guarantee on all hardy plants.
>
> **Special services:** restaurant.

GARDENERS' RECOMMENDATIONS: ❀ *"One of the better outlets for miles around."* Mr and Mrs D E Pounce.

See map page 389.

Peveril Clematis Nursery   Clematis are tricky to grow, demanding different treatment for different groups. It makes sense to go to a specialist to get full advice. This list is good and comprehensive.

> **Peveril Clematis Nursery**, Christow, Exeter, Devon EX6 7NG
>
> **Tel:** 01647 252937
>
> **Opening hours:** 10.00–13.00, 14.00–17.00 Monday to Wednesday, Friday and Saturday (closed Thursday), 10.00–13.00 Sunday from March to end November.

Visitors welcome: yes.

Catalogue: send 2 first class stamps.

Payment: cash or cheque.

Mail order: no.

Availability: most plants are available all year. Supplies of rare or unusual plants may be limited.

Refund/replacement: yes.

Special services: an established garden for customers' reference.

GARDENERS' RECOMMENDATIONS: *"Everything home grown. Excellent."* Major and Mrs John Poe.

See map page 389.

Pine Cottage Plants

The nursery, started in 1997, now holds the national collection of agapanthus of which they have over 150 different cultivars. There is also a list of tender plants, trees, shrubs and grasses. The nursery will try to identify plants.

Pine Cottage Plants, Four Ways, Eggesford, Chulmleigh, Devon EX18 7QZ

Tel/fax: 01769 580076

Opening hours: by appointment only.

Visitors welcome: yes.

Catalogue: £1. Send 3 first class stamps for list.

Payment: cash or cheque.

Mail order: yes. Minimum order £15.

Post and packing: £5.50 for up to 5 plants, £6.50 for 6–10, £7.50 for 16–20, £8 thereafter.

Delivery: allow up to 1 week.

Availability: supplies can be limited and some plants are available only at certain times of year.

Refund/replacement: yes.

Special services: garden consultation, plant identification.

GARDENERS' RECOMMENDATIONS: *"This is a new small nursery specialising in agapanthus, half-hardy perennials and unusual hardy perennials and shrubs. As well as finding something different here,*

the owner, Richard Fulcher, has a wealth of horticultural experience and expertise at his fingertips which he is happy to impart."
Maureen Jones.

See map page 389.

Plant World Botanic This plantsman's garden (with nursery to go with it) is set out in the countries of the world. Not only is this highly instructive but can be helpful in deciding what to put where (desert plants in hot, dry areas etc.) There are three national primula collections here plus new introductions from expeditions around the world. Less exotically, there are good selections of geraniums, meconopsis and columbines.

> **Plant World Botanic**, St Marychurch Road, Newton Abbot, Devon TQ12 4SE
> **Tel/fax:** 01803 872939
> **Opening hours:** 9.30–17.00 daily from Easter to end September.
> **Visitors welcome:** yes.
> **Catalogue:** seeds only, send 3 first class stamps.
> **Payment:** cheque, major credit cards.
> **Mail order:** seeds only. Minimum order £8.
> **Post and packing:** free for seed orders over £8.
> **Delivery:** seeds are sent by first class post.
> **Availability:** seeds are available all year round, plants for 6 months.
> **Refund/replacement:** yes.

GARDENERS' RECOMMENDATIONS: ⊕ *"Very interesting garden. Many unusual alpines/plants from abroad. Specialises in seed sales."* Mrs N Bitschi. ⊕ *"We visit several times a year and have watched the garden, and their knowledge, grow. It is a garden full of interesting plants. Lovely peaceful view."* Mr and Mrs Robert Knight. ⊕ *"Highly recommended – best germination rate for years."* Mrs Jessica Duncan.

See map page 388.

The Plantsman Nursery This is an unusual nursery because it operates only by mail-order: because of restrictions by the

Dartmoor National Park it is not allowed to accept visitors. Seems a pity when it specialises in climbing hardy and tender vines. The catalogue is extremely helpful and includes colour photographs and the nursery runs a plant surgery for existing customers via e-mail.

The Plantsman Nursery, North Wonson Farm, Throwleigh, Okehampton, Devon EX20 2JA

Tel: nursery 01647 231618, office 01647 231699

Fax: 01647 231157

E-mail: pnursery@aol.com

Website: http://www.plantsman.com

Opening hours: not open to the public. Office hours 8.00–17.00 Monday to Friday.

Visitors welcome: no visitors whatsoever except to view national collection.

Catalogue: £2, refundable against purchase.

Payment: cash, cheque, major credit cards.

Mail order: yes. Minimum order £25 plus delivery charge.

Post and packing: £11.75 for up to 10kg in mainland UK.

Delivery: usually within 5 days.

Availability: certain plants may sell out.

Refund/replacement: yes. if complaints are reported within 3 days of receipt.

Special services: quarterly newsletter, yearly report on annual plant collecting expedition.

GARDENERS' RECOMMENDATIONS: ✿ *"Hardy and tender climbing plants all grown on premises."* Mrs P Tham.

Pleasant View Nursery and Garden   The garden is of four acres with an arboretum suitable for all seasons. The nursery has the NCCPG national collections of salvia, with over 200 varieties, and abelia. It is 350 feet above sea level and very exposed, cool and quite dry so the plants are suitable for similar conditions.

Pleasant View Nursery, Two Mile Oak, Newton Abbot, Devon TQ12 6DG

Tel/fax: 01803 813388

Opening hours: 10.00–12.45, 13.30–17.00 Wednesday to Friday, and on Saturday for collection of orders only, from mid-March to end September.

Visitors welcome: yes.

Catalogue: send 5 second class stamps.

Payment: cash or cheque.

Mail order: yes.

Post and packing: from £3.80 for 6 salvias by post to £8 for shrubs by carrier.

Delivery: varies according to season.

Availability: salvias from April to September. Shrubs available all year round but supplies of certain varieties are limited.

Refund/replacement: no.

Special services: Garden open to visitors on Wednesday and Friday afternoons from May to September, entrance £2. Open to groups by appointment. Lectures to groups all over the country.

GARDENERS' RECOMMENDATIONS: ✿ *"Salvia specialist and, as such, unequalled in this country, but she also has an interesting range of half hardy shrubs at pretty realistic prices."* Mr Tim Longville.

See map page 388.

Pounsley Plants Jane Hollow has her nursery in a garden setting and grows what her customers want. She says, although she's in south Devon, the area is windy, salty, wet in winter and very dry in summer so her plants are tough. She gets wild seed collections and therefore has interesting rarities as well as good collections of kniphofia, iris, campanula and geraniums.

Pounsley Plants, Pounsley Coombe, Spriddlestone, Brixton, Plymouth, Devon PL9 0DW

Tel/fax: 01752 402873

E-mail: janehollow@pou599@aol.com

Opening hours: 10.00–17.00 Monday to Saturday.

Visitors welcome: yes, ring first to avoid disappointment.

Catalogue: send 2 first class stamps.

Payment: cheque.

Mail order: yes. Minimum order £10 or 4 plants.

Post and packing: £15.

Delivery: allow 28 days.

Availability: mail order service from October to February.

Refund/replacement: yes.

Special services: planning and planting advice.

GARDENERS' RECOMMENDATIONS: *"Wonderfully unusual plants. Very reasonable. Expertly grown. Passes on knowledge."* Mr and Mrs D Fenwick. *"Jane propagates a wonderful range of unusual and rare plants. She exhibits at local plant fairs and sales and is available to give cultural hints and advice to customers."* Mr and Mrs D Willis. *Also recommended by* Mr John Carter, Rowden Gardens.

See map page 388.

R D Plants   "We are," Rodney Davey and Lynda Windsor, say proudly "a low-tech old fashioned type of nursery with a resident propagator/nurseryman. We grow quality plants of hellebores and woodland plants plus unusual varieties and firm favourites of herbaceous perennials. Advice for visiting customers is given by the person who grows them." The formula obviously works for so many gardeners have recommended the firm.

R D Plants, Homelea Farm, Chard Road, Tytherleigh, Axminster Devon EX13 7BG

Tel: (only between 8.30–9.30 am) 01460 220206

Opening hours: 9.00–13.00, 14.00–17.00 most days from 1 March to 31 August. February by appointment for flowering hellebores.

Visitors welcome: yes, during opening hours.

Catalogue: Send 4 loose second class or 3 first class stamps.

Payment: cash, (cheque minimum £10).

Mail order: no.

Availability: Hellebores and woodland plants in early spring. 1,000 varieties of herbaceous perennials, mainly in 2 litre pots.

Refund/replacement: yes.

Special services: experienced propagator on site to give advice.

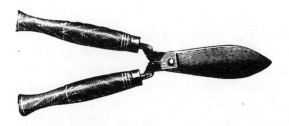

GARDENERS' RECOMMENDATIONS: ✸ *"Excellent plants divided into sections ie: shade, hot border etc. Helpful for new gardeners. Owners very knowledgeable."* ✸ *"Excellent range of unusual plants and detailed help given – display garden. Owners are real enthusiasts."* Rob Hubble and Stella Tracey. ✸ *"A superb selection of unusual perennials. Some wonderful hellebores coming on!"* Mr and Mrs M Perry. ✸ *"The most beautifully presented, and the finest selection of unusual herbaceous plants we know of."* Mr and Mrs Brown, Plant World. ✸ *"Superb range of rare and good garden plants, expertly grown. The highest standard of any nursery I know."*

See map page 389.

Rowden Gardens

The nursery holds national collections for fallopia, persicaria and Ranunculus ficaria. It specialises in rare and unusual aquatic and damp loving plants with a good range of irises, gunnera, ferns, grasses and rushes.

Rowden Gardens, Brentor, nr Tavistock, Devon PL19 0NG
Tel/fax: 01822 810275
Opening hours: 10.00–17.00 at weekends and bank holidays from April to September and at other times by appointment.
Visitors welcome: yes, during opening hours or by appointment.
Catalogue: £1.50.
Payment: cheque.
Mail order: yes.
Post and packing: from £4.50 to £12.50 depending on value of order.
Delivery: plants are sent out when they are ready and weather conditions are suitable.
Availability: aquatics despatched from last April to mid-August.
Refund/replacement: only if wrong variety sent.

GARDENERS' RECOMMENDATIONS: ✸ *"A specialist water garden in an unlikely position on top of a hill. Owner a great character and raconteur, full of anecdote and knowledge."* Mr Michael Stone. ✸ *"A very wide range of moisture-loving plants but displayed in the show garden in unusual fashion. Originally this was a series of long rectangular tanks for growing watercress. The parallel tanks make for interesting perspectives – ever changing."* Mr and Mrs K Ashburner,

Stone Lane Gardens. ✿ *"John Carter hold the NCCPG Polygonum collection and specialises in aquatics, so spring is the best time for a visit."* Mrs Jessica Duncan.

See map page 388.

Sampford Shrubs   When I asked if this nursery offered any special services, they replied "No! We stick to growing good plants." They might also add that they don't stick to shrubs, either. Like many smaller nurseries, they grow exactly what they like and this varies from grasses to rhododendrons.

Sampford Shrubs, Sampford Peverell, Tiverton, Devon EX16 7EN
Tel/fax: 01884 821164
E-mail: martin.h@virgin.net
Website: http://www.freespace.virgin.net/martin.h/sampford/
Opening hours: 9.00–17.00 Thursday to Saturday, 10.00–16.00 Sunday from February to November.
Visitors welcome: yes.
Catalogue: send A5 sae.
Payment: cash or cheque.
Mail order: yes. Minimum order £15 plus carriage.
Post and packing: £7 for up to 20 kg. Highlands and Islands by quotation.
Delivery: allow 6 weeks if weather is suitable. Orders including less hardy items may be delayed until early March.
Availability: most plants should be available for most of the year, but this is not always possible.
Refund/replacement: yes, if notified within one month. No liability accepted for mistreatment or weather damage.

GARDENERS' RECOMMENDATIONS: ✿ *"A wonderful simple nursery where it is possible to find a lot of well grown old friends, as well as an interesting variety of unusual plants. Very friendly and always seem to have time to discuss problems and give splendid advice. All material produced on the spot."* Mr and Mrs J Kenney. ✿ *"Unusual, well-produced plants at reasonable prices. The owners are always generous with their plant knowledge."*

See map page 389.

Silver Dale Nurseries   Fuchsia specialists and members of the fuchsia society who hold the national collection of hardy cultivars and species. Cuttings can be taken against orders and are very cheap. The only deplorable thing about fuchsias is the silly names that breeders give them — one group is named after the seven dwarfs in Snow White.

> **Silver Dale Nurseries**, Shute Lane, Combe Martin, Devon EX34 0HT
> **Tel:** 01271 882539
> **Opening hours:** 10.00–18.00 daily.
> **Visitors welcome:** yes.
> **Catalogue:** £1.
> **Payment:** cheque, Visa, Mastercard, Eurocard, Switch.
> **Mail order:** yes.
> **Post and packing:** from £3.25 for up to 10 cuttings to £6.75 for up to 50 by first class post.
> **Delivery:** allow 6 weeks.
> **Availability:** mail order from January to May. Pots available throughout the year.
> **Refund/replacement:** yes, reply paid cards send with order to monitor any comments.
> **Special services:** display area, leaflets and advice, talks by arrangement.

GARDENERS' RECOMMENDATIONS: ❀ *Recommended by* Mrs Edna Squires, Hon Sec Devon Group NCCPG.

See map page 389.

Stone Lane Gardens   The nursery adjoins the birch and alder arboretum and likes to supply trees which match what visitors can see there — "an ideal", says Kenneth Ashburner, "which cannot be wholly reached." However, the list has birch collected from Wisconsin to Yunnan, from North Honshu to Poland and is extremely exciting. The alnus varieties also seem to cover the globe. The list includes a very few other trees such as a pin oak and Arizona ash. The nursery holds a sculpture exhibition every summer called *The Mythic Garden* and sells works by some of the best modern sculptors working in Britain today.

Stone Lane Gardens, Stone Farm, Chagford, Devon TQ13 8JU
Tel/fax: 01647 231311
Opening hours: by appointment at any time.
Visitors welcome: yes.
Catalogue: £2 inc p&p.
Payment: cash or cheque.
Mail order: yes.
Post and packing: £5 to £7.
Delivery: allow 2-3 months, less in spring.
Availability: bare-rooted wild-origin birch and alder, also fraxinus, platanus and Malus sieboldii from November to April.
Refund/replacement: yes.

GARDENERS' RECOMMENDATIONS: ✿ *"I wouldn't really class this as a nursery as such, more of an experience. Kenneth Ashburner collects tree seed from the wild, particularly birch and alder. The largely "wild" display garden with close planting of trees in groves (wonderful pink and white stemmed birches) doubles as a sculpture garden, with exhibitors choosing the placement of their pieces and the exhibition changing yearly. Lovely location down winding lanes on the edge of Dartmoor. (The Ashburners were featured in RHS* The Garden *a couple of years ago)."* Mrs Jessica Duncan.

See map page 389.

Stuckey's Alpines

The Stuckeys are keen growers and creators of rock gardens and will talk to clubs about their construction. Plants include, obviously, alpines but also arisaema, dwarf shrubs, primulas and auriculas.

Stuckey's Alpines, 38 Phillipps Avenue, Exmouth, Devon EX8 3HZ
Tel: 01395 273636
Opening hours: on NGS open days or by appointment.
Visitors welcome: yes, by appointment.
Catalogue: none.
Payment: cash or cheque.
Mail order: no.
Availability: all year round.
Refund/replacement: yes.
Special services: rock garden construction, trough collection, talks to clubs.

Gardeners' Recommendations: *"Excellent alpines."* Mrs N Bitschi.

See map page 389.

Suttons Seeds

Suttons Seeds A very famous seed firm which has been winning gold medals at Chelsea for nearly 100 years. But they also offer a selection of bulbs, patio plants such as fuchsia and petunia along with a huge list of flower and vegetable seeds.

Suttons Seeds, Woodview Road, Paignton, Devon TQ4 7NG
Tel: 01803 696363 **Fax:** 01803 696345
E-mail: retail@suttons.co.uk
Opening hours: mail order only.
Visitors welcome: no.
Catalogue: free.
Payment: cheque, Visa, Mastercard, Switch, Delta.
Mail order: yes.
Post and packing: 75p for seed orders up to £8, free thereafter. £1.95 to £2.50 for bulbs.
Delivery: seeds despatched as quickly as possibly. Plants and bulbs in season.
Availability: seeds all year round, plants and bulbs despatched during planting season.
Refund/replacement: yes.
Special services: advisory service by post or telephone.

Gardeners' Recommendations: *Recommended by* Lady Barbirolli *and* The Earl Haig.

Thornhayes Nursery

Thornhayes Nursery The firm grows ornamental and fruit trees. In the ornamental bracket are over 40 birch varieties, over 30 beeches and nearly 100 sorbus. Among the fruit trees are ancient apples like Cornish Aromatic, Colonel Vaughan and Catshead, figs, mulberries, walnuts and medlars. An inspiring list.

Thornhayes Nursery, St Andrews Wood, Dulford, Cullompton, Devon EX15 2DF
Tel: 01884 266746 **Fax:** 01884 266739

E-mail: trees@thornhayes.demon.co.uk
Opening hours: 8.00–16.30 Monday to Friday.
Visitors welcome: yes, by appointment.
Catalogue: send 5 first class stamps.
Payment: cash or cheque.
Mail order: yes.
Post and packing: from £15.
Delivery: varies according to time of year.
Availability: choice rarities need to be ordered well in advance.
Refund/replacement: yes, if justified.

GARDENERS' RECOMMENDATIONS: ❀ *"Very comprehensive range of apple trees (particularly West Country varieties, as well as interesting range of broad-leaved trees. Kevin Croucher is an acknowledged expert on matters such as grafting etc."* Mrs Jessica Duncan. ❀*"Excellent tree and fruit nursery."* Major and Mrs George Llewellyn. ❀ *"Has supplied us with excellent fruit trees and holds a huge range."* Sarah Conibear.

See map page 389.

Veryans Plants Rebecca Veryan Millar produces an idiosyncratic list of plants she clearly likes with helpful growing advice. Emocomon chionanthum "runs around like mad", Maianthemum bifolium is "a dear little relative of the lily of the valley." Sadly, she does mail order only, as she sounds worth a visit.

Veryans Plants, The Barn, Coryton House, Coryton, Okehampton, Devon EX20 4PB
Tel: 01822 860130
Opening hours: not open to the public.
Visitors welcome: no.
Catalogue: send 3 first class stamps.
Payment: cash or cheque.
Mail order: yes.
Post and packing: £4.50 for up to 4 plants, £6 for 5–10 plants, £7 thereafter.
Delivery: up to 12 months depending on weather and availability.
Availability: supplies can be limited and some plants are available only at certain times of year.
Refund/replacement: by arrangement.

GARDENERS' RECOMMENDATIONS: ✿ *"Unusual, well-produced plants at reasonable prices."* ✿ *"Small selection of spring flowering woodlanders, flowers for semi-wild gardens, something not always easy to find."*

Whitehouse Ivies

No garden should be without at least one ivy scrambling over walls, banks, rockeries or as ground cover. Within its limits, the range is huge with an extraordinary diversity of size and shape of leaf, veining, variations and behaviour. The catalogue is extremely helpful in showing a silhouette of each leaf shape along with a helpful description.

> **Whitehouse Ivies**, Eggesford Gardens, Chulmleigh, Devon EX18 7QU
> **Tel:** 01769 580250 **Fax:** 01769 581041
> **Opening hours:** 9.00–17.30 daily.
> **Visitors welcome:** yes.
> **Catalogue:** £1.50.
> **Payment:** cash, cheque, major credit/debit cards.
> **Mail order:** yes.
> **Post and packing:** by quotation.
> **Delivery:** 2-3 weeks.
> **Availability:** all year round.
> **Refund/replacement:** yes, 2-year guarantee (providing instructions are followed).
> **Special services:** plant finding service.

GARDENERS' RECOMMENDATIONS: ✿ *"Excellent selection of ivies – mail order plants arrived in very good condition and grew very well."* Ms Venner and Mr Glassborow.

See map page 389.

Withleigh Nurseries

No catalogue here for the general lists of shrubs, bedding, roses, climbers, herbaceous etc. but, says the nursery, "just good plain value for money, variety and knowledgeable service." No e-mail, no fax, no website — "not very 1990s are we?" they add. It's not really necessary.

Withleigh Nurseries, Sunrise Hill, Tiverton, Devon EX16 8JG
Tel: 01884 253351
Opening hours: 9.00–17.30 Monday to Saturday from March to June, and Tuesday to Saturday from July to February.
Visitors welcome: yes.
Catalogue: none.
Payment: cash or cheque.
Mail order: no.
Availability: many items are seasonal.
Refund/replacement: sympathetic to all losses.

GARDENERS' RECOMMENDATIONS: ⊛ *"Withleigh is run by the owner. The plants are good and reasonable."* Mr and Mrs Shapland. ⊛ *"Good range of plants, including the rarer varieties, well tended and tidy. A good garden to view."*

See map page 389.

Nigel Wright Rhododendrons

The nursery sells only rhododendrons — and those to very grand places indeed. "We do not supply forced potted plants as required by garden centres," they say firmly. The list is huge with only a few species but, if you want a special colour or habit, this is your place.

Nigel Wright Rhododendrons, The Old Glebe, Eggesford, Chulmleigh, Devon EX18 7QU
Tel: 01769 580632
Opening hours: by appointment.
Visitors welcome: by appointment only.
Catalogue: send 2 first class stamps.
Payment: cash or cheque.
Mail order: no.
Availability: stock of 6,000 plants of over 200 varieties.
Refund/replacement: replacement.
Special services: individual attention including tour of 7-acre rhododendron garden. Free advice and planting plans.

GARDENERS' RECOMMENDATIONS: ⊛ *"Nigel does a superb list and his plants are well grown and hardy."*

See map page 389.

DORSET

Abbey Plants Connected with a cottage garden which is stocked with interesting plants, the nursery offers a wide range of garden plants along with a list of the trees and shrubs.

> **Abbey Plants**, Chiffchaffs, Chaffeymoor, Bourton, Dorset SP8 5BY
> **Tel:** 01747 840841
> **Opening hours:** 10.00–13.00, 14.00–17.00 Tuesday to Saturday from mid-March to mid-November and on Chiffchaffs' NGS open days.
> **Visitors welcome:** yes.
> **Catalogue:** none.
> **Payment:** cash or cheque.
> **Mail order:** yes.
> **Post and packing:** generally at cost.
> **Delivery:** depends on distance.
> **Availability:** limited supplies of the more unusual varieties.
> **Refund/replacement:** yes, if genuine.

GARDENERS' RECOMMENDATIONS: ✤ *"They have a good selection of plants both common and unusual and usually well-grown."* Mrs Anne Stevens. ✤ *"A small nursery of good plants, attached to the owners' delightful cottage garden."* Mrs G C Royle

See map page 389.

Cherry Tree Nursery This is a different kind of nursery, added to this list because it is the first project of the Sheltered Work Opportunities Project (SWOP) offering "therapeutic horticultural work in a supportive and stress-free environment." Using workers with some degree of mental ill-health, the nursery now produces over 80,000 hardy shrubs each year from cuttings. Growing things, like looking after animals, is a great restorative.

> **Cherry Tree Nursery**, off New Road Roundabout, Northbourne, Bournemouth, Dorset BH10 7DA
> **Tel:** 01202 593537 **Fax:** 01202 590626
> **Opening hours:** 8.30–15.30 Monday to Friday, 9.00–12.00 most Saturdays.

Visitors welcome: yes.
Catalogue: free.
Payment: cash or cheque.
Mail order: no.
Delivery: available locally within one or two days.
Availability: varies according to season.
Refund/replacement: yes.

GARDENERS' RECOMMENDATIONS: *"A very efficient nursery run by Mrs E Pitkin but employing handicapped staff. Good quality plants at low prices."* Dr and Mrs J Fisher. *"Cherry Tree Nursery is run by SWOP. It is going from strength to strength. It provides excellent quality young plants, at reasonable prices, as well as a happy, healthy working environment for the people working there. I recommend a visit or at least a phone call. The Manager and her staff are dedicated – to the plants and to their workers."* Mrs J Smith.

See map page 390.

Christina's Cottage Plants The garden alongside the nursery is open under the NGS scheme and many plants for sale can be seen in situ. The firm has no catalogue other than a list of 70 varieties of geraniums but specialises in those which tolerate dry situations, whether sunny or shaded, and alkaline soil

Christina's Cottage Plants, Friars Way Nursery, Church Street, Upwey, Weymouth, Dorset DT3 5QE
Tel/fax: 01305 813243
Opening hours: 11.00–18.00 Thursday and by appointment.
Visitors welcome: yes, but please telephone first.
Catalogue: send 3 first class stamps for geranium list.
Payment: cash or cheque.
Mail order: no.
Availability: supplies can be limited.
Refund/replacement: if there is a fault with the plant.

GARDENERS' RECOMMENDATIONS: *"Very good and the owners helpful."* Mrs Anne Stevens.

See map page 389.

Cold Harbour Nursery

Cold Harbour Nursery A place for plantsmen with a good selection of both unusual and rare perennials, plants ideal for woodland (the nursery is set in woodland) and grasses. The nursery was founded in 1992 in an area being reclaimed from an overgrown oak wood. Holly and brambles have given away to rhododendrons, azaleas and shrubs to form the backbone of the garden.

> **Cold Harbour Nursery**, Bere Road, Wareham, Dorset.
> Office address: 19 Hilary Road, Poole, Dorset BH17 7LZ
>
> **Tel:** 01202 696875 (evenings)
>
> **E-mail:** coldharbour@hilaryroad.freeserve.co.uk
>
> **Opening hours:** 10.00–17.00 Tuesday to Friday and most weekends (best to telephone first) from 1 March to end October.
>
> **Visitors welcome:** yes.
>
> **Catalogue:** send 3 second class stamps.
>
> **Payment:** cheque.
>
> **Mail order:** yes. Minimum order £10.
>
> **Post and packing:** £14 for next-day service.
>
> **Delivery:** within 2 weeks.
>
> **Availability:** most plants are available from late spring.
>
> **Refund/replacement:** yes.

See map page 389.

Frampton Roses

Frampton Roses The rose fields around this nursery are open to the public every summer so that people can see the varieties before they buy. Go anytime from June to September to catch their full glory. On view are some splendid old varieties such as Rosa mundi, R gallica and, a favourite of mine, R mutabilis. There are species roses, floribunda and hybrid teas. The nursery will give advice to new rose growers.

> **Frampton Roses**, 34 Dorchester Road, Frampton, Dorchester, Dorset DT2 9NF
>
> **Tel:** 01300 320453
>
> **Opening hours:** 9.00–17.00 Thursday to Monday in summer, 9.00–16.00 Thursday to Monday in winter, closed Tuesday and Wednesday.
>
> **Visitors welcome:** yes.
>
> **Catalogue:** free. Second class stamp appreciated.

Payment: cash or cheque.

Mail order: yes.

Post and packing: £4.99 for up to 10 plants, £7.50 thereafter.

Delivery: 3 working days from receipt of payment.

Availability: all year round, although supplies of some popular varieties may be limited.

Refund/replacement: replacement.

GARDENERS' RECOMMENDATIONS: ❀ *"A specialist rose nursery run by husband and wife; excellent selection of old and English roses, very well grown. Knowledgeable, helpful service."* ❀ *"Excellent new rose nursery, run by owner and his wife. He worked for Hilliers for many years. A very good selection of roses, excellent plants and reasonably priced."* Mr and Mrs H Lindsay. ❀ *"Very good stock."* Major & Mrs John Poe.

See map page 389.

Knoll Gardens Nursery
Holders of the national collections of phygelius (cape fuchsias) and deciduous ceanothus, the nursery also has excellent lists of grasses, hardy and tender perennials.

Knoll Gardens Nursery, Stapehill, Hampreston, nr Wimborne, Dorset BH21 7ND

Tel: 01202 873931 **Fax:** 01202 780842

Website: http://www.knollgardens.co.uk

Opening hours: 10.00–17.00 daily from April to September, 10.00–16.00 Wednesday to Sunday in October and March, 10.00–16.00 Wednesday to Friday and Sunday from November to Christmas.

Visitors welcome: yes.

Catalogue: none.

Payment: cash, cheque, Visa, Access, Switch, Delta.

Mail order: possibly soon.

Availability: supplies of some plants can be limited.

Refund/replacement: yes.

GARDENERS' RECOMMENDATIONS: ❀ *"This nursery, attached to the gardens, has an excellent range of perennials and grasses, shown growing in the gardens. The National Collections of phygelius and ceanothus are held here. The plants are of good quality and the staff knowledgeable and helpful."* Mrs Penny Slade, secretary of the East

Dorset NCCPG. ❀ *"Good quality, interesting general plants. Good Price. Attractive garden."* The Reverend and Mrs Hamilton-Brown. ❀ *"Water gardens with waterfalls, pools and stream, mixed borders and woodland setting."*

See map page 390.

MacPennys of Bransgore
As well as lists of shrubs etc, the nursery sensibly divides its catalogues into ferns, azaleas and rhododendrons, camellias and heather, among others. Sensibly because this is a huge list of interesting plants.

MacPennys of Bransgore, 154 Burley Road, Bransgore, Christchurch, Dorset BH23 8DB

Tel: 01425 672348

Opening hours: 9.00–17.00 Monday to Saturday, 14.00–17.00 (9.00–17.00 April to June) Sunday.

Visitors welcome: yes.

Catalogue: send A4 sae plus 4 first class stamps.

Payment: cash, cheque, major credit/debit cards.

Mail order: yes.

Post and packing: from £4.25.

Delivery: within 10 days if available.

Availability: supplies can be limited and some varieties are available only at certain times of year.

Refund/replacement: yes.

Special services: guided tours of 4-acre woodland garden for groups by appointment at certain times.

GARDENERS' RECOMMENDATIONS: ❀ *"They have a woodland garden where one can see their plants growing and most of the plants are of their own raising."* ❀ *"Pleasantly 'old fashioned'. Good range of plants plus some tender specialities. All 'home-grown'."* Mr and Mrs P Jackson. ❀ *"An old family business. They know about plants, providing a large range of conifers, heathers, shrubs, trees, herbaceous plants. Has a sunken garden of camellias and many different shrubs and trees."* Mr and Mrs O Ziegler.

See map page 390.

The Scented Garden   There is more to gardens than colour. Scented gardens are becoming increasingly planted and this nursery, which holds the national collection of lavenders, has many more plants than on its small list. Phone if you have something special in mind.

> **The Scented Garden**, Gardens Cottage, Littlebredy, Dorchester, Dorset DT2 9HG
> **Tel:** 01308 482307
> **Opening hours:** 14.30–20.00 Tuesday only in June and July.
> **Visitors welcome:** by prior appointment.
> **Catalogue:** send 2 second class stamps.
> **Payment:** cash or cheque.
> **Mail order:** no.
> **Availability:** best choice available from May to August.
> **Refund/replacement:** yes.
> **Special services:** advice on colour themes and plant association.

GARDENERS' RECOMMENDATIONS: ❀ *"National collection of lavenders. Very good herbaceous plants, excellent quality."* Mr and Mrs H Lindsay.

See map page 389.

Trehane Nursery   Specialists in camellias and blueberries, the nursery also has cranberries, azaleas and rhododendrons, pieris and magnolias, all lovers of acid soil. The helpful catalogue does a question and answer routine on cultivating camellias.

> **Trehane Nursery**, Stapehill Road, Hampreston, Wimborne, Dorset BH21 7ND
> **Tel/fax:** 01202 873490
> **Opening hours:** 8.30–16.30 Monday to Friday. 10.00–16.00 at weekends during spring only. By appointment at other times.
> **Visitors welcome:** yes.
> **Catalogue:** £1.70.
> **Payment:** cash, cheque, major credit cards.
> **Mail order:** yes.
> **Post and packing:** £8.50 for orders up to £39, £10.50 for orders from £39 to £78, by quotation thereafter.

Delivery: 2-3 days by carrier, 5–10 working days by Parcelforce.

Availability: despatch all year round except during extreme weather. Certain varieties are in short supply.

Refund/replacement: yes, within a year if customer has followed planting and growing instructions.

GARDENERS' RECOMMENDATIONS: ✿ *"Wide selection of camellias, well grown plants, my source of camellias. Good advice available."* Mr and Mrs Gueterbock. ✿ *"Specialist and reliable."* Mr Bruce Archibold, former chairman RHS Rhododendron, Camellia and Magnolia Group. ✿ *"The place for camellias – exceptional range. Not cheap but good quality."* Mr and Mrs P Jackson. ✿ *"Wide range of camellias."* Mr and Mrs E G Millais, Millais Nursery.

See map page 390.

ESSEX

Beeches Nursery   This is a small nursery with a big list, so it's sensibly divided into herbaceous, grasses and ferns in one, trees and climbers, shrubs, fruit, roses and bamboos in another. It offers advice on site over a large range of plants.

Beeches Nursery, The Beeches, Ashdon, nr Saffron Walden, Essex CB10 2HB

Tel: 01799 584362   **Fax:** 01799 584362

E-mail: sales@beechesnursery.co.uk

Website: http://www.beechesnursery.co.uk

Opening hours: 8.30–17.00 Monday to Saturday, 9.30–17.00 Sunday and bank holidays.

Visitors welcome: yes.

Catalogue: send 3 second class stamps.

Payment: cheque, Visa, Mastercard, Access, debit cards.

Mail order: yes.

Post and packing: £8.95 for up to 25 kg by 24-hour carrier.

Delivery: 1-3 weeks according to season and availability.

Availability: supplies can be limited.

Refund/replacement: yes, if damaged in transit.
Special services: on site advice.

GARDENERS' RECOMMENDATIONS: ✿ *"Small nursery with wide range of herbaceous perennials, alpines, shrubs, trees, grasses. Also some half-hardy plants and, in season, bedding and vegetable plants. Many grown on premises. Knowledgeable advice. Garden atmosphere. Best nursery we know – anywhere!"* Mr and Mrs P E Lewis. ✿ *"Unusual and rare plants especially perennials. Kevin Marsh sources seed from all over the world. A small nursery with very friendly service and advice. Also a very good range of roses, shrubs and trees. Good mail order service."* Mr and Mrs Swete. ✿ *"Huge range of perennials – all substantial plants e.g. 19 eryngiums, 35 euphorbias, wonderful value."* Mr P J Oliver-Smith.

See map page 393.

The Beth Chatto Gardens   A famous nursery, with gardens attached, run by a famous garden writer. Beth Chatto made her name with interesting planting for difficult areas — dry shade, gravel, cool shade, full sun — and her gardens show the plants in situ. Because she tries out what she preaches (and East Anglia has a comparatively dry, windswept climate) the plants do what she tells us. It is, however, a very large concern now and consequently, in my experience, could be more friendly.

The Beth Chatto Gardens Ltd, Elmstead Market, nr Colchester, Essex CO7 7DB
Tel: 01206 862007 **Fax:** 01206 825933
Opening hours: 9.00–17.00 Monday to Saturday from March to end October, 9.00–16.00 Monday to Friday from November to end February.
Visitors welcome: yes.
Catalogue: £3.
Payment: cheque, Visa, Access, Switch.
Mail order: yes. Minimum order £20.
Post and packing: £6.50 for orders up to £65, 10% of order value thereafter.
Delivery: orders despatched from September to early December and early spring to end April.
Availability: some plants are scarce.

Refund/replacement: by arrangement. Complaints should be made within 14 days.

Special services: gift vouchers.

GARDENERS' RECOMMENDATIONS: ✸ *"I travel regularly to this well-established nursery to add plants to my own collections …definitely highly recommended by me."* Mr N Lucas, Knoll Gardens. ✸ *"This was my local nursery when I started gardening 28 years ago and now in Devon I am still occasionally using her very good mail order service for irresistible 'treasures'. A visit to her garden as well as the nursery is an education both horticulturally and artistically."* Mrs Jessica Duncan. ✸ *"…impossible to leave without loads of plants, sensible, hardy and mostly easy ones chosen by Beth with an artist's eye."* ✸ *"The best. We go all over the country in our quest for unusual plants. We have visited the garden and nursery since 1990. We met Beth Chatto pushing a wheelbarrow in her garden. Wonderful."* Mr and Mrs P Fowler.

See map page 393.

The Cottage Garden

When I visit this nursery, I tend to come away with hardware rather than plants, for it sells antique garden rollers, old glass cloches and terracotta pots. The plants are excellent, too, and tend towards the simple cottage garden varieties.

The Cottage Garden, Langham Road, Boxted, Colchester, Essex CO4 5HU

Tel: 01206 272269

Opening hours: 8.00–17.30 Monday to Saturday, 9.30–17.00 Sunday. Closed Tuesday and Wednesday between September and February.

Visitors welcome: yes.

Catalogue: none.

Payment: cash or cheque.

Mail order: no.

Availability: good range throughout the year.

Refund/replacement: yes, if justified.

GARDENERS' RECOMMENDATIONS: ✸ *"Always helpful and knowledgeable."* Mr and Mrs D R Brightwell.

See map page 393.

County Park Nursery Graham Hutchins specialises in the plants of New Zealand and Tasmania and his plant list helpfully indicates just how hardy each variety is. Though many of these look exotic, a good few will cope in a sheltered area and some, like olearias and hebes, are pretty tough. He holds the national collection of over 100 coprosma, has 300 hebes, 40 leptospermum and 90 carmichaelia or related plants. He has also introduced and named over 500 new plants, continuing at the rate of about 30 a year.

> **County Park Nursery**, Essex Gardens, Wingletye Lane, Hornchurch, Essex RM11 3BU
>
> **Tel:** 01708 445205
>
> **Opening hours:** 9.00–18.00 Monday, Tuesday and Thursday to Saturday, 10.00–17.00 Sunday from April to October. By appointment only from November to March.
>
> **Visitors welcome:** yes, advisable to ring first as the nursery is a one-man business.
>
> **Catalogue:** none.
>
> **Payment:** cash or cheque.
>
> **Mail order:** no.
>
> **Availability:** supplies can be limited and some plants are available only at certain times of year.
>
> **Refund/replacement:** never had a dissatisfied customer.
>
> **Special services:** many specimen plants on show from New Zealand and Australia.

GARDENERS' RECOMMENDATIONS: *"The New Zealand specialist. Confounded nuisance that he doesn't do mail order. The only possible reason for visiting Hornchurch…"* Mr Tim Longville. *"Graham Hutchins specialises in antipodean plants. It is a tiny place crammed full of propagated plants mainly from New Zealand. You need an hour or so to visit because once you get chatting to Graham, listening to his tales of collecting sprees in New Zealand, time flies!"* Glenys Payne and Peggy Harvey.

See map page 392.

Glen Chantry Particular interests, say Sue and Wol Staines, are irises, geraniums, hostas, euphorbias and plants for the white garden — but that's not the half of it. This is a plantsman's paradise, full of extremely rare and beautiful varieties. The three-acre garden shows what can be done with them.

Glen Chantry, Ishams Chase, Wickham Bishops, Essex CM8 3LG
Tel/fax: 01621 891342
Opening hours: 10.00–16.00 Friday and Saturday from end March to mid-October, and as listed in NGS yellow book.
Visitors welcome: yes, during opening hours.
Catalogue: send 4 first class stamps.
Payment: cash or cheque.
Mail order: no.
Availability: rare plants are always in limited supply.
Refund/replacement: cases are assessed individually.
Special services: Teas, 3-acre garden open to visitors (entrance £2).

GARDENERS' RECOMMENDATIONS: ❀ *"Well grown, large range of interesting perennials – value for money – knowledgeable owners with super garden of their own."* Mr and Mrs Holdaway and Mrs Burton. ❀ *"Very good for perennials and alpines. Wide and excellent choice."* Mr Ken Akers. ❀ *"A true plantsman's nursery run by a couple devoted to their garden and plant growing. Always full of helpful advice and knowledge."* Mrs Catherine Horwood. ❀ *"Sells excellent plants all home produced from a superb garden."* Mr and Mrs G Smith. ❀ *Also recommended by* Mr and Mrs M Metianu, Church Hill Cottage.

See map page 393.

Langthorns Plantery
This is a huge selection of interesting plants — some extremely rare which may be propagated to order. There is no mail-order — why bother, they say, when people come from all over the world to visit them?

Langthorns Plantery, Little Canfield, nr Dunmow, Essex CM6 1TD
Tel/fax: 01371 872611
Opening hours: 10.00–17.00 (dusk if earlier) daily, except Christmas fortnight and Easter Sunday.
Visitors welcome: yes.
Catalogue: £1.50.
Payment: cash, cheque, Visa, Access, Mastercard, Switch.
Mail order: no.
Refund/replacement: yes, if a plant dies within 6 months of purchase unless as a result of customer negligence.

GARDENERS' RECOMMENDATIONS: ✺ *"An excellent selection of more unusual plants – herbaceous, shrubs and trees. There is also a wide selection of container grown roses, particularly good for old-fashioned and shrub roses. Helpful advice if required and good labelling on plants."* Mr and Mrs E G Billington. ✺ *"Langthorns shows good healthy plants with large and interesting scope – also reasonable prices."* Mr and Mrs R Pilkington. ✺ *"Excellent collection of unusual perennials and shrubs all beautifully grown. Impossible to come away empty handed."* Mrs Catherine Horwood.

See map page 393.

Manor Nursery

Excellent range of choice herbaceous plants of unusual forms and colours detailed in helpful catalogue. More available to personal shoppers for whom there are good discounts. There's also a garden to show off the plants.

Manor Nursery, Thaxted Road, Wimbish, Saffron Walden, Essex CB10 2UT

Tel/fax: 01799 513481

E-mail: flora@gardenplants.co.uk

Website: http://www.gardenplants.co.uk

Opening hours: 9.00–17.00 from March to October, 9.00–16.00 from November to February.

Visitors welcome: yes.

Catalogue: £1.50.

Payment: cheque, major credit/debit cards.

Mail order: yes. Minimum order 10 plants.

Post and packing: £5 for up to 25 plants, free thereafter.

Delivery: by 24-hour carrier. Allow 1-4 weeks depending on availability.

Availability: most plants in stock all year round.

Refund/replacement: yes, no quibble guarantee.

Special services: garden usually open.

GARDENERS' RECOMMENDATIONS: ✺ *"Unusual plants."* Mrs W H Mason. ✺ *"Excellent plants, well-chosen list, interested in one's requirements."* Dr and Mrs D W Eyre-Walker.

See map page 393.

Mill Race Nursery

Mill Race Nursery   This is a huge nursery with 500,000 containerised plants over 12 acres. Other plants are grown under contract by other nurseries. The list provides few surprises but, if you are keen to start a garden with plants which respond well and are good value, this is a good place to start.

> **Mill Race Nursery**, New Road, Aldham, Colchester, Essex CO6 3QT
>
> **Tel:** 01206 242521   **Fax:** 01206 241616
>
> **Opening hours:** 9.00–17.30 daily.
>
> **Visitors welcome:** yes.
>
> **Catalogue:** 50p.
>
> **Payment:** cash, cheque, major credit cards.
>
> **Mail order:** no.
>
> **Availability:** supplies can be limited and some plants are available only at certain times of year.
>
> **Refund/replacement:** depends on circumstances.
>
> **Special services:** coffee shop, riverside picnic garden, boating on River Colne, dried and silk flowers, design and landscaping.

GARDENERS' RECOMMENDATIONS: ❀ *"An excellent choice of plants, some unusual, of high quality and, on the whole, reasonably priced."* Lady Cave.

See map page 393.

Frances Mount Hardy Perennial Plants

Frances Mount Hardy Perennial Plants   Frances specialises in those belles of the border and bog — hardy geraniums. With elegant leaves, the ability to smother weeds and a long flowering period, these are most helpful plants. The flowers may vary from dark purple to soft grey with strong veining. Some are British natives and can still be found in hedgerows. A helpfully described selection along with a few other perennials such as campanula, irises and pulmonaria.

> **Frances Mount Perennial Plants**, 1 Steps Farm, Polstead, Colchester, Essex CO6 5AE
>
> **Tel:** 01206 262811
>
> **Opening hours:** 10.00–17.00 Tuesday, Wednesday and Saturday, 14.00–18.00 Friday. Closed December and January.
>
> **Visitors welcome:** yes.
>
> **Catalogue:** send 3 first class stamps.

Payment: cheque.

Mail order: yes. Minimum order £5 plus p&p.

Post and packing: £7 for up to 10 plants, £8 for 11 to 20, £10 for 21 to 30, 35p per plant thereafter.

Delivery: 1 to 4 weeks depending on weather conditions. No delivery in December and January.

Availability: orders despatched from September to November and from February to May.

Refund/replacement: yes.

GARDENERS' RECOMMENDATIONS: ⊛ *"Very small nursery specialising in hardy geraniums. Interesting plants. Miss Mount is a very knowledgeable plantswoman, including wild flowers. Encyclopaedic knowledge."*

See map page 393.

Oasis Paul Spraklin is a garden designer who works with tropical-looking plants and, because they were hard to find, he began propagating his own. What he doesn't need, he sells on. Because of this, numbers may be limited or sold out — and he pleads with buyers to ring him first. His interests include agaves and tree ferns, chusquea bamboo, red hot pokers, yuccas and arum lilies. A most interesting selection.

Oasis, 42 Greenwood Avenue, South Benfleet, Essex SS7 1LD

Tel: 01268 757666 **Fax:** 01268 795646

E-mail: exotic@globalnet.co.uk

Website: http://www.user.globalnet.co.uk/~exotic

Opening hours: generally 11.00–16.00 Saturday from April to October, but telephone first. By appointment at other times.

Visitors welcome: yes.

Catalogue: send 2 first class stamps.

Payment: cash or cheque.

Mail order: yes.

Post and packing: from £6.50.

Delivery: depends on availability.

Availability: some plants unavailable during winter.

Refund/replacement: individual complaints considered on merit.

Special services: garden design.

GARDENERS' RECOMMENDATIONS: *"Specialist in half hardy plants for hot dry climates, such as tropical Essex! A devoted enthusiast, with an ever increasing range (the nursery is only 2 or 3 years old) – and no longer just plants for heat and dryness either. Sensible prices too."* Mr Tim Longville.

See map page 392.

Rhodes and Rockcliffe

The firm sells nothing but begonias but these include rhizomatous varieties, shrubby ones and cane-stemmed species. There are also hybrids. They have won numerous RHS medals, including three silver-gilts at Chelsea.

> **Rhodes & Rockliffe**, 2 Nursery Road, Nazeing, Essex EN9 2JE
> **Tel:** 01992 463693 **Fax:** 01992 440673
> **Opening hours:** strictly by appointment.
> **Visitors welcome:** yes, by appointment.
> **Catalogue:** send 2 first class stamps.
> **Payment:** cash or cheque.
> **Mail order:** yes.
> **Post and packing:** £2 for up to 5 plants, £3 for 6–10, £5 thereafter.
> **Delivery:** by arrangement.
> **Availability:** spring and summer only.
> **Refund/replacement:** yes.

GARDENERS' RECOMMENDATIONS: *Recommended by* Christopher Lloyd, Great Dixter.

See map page 392.

R & R Saggers

A small nursery which has neither catalogue nor mail order service. It sells a general list and also stocks Whichford terracotta pots.

> **R and R Saggers**, Waterloo House, Newport, Saffron Walden, Essex CB11 3PG
> **Tel:** 01799 540858
> **Opening hours:** Tuesday to Sunday 10.00–17.00. Closed on Sundays from January to March and in August.
> **Visitors welcome:** yes.
> **Catalogue:** none as varieties are always changing.

Payment: cheque, major credit cards.

Mail order: no.

Availability: supplies can be limited and some plants, eg bare-rooted roses, hedging and trees are available only at certain times of the year.

Refund/replacement: replacement.

GARDENERS' RECOMMENDATIONS: ✿ *"Very prettily laid out nursery featuring unusual plants, endlessly helpful and pleasant to deal with. Will always attempt to secure a desired plant. Topiary and statuary a speciality. Impossible to come away without having something. Also flower arranging and stunning wedding work."* Dr and Mrs Sanders. ✿ *"A wonderful and immaculate town garden filled with treasures. Unusual plants, statuary, Whichford pots, garden sundries, fresh flowers. Very friendly service and definitely an 'Aladdin's Cave'. All on a small scale."* Mr and Mrs P Swete. ✿ *"Very helpful, sound advice which takes soil type and climatic conditions into consideration."* Mr and Mrs S Cooke. ✿ *"Excellent service in an attractive garden with a good arrangement of plants for sale."* Mr and Mrs R A Lloyd.

See map page 393.

See also: Sheila Chapman Clematis, page 350.

GLOUCESTERSHIRE

Batsford Garden Centre   Here they say that "the customer is king" and whatever the customer wants, they will stock. What they do stock as a result are over 100,000 ferns in over 50 varieties, four different cranberries, ginseng, Dicksonia antarctica, Japanese maples, magnolias and lots of interesting and uncommon trees.

Batsford Garden Centre, Batsford, Moreton-in-Marsh, Gloucestershire GL56 9QB

Tel: 01386 700409 **Fax:** 01386 701148

E-mail: batsford@martex.net

Opening hours: 10.00–17.00 daily.

Visitors welcome: yes.

Catalogue: none.

Payment: cash, cheque, major credit/debit cards or barter.

Mail order: yes.

Post and packing: at cost.

Delivery: 7 days.

Availability: some unusual plants only produced in small numbers.

Refund/replacement: the plants are guaranteed to grow.

Special services: limited garden design free of charge, plant search service, delivery.

GARDENERS' RECOMMENDATIONS: ❀ *"Part of Batsford Estate and owned by Lord Dulverton who also owns the adjoining Arboretum planted by his ancestors. This is an added advantage as visitors to the centre can view a myriad of trees growing in spectacular surroundings. The garden centre is leased to Mr Nick Dicker who is a most helpful and knowledgeable plantsman. His stock is mainly perennials from outside sources. Sometimes a little expensive but his knowledge and time given free is worth a lot."* Mrs M Stuart-Turner.

See map page 393.

Close Nursery

A small nursery without a catalogue which specialises in herbaceous plants along with climbers, roses, herbs, bedding plants and ornamental pots.

Close Nursery, Shipton Moyne Road, Tetbury, Gloucestershire GL8 8PJ

Tel: 01666 505021

Opening hours: 9.00–17.00 Monday to Saturday, 10.00–16.30 Sunday. Closed January.

Visitors welcome: yes.

Catalogue: none.

Payment: cash, cheque, major credit cards.

Mail order: no.

Availability: plants are normally available all year.

Refund/replacement: yes.

Special services: refilling hanging baskets and tubs. Plant identification – shrubs, herbaceous.

GARDENERS' RECOMMENDATIONS: ❦ *"Run by a husband and wife team. Much of their production is taken by two prestigious outlets which guarantees their quality. They have an exceptionally wide range of excellent varieties. Prices are good and the stock is fresh, much of it propagated on site."* D S Taylor.

See map page 394.

Compton Lane Nurseries   A good range of hardy alpines, herbaceous and shrubs with additional ferns, grasses and tender perennials. They will design areas for you.

Compton Lane Nurseries, Little Compton, Moreton-in-Marsh, Gloucestershire GL56 0SJ

Tel: 01608 674578 **Fax:** 01295 721459

Opening hours: 10.00–17.00 Wednesday, Thursday and Saturday from March to October.

Visitors welcome: yes, by appointment.

Catalogue: send 5 first class stamps.

Payment: cash or cheque.

Mail order: yes, from October to March only. Minimum order £15 plus p&p.

Post and packing: at cost.

Delivery: depends on plants ordered.

Availability: some plants are produced in smaller quantities depending on rarity and ease of propagation. The less common varieties are only available at certain times.

Refund/replacement: replacement.

Special services: garden design, consultancy.

GARDENERS' RECOMMENDATIONS: ❦ *"A new nursery but very promising in an area where there are lots of good gardens and very few nurseries of any quality."* Mr and Mrs J D Sword. ❦ *"Specialist nursery alpine/herbaceous, unusual shrubs. Excellent nurseryman, Christopher Brown."* ❦ *"Very helpful, excellent plants and a big display border."* Mrs G C Royle. ❦ *"Chris Brown is always looking to widen the range of unusual plants that he grows and improve the quality of his stock by selection and cross pollination. From his great knowledge and experience he is always willing to give helpful advice."*

See map page 393.

Hoo House Nursery Specialises in herbaceous perennials and alpines with two national collections — for platycodons and the willow gentians, Gentiana asclepiadea. A small, husband and wife run nursery growing a wide range of over 800 plants, mostly easy to grow. "I have been known to talk people out of buying some plants," says the owner. "I would rather lose the sale than see some of my babies going to the wrong home."

Hoo House Nursery, Hoo House, Gloucester Road, Tewkesbury, Gloucestershire GL20 7DA

Tel/fax: 01684 293389

Opening hours: 14.00–17.00 Monday to Saturday.

Visitors welcome: yes.

Catalogue: send 3 first class stamps.

Payment: cash or cheque.

Mail order: no.

Availability: supplies can be limited and some plants are available only at certain times of year.

Refund/replacement: yes.

GARDENERS' RECOMMENDATIONS: ✿ *"Wide selection of hardy perennials and alpines."* Mr and Mrs R Paice. ✿ *"Wide range of herbaceous and alpine plants."* Tessa King-Farlow.

See map page 394.

Hunts Court Garden and Nursery Mainly a rose specialist offering over 350 varieties, some not available anywhere else. They also sell a small but good list of shrubs and geraniums and penstemons which can be seen growing in the gardens.

Hunts Court Garden and Nursery, North Nibley, Dursley, Gloucestershire GL11 6DZ

Tel: 01453 547440 **Fax:** 01453 547440

Opening hours: 9.00–17.00 Tuesday to Saturday except August, 25 and 26 December and Good Friday.

Visitors welcome: yes.

Catalogue: send 5 first class stamps.

Payment: cash or cheque.

Mail order: no.

Availability: supplies can be limited depending on crop and season.

Refund/replacement: replacement.

Special services: assistance in choosing plants always available.

GARDENERS' RECOMMENDATIONS: ❀ *"Very large selection of extremely healthy roses (which grow as well as they look)."* Mrs Susan Beck. ❀ *"Speciality roses and hardy geraniums. (Rather untidy when we saw it). Very large selection of roses."* Mr and Mrs G Gough. ❀ *"A small nursery specialising in a wide range of old roses. Also an interesting range of shrubs and herbaceous plants."* ❀ *"Great for unusual roses and other shrubs. Run by an attractively crazed enthusiast."*

See map page 394.

Just Phlomis The nursery holds, as you might expect, the national collection of phlomis, a genus of the Labiatae family with generally hairy, greyish leaves and stems. They come from the Mediterranean as well as Russia and the east and are excellent for dry areas. The list includes 16 perennial phlomis and 20 evergreen shrubby ones.

Just Phlomis, Sunningdale, Grange Court, Westbury-on-Severn, Gloucestershire GL14 1PL
Tel: 01452 760268 **Fax:** 0870 0881823
E-mail: j.mann.taylor@clara.co.uk
Website: http://www.j.mann.taylor.clara.net/phlomis.html
Opening hours: by appointment.
Visitors welcome: yes.
Catalogue: send 2 second class stamps.
Payment: cash or cheque.
Mail order: yes. Minimum order 3 plants.
Post and packing: from £4 for 3 plants by first class post. At cost by parcel post for 8 plants and over.
Delivery: allow 1 week.
Availability: limited as only small numbers are propagated.
Refund/replacement: by arrangement.

GARDENERS' RECOMMENDATIONS: ❀ *Recommended by* Mrs Caroline Todhunter.

See map page 394.

Miserden Nurseries A friendly nursery who say it's their pleasure "to share knowledge and experience of producing and nurturing our stock." Their speciality is unusual herbaceous perennial plants such as species foxgloves, and anemones, irises, lupins and paeonies. There's a restored Victorian greenhouse in which stock is shown.

> **Miserden Nurseries**, Miserden Park, Miserden, nr Cirencester, Gloucestershire GL6 7JA
>
> **Tel:** 01285 821638 **Fax:** 01453 884610
>
> **Opening hours:** 10.00–17.00 Tuesday to Sunday from mid-March to mid-October. Open on bank holidays and in December for Christmas trees, wreaths etc.
>
> **Visitors welcome:** yes.
>
> **Catalogue:** none.
>
> **Payment:** cash, cheque major credit/debit cards.
>
> **Mail order:** service planned.
>
> **Availability:** the nursery aims to offer a comprehensive range throughout the year but supplies of certain plants can be limited and some are ready at specific times of year.
>
> **Refund/replacement:** yes.
>
> **Special services:** Victorian-style greenhouse complex.

GARDENERS' RECOMMENDATIONS: ⊛ *"Knowledgeable and reliable."* Mrs Mary Keen. ⊛ *"Good range of unusual herbaceous plants."*

See map page 394.

Mount Pleasant Trees If you want to make a whole wood, an arboretum or a formal hedged garden, this is the specialist nursery — which also offer plants for specimen planting. The catalogue is extremely helpful with notes on spacing, heeling in and propagating.

> **Mount Pleasant Trees**, Rockhampton, Berkeley, Gloucestershire GL13 9DU
>
> **Tel:** 01454 260348
>
> **Opening hours:** By appointment only 8.00–18.00 Monday to Saturday.
>
> **Visitors welcome:** only by prior appointment. No display areas.
>
> **Catalogue:** send £1 coin or equivalent in loose stamps.
>
> **Payment:** cash or cheque.
>
> **Mail order:** no.

Availability: late October to mid-March.

Refund/replacement: yes, depending on circumstances.

GARDENERS' RECOMMENDATIONS: *"A great nursery where a range of trees are grown, mainly native species for hedging, forestry, woodland and gardens."*

See map page 394.

Pan-Global Plants   Not exactly a modest title but Nick Macer is right — his plants come from wild seed collecting expeditions. He offers some interesting bamboos such as Chusquea culeou, carnivorous plants and exotics like the Japanese banana. And more to come. His design consultancy is for those "who think big" and arboreta are a speciality.

Pan-Global Plants, Spoonbed Nursery, Rococo Garden, Painswick, Gloucestershire GL6 6TH

Tel: 01452 814242 **Fax:** 01452 813204

Opening hours: 11.00–17.00 Wednesday to Sunday from second Wednesday in January to end November.

Visitors welcome: yes.

Catalogue: send 3 first class stamps.

Payment: cash, cheque, Visa, Mastercard.

Mail order: plants can be sent via Interlink.

Post and packing: £13 for up to 10 kg.

Delivery: normally next day.

Availability: some plants are propagated in small quantities.

Refund/replacement: yes, if justified.

Special services: landscape design and consultancy.

GARDENERS' RECOMMENDATIONS: *Recommended by* Mrs Caroline Todhunter *and* Mr and Mrs J Taylor.

See map page 394.

Chris Pattison (Nurseryman)   Like many of the smaller nurserymen, Chris Pattison prides himself on the rarity of his plants — in this case alpines and shrubs plus Japanese maples. He also offers planting designs and plans for the garden.

Chris Pattison (Nurseryman), Brookend, Pendock, Gloucestershire GL19 3PL

Tel/fax: 01531 650480

E-mail: cp@redmarley.freeserve.co.uk

Website: http://www.redmarley.freeserve.co.uk

Opening hours: 9.00–17.00 Monday to Friday and by appointment.

Visitors welcome: yes.

Catalogue: send 3 first class stamps.

Payment: cash or cheque.

Mail order: no.

Availability: some plants are seasonal.

Refund/replacement: yes.

Special services: planting designs and plans.

GARDENERS' RECOMMENDATIONS: ✿ *"Excellent source of unusual and high quality plants with personal service. Nothing too much trouble and modest prices."* Mr and Mrs W K Turner. ✿ *"A wide range of trees and shrubs are grown but they specialise in Japanese maples. The plants are good and strong coming in a range of sizes."* ✿ *"Acers and wide range of rare and high quality plants. Sensible prices. Well worth the trek to find the nursery."* Mr and Mrs E W Dyer.

See map page 394.

Derry Watkins at Special Plants

A gardener who still opens under the NGS scheme and offers a fine list of plants along with lectures, courses and garden visits. The nursery stocks both hardy and tender perennials and Mrs Watkins has a special interest in South African plants following a travelling fellowship there in 1993. Many of the seeds she collected grow at over 8,000 feet and should be quite happy growing in Britain.

Special Plants, Greenways Lane, Cold Ashton, Chippenham, SN14 8LA

Tel: 01225 891686

E-mail: specialplants@bigfoot.com

Website: http://www.co.uk/cat.html

Opening hours: 11.00–15.00 daily from March to end September. At other times by appointment.

Visitors welcome: yes.

Catalogue: send 4 second class stamps.

Payment: cash or cheque.

Mail order: yes, September to March only.

Post and packing: £9.50.

Delivery: 1 week to 6 months depending on availability. Plants can be delivered to shows.

Availability: supplies can be limited and some plants are only available at certain times of year.

Refund/replacement: yes.

Special services: garden visits and tours, lectures and courses. Garden open for NGS and by appointment.

GARDENERS' RECOMMENDATIONS: ✿ *"This nursery is in a most attractive setting about 5 miles north of Bath. Mrs Watkins is developing a specialised garden round the house where visitors can see her unusual plants growing."* Mrs M Bailey. ✿ *"Half hardy specialist. Lots of conservatory or greenhouse rarities, just about try-able outside in really mild gardens. Many plants grown from her own seed-hunting trips, particularly to South Africa. Visitors should try to visit the old nursery as well as the new one: the stock isn't the same."* Mr Tim Longville.

See map page 390.

Spinneywell Nurseries   Offers a wide range of unusual trees, shrubs and herbaceous plants along with box and yew hedging.

Spinneywell Nurseries, Waterlane, Oakridge, Bisley, Gloucestershire GL6 7PH

Tel: 01452 770092 **Fax:** 01452 770151

Opening hours: 10.00–17.00 daily March to December. 10.00–16.00 January and February.

Visitors welcome: yes.

Catalogue: send 6 first class stamps.

Payment: cash, postal order, cheque.

Mail order: yes.

Post and packing: by quotation.

Delivery: allow 28 days.

Availability: supplies can be limited or available only at certain times of the year.

Refund/replacement: yes.

Special services: plant sourcing.

GARDENERS' RECOMMENDATIONS: *"Excellent."* Mrs Mary Keen.

See map page 394.

Tinpenny Plants
Elaine Horton explains that Tinpenny Farm has a largish garden to act as inspiration and propagation for the nursery. Both garden and nursery (wheelchair friendly) are open. She specialises in a wide range of garden-worthy plants, especially old-fashioned ones, which are generally hard to find. Also there are irises, hellebores and shade-loving plants.

> **Tinpenny Plants**, Tinpenny Farm, Fiddington, Tewkesbury, Gloucestershire GL20 7BJ
>
> **Tel:** 01684 292668
>
> **Opening hours:** 12.00–17.00 Tuesday to Thursday, bank holiday Mondays and one Sunday per month. Otherwise by appointment at any time.
>
> **Visitors welcome:** yes.
>
> **Catalogue:** send 2 first class stamps.
>
> **Payment:** cash or cheque.
>
> **Mail order:** no.
>
> **Availability:** supplies can be limited and some plants are available only at certain times of year.
>
> **Refund/replacement:** yes.
>
> **Special services:** propagation of specific plants to order. Garden planning and design. Advisory garden visits.

GARDENERS' RECOMMENDATIONS: *"Recently moved to a large site but has all the signs of being better than the older garden. The ultimate of rare and unusual plants and plenty of design. Supremely well grown on a very difficult site."*

See map page 394.

See also: Trevi Garden, page 361.

HAMPSHIRE

Agar Nursery The owners of this nursery have 60 years combined experience to offer buyers — and they are very happy to give advice. About 80% of their stock is herbaceous plants, both tender and hardy, the rest includes shrubs, climbers, conifers and heathers.

> **Agar Nursery**, Agar Lane, Hordle, nr Lymington, Hampshire SO41 0FL
>
> **Tel:** 01590 683703
>
> **Opening hours:** 10.00–17.00 from March to October, 10.00–16.00 from 1 November to 20 December. Closed Thursday.
>
> **Visitors welcome:** yes.
>
> **Catalogue:** none.
>
> **Payment:** cash or cheque.
>
> **Mail order:** no.
>
> **Availability:** certain items always sell out.
>
> **Refund/replacement:** yes.

GARDENERS' RECOMMENDATIONS: ✻ *"Nursery owned and run by Mr and Mrs George and Diana Tombs. All plants grown and nurtured to selling size on the nursery. Genuine plantsmen and extremely helpful."* Mr and Mrs P J Pitman.

See map page 390.

Apple Court Mainly known for its hostas, daylilies and ferns, there is also a smallish general perennial list which tends towards interesting leaves rather than flowers.

> **Apple Court Nursery**, Hordle Lane, Hordle, Lymington, Hampshire SO41 0HU
>
> **Tel:** 01590 641230 **Fax:** 01590 644220
>
> **E-mail:** applecourt@btinternet.com
>
> **Website:** http://www.applecourt.com
>
> **Opening hours:** 10.00–13.00, 14.00–17.00 from March to end October. Closed on Wednesdays and from November to February.
>
> **Visitors welcome:** yes.

Catalogue: send 4 first class stamps.

Payment: cash, cheque, postal order.

Mail order: yes. Minimum order £15 plus p&p.

Post and packing: 1-5 plants £5, 5–10 £5.50, 10–15 £6, 15-20 £6.50, over 20 pro rata @ 35p per plant.

Delivery: 3-5 weeks. Sometimes varies according to weather and availability.

Availability: throughout the year but supplies of very rare plants are limited.

Refund/replacement: yes.

Special services: lectures, garden design.

GARDENERS' RECOMMENDATIONS: ✿ *"Quite wonderful collection of hemerocallis and always fantastic garden plants. Also marvellous collection of hostas and grasses, plus other interesting perennials. Lovely display gardens well worth visiting."* Mrs Susan Beck. ✿ *"… list is varied and different. Plants arrived in good condition and established well. Has a good garden."* Mrs Danae Johnston. ✿ *"A long-established specialist nursery with a mail order facility. A fairly wide range of less usual items are catalogued. My enquiries have always received very individual attention and the plants I have ordered have arrived promptly, well packed and in good condition."* Maureen Jones, Little Upcot Gardens.

See map page 390.

Blackmoor Nurseries
Fruit trees and soft fruit for amateurs and professional gardeners with a good list of apples and pears, along with peaches, apricots, raspberries, tayberry, black, red and white currants and a few grapes.

Blackmoor Nurseries, Blackmoor, nr Liss, Hampshire GU33 6BS

Tel: 01420 473141 **Fax:** 01420 474410

E-mail: nurserysales@blackmoor.co.uk

Website: http://www.blackmoor.co.uk

Opening hours: 9.00–16.00.

Visitors welcome: to the retail outlet only.

Catalogue: free.

Payment: cheque.

Mail order: yes.

Post and packing: minimum £20.

Delivery: allow 21 days.
Availability: November to April.
Refund/replacement: yes.

GARDENERS' RECOMMENDATIONS: *Recommended by* Lady Scott, Rotherfield Park.

See map page 390.

Blackthorn Nursery
The firm grows and propagates all its own plants which include hellebores, daphnes, hepaticas and epimediums; there's also a good range of alpine and rock plants.

Blackthorn Nursery, Kilmeston, Alresford, Hampshire SO24 0NL
Tel: 01962 771796 **Fax:** 01962 771071
Opening hours: first Thursday to Sunday of each month from February to June inclusive.
Visitors welcome: yes, strictly during opening hours only.
Catalogue: send 3 first class stamps.
Payment: cash or cheque.
Mail order: no.
Availability: supplies can be limited.
Refund/replacement: by arrangement.

GARDENERS' RECOMMENDATIONS: *"A very small spring garden but another wonderful source of epimediums and hellebores. The best for epimediums."* Mr and Mrs G Gough, Trevi Garden. *"Excellent specialist nursery. Hellebores, epimediums, daphnes and alpines. Many rare trees and shrubs especially magnolia. N. c. trillium."* Mr and Mrs P Short. *"Unusual perennials and alpines – quality plants presented immaculately in a most beautiful area – friendly husband and wife proprietors are experts in their field. Only open early in the year. Hellebore specialists."* Mr and Mrs F Leocadi.

See map page 390.

Drysdale Garden Exotics
Very much the current trend in gardening, this nursery offers plants for Mediterranean gardens, for exotic gardens, for people who prefer leaves to flowers and also has a

specialist collection of bamboos. This is the sort of nursery to visit to get inspiration rather than buying from the catalogue.

Drysdale Garden Exotics, Bowerwood Road, Fordingbridge, Hampshire SP6 1BN

Tel: 01425 653010

Opening hours: 9.30–17.30 Wednesday to Friday, 10.00–17.30 Sunday.

Visitors welcome: yes, during opening hours.

Catalogue: send 3 first class stamps.

Payment: cash or cheque.

Mail order: yes.

Post and packing: from £6.25 for 1 plant to £17.75 for 8.

Delivery: plants despatched when ready.

Availability: supplies can be limited and some plants are available only at certain times of year.

Refund/replacement: only if plants are defective on arrival.

GARDENERS' RECOMMENDATIONS: ✿ *"A small specialist nursery holding national reference collection of bamboos in an attractive garden area. A large variety of bamboos can be purchased with good advice given if needed."* Mr F G Jacob. ✿ *"Your car won't be big enough."* Diana Yakeley *"THE people for bamboos – some other interesting plants."* The Hon Mr and Mrs Robin Borwick, Neptune House Gardens.

See map page 390.

Exbury Gardens Plant Centre
Plants from the famous rhododendron garden are, obviously, rhodos, azaleas and camellias. As well as these there is a good range of clematis, roses, conifers, herbs, alpines and bedding.

Exbury Gardens Plant Centre, The Estate Office, Exbury, Southampton, Hampshire SO4 1AZ

Tel: 023 8089 8625   **Fax:** 023 8089 9940

Website: http://www.exbury.co.uk

Opening hours: 10.00–17.50 (dusk if earlier) daily. Closed from Christmas to end February.

Visitors welcome: yes.

Catalogue: none.

Payment: cash, cheque, credit cards except American Express.

Mail order: no.

Availability: best selection of ericaceous stock from March to May.

Refund/replacement: replacement.

GARDENERS' RECOMMENDATIONS: *"Very good plants, service, delivery."* Mrs Craig.

See map page 390.

Family Trees An excellent selection of fruit trees, well grown. There are apples and pears, plums, gages and damsons, cherries, peaches, nectarines and apricots plus quinces, figs, nuts and medlars. The nursery stocks a few non-fruit trees and a nice selection of old roses.

Family Trees, Sandy Lane, Shedfield, Hampshire SO32 2HQ

Tel: 01329 834812

Opening hours: 9.30–12.30 Wednesday and Saturday from mid-October to mid-April.

Visitors welcome: yes, during opening hours.

Catalogue: free.

Payment: cash or cheque.

Mail order: yes.

Post and packing: £9 to £15 minimum. 10% of order value for trees up to 6ft, 20% for trees 6–10ft.

Delivery: next day.

Availability: October to April.

Refund/replacement: replacement at half price if reasonable care has been taken.

Special services: advice and demonstrations of pruning and grafting etc.

GARDENERS' RECOMMENDATIONS: *Recommended by* Lady Scott, Rotherfield Park *and* Mr and Mrs H Collum.

See map page 390.

Hardy's Cottage Garden Plants One of the glories of England is the cottage garden, a small plot filled with colourful herbaceous perennials. Hardy's stocks over 1,200 varieties, won a gold at Chelsea in 1997 and, to ensure their hardiness (no pun) grow their plants on a windy hill in Hampshire. The list is wide rather than deep but full of charmers like geraniums, columbines and pulmonarias.

Hardy's Cottage Garden Plants, Priory Lane, Freefolk Priors, Whitchurch, Hampshire RG28 7NJ

Tel: 01256 896533 **Fax:** 01256 896572

E-mail: rosyhardy@cottagegardenplants01.freeserve.co.uk

Opening hours: 10.00–17.00 from March to October.

Visitors welcome: yes.

Catalogue: £1.

Payment: cash, cheque, Visa, Mastercard.

Mail order: yes.

Post and packing: £7.50 for orders up to £75, £12.50 thereafter.

Delivery: spring despatch 15 March to 30 April, autumn despatch 1 October to 15 November.

Availability: supplies can be limited and some plants are available only at certain times of year.

Refund/replacement: yes.

GARDENERS' RECOMMENDATIONS: ❀ *"A family-run nursery specialising in herbaceous perennials, both old and new. Very helpful people too."* Mr and Mrs H Lock. ❀ *"Good selection of plants with good rootball and lots of help with choosing plants."* ❀ *"Good range of excellent perennials."* Mr and Mrs E W Dyer.

See map page 390.

Highfield Hollies   They claim this is the only specialist holly nursery in Britain and it sells both hollies for hedges and topiary — commoner varieties, that is — and some of the really spectacular blue hollies, variegated hollies and, my favourite, ferox which manages to have prickles on the leaf as well as round the edges. The firm offers planting advice — rather necessary since hollies have to be sexed and their names don't always help. Silver Queen, for instance, is a chap.

Highfield Hollies, Highfield Farm, Hatch Lane, Liss, Hampshire GU33 7NH

Tel: 0173 892372 **Fax:** 01730 894853

Opening hours: by appointment.

Visitors welcome: yes, by appointment.
Catalogue: send 2 first class stamps.
Payment: cheque.
Mail order: yes.
Post and packing: at cost.
Delivery: allow a day or two.
Availability: all year round.
Refund/replacement: yes, depending on circumstances.
Special services: garden planning, topiary, propagation, identification service.

GARDENERS' RECOMMENDATIONS: ✿ *"Specialises in hollies and has many of the rarer small-leafed ones. She prepares young specimens for topiary and has some quite big ones available for instant results."*

See map page 390.

Langley Boxwood Nursery
The place for box trees and holder of the national collection. The nursery offers all kinds of topiary shapes — birds, animals, spirals and obelisks — plus a huge selection of box varieties. If you thought there was only one box, here you will be disillusioned.

Langley Boxwood Nursery, Rake, nr Liss, Hampshire GU33 7JL
Tel: 01730 894467 **Fax:** 01730 894703
E-mail: langbox@msn.com
Website: http://www.boxwood.co.uk
Opening hours: 9.00–16.30 weekdays, 10.00–16.00 Saturday.
Visitors welcome: yes.
Catalogue: send 4 first class stamps.
Payment: cash or cheque.
Mail order: yes.
Post and packing: at cost.
Delivery: 48 hours.
Availability: all year round.
Refund/replacement: yes.
Special services: advice on boxwood and topiary.

GARDENERS' RECOMMENDATIONS: ✿ *"Excellent range of box and yew."* Mr and Mrs G Bearman. ✿ *"A specialist nursery with helpful advice given when designing a knot garden, then lovely plants supplied."* *"Widest range of box, including topiary."* Mr and Mrs E G Millais, Millais Nursery. *"Undoubtedly one of the very best specialist nurseries with an enormous collection of box species and cultivars always offered in superb condition."* Mr and Mrs A J Young.

See map page 390.

Longstock Park Nursery

Longstock Park Nursery The holders of the national collections of buddleja and viticella clematis are very willing to pass on their advice and even identify mystery plants. They also have alpines, ferns, aquatics and conservatory plants among a more general range, mostly grown at the nursery.

> **Longstock Park Nursery**, Longstock, Stockbridge, Hampshire SO20 6EH
> **Tel:** 01264 810894 **Fax:** 01264 810924
> **Opening hours:** 8.30–16.30 Monday to Saturday all year round. 14.00–17.00 on Sunday from March to October.
> **Visitors welcome:** yes.
> **Catalogue:** £1.50.
> **Payment:** cash, cheque, Visa, Mastercard, Access, Switch, Delta.
> **Mail order:** no.
> **Availability:** while stocks last.
> **Refund/replacement:** yes, on proof of purchase.

GARDENERS' RECOMMENDATIONS: *"A wide and interesting range of plants displayed in the old walled gardens. A very nice place to visit. If you go in the late summer you can see the very splendid herbaceous border."* Mr and Mrs T F Clarke. *"Very helpful. Very knowledgeable. Super range of unusual shrubs, herbaceous etc."* Professor and Mrs A R Elkington. *"Very good trees and shrubs."*

See map page 390.

MacGregors Plants

MacGregors Plants The nursery holds the national collection of phygelius and also stocks other unusual plants and those which tolerate shade. There are, for example, lots of epimediums, penstemons and columbines. Plants are produced in small batches and may well sell out.

MacGregors Plants, Carters Clay Road, Lockerley, nr Romsey, Hampshire SO51 0GL

Tel: 01794 340256 **Fax:** 01794 341828

Opening hours: 10.00–16.00 Friday to Sunday and bank holidays from March to October and by appointment.

Visitors welcome: yes.

Catalogue: send 3 first class stamps for plant list.

Payment: cheque.

Mail order: a limited service.

Post and packing: £10 to £20 for parcels up to 10 kg by 24-hour carrier.

Delivery: 7–10 days if available.

Availability: some varieties sell out.

Refund/replacement: yes.

Special services: lectures, group visits, horticultural/gardening education.

GARDENERS' RECOMMENDATIONS: ✿ *"I would highly recommend this nursery. There is no garden alongside, as such, simply three excellent tunnels of high quality interesting plants. A small point of interest perhaps is that I have just bought from this nursery 2 Lysimachia minoricensis – this charming plant is listed in the current Threatened Plants Appeal run by Friends of Kew."* Mrs C Ellert.

See map page 390.

Pandora Nursery Mostly shrubs but with a few perennials and grasses. The main areas of speciality in a good general list are cistus with over 30 on offer and the delightful euphorbias some of which like full sun and others damp shade. As Paul and Amanda O'Carroll say, it's just a question of picking the right one.

Pandora Nursery, The Walled Garden, Bury Lodge Estate, West Street, Hambledon, Hampshire
Office: 17 Quail Way, Horndean, Hampshire PO8 9YN

Tel: 023 9259 7323

Opening hours: 10.00–16.00 Wednesday to Friday and by appointment.

Visitors welcome: yes.

Catalogue: send 5 second class stamps.

Payment: cash or cheque.

Mail order: no.

Availability: can be limited but will grow to order (allow 3 months).

Refund/replacement: yes.

Special services: garden design service offering advice and a small scale planting scheme.

GARDENERS' RECOMMENDATIONS: *"A small, friendly nursery with an interesting collection of euphorbias."* Mrs Gillian Baird. *"Very good catalogue of unusual plants. Specialising in cistus and euphorbia."* *"A young couple, very knowledgeable and enthusiastic. Have interesting plants."* The Hon Mr and Mrs Robin Borwick.

See map page 390.

Rose Cottage Nursery

With summers ever drier, this nursery has the answer in a list of drought-tolerant plants, even though it was started only in 1998, one of the wettest summers of recent years. It goes from ivies and herbs to trees like eucalyptus. The nursery is beside the owners' garden, which opens under the NGS scheme, and plants can be seen in situ. Advice and planting plans are offered.

Rose Cottage Nursery, Kingsley Common, nr Bordon, Hampshire GU35 9NF

Tel: 01420 489071 **Fax:** 01420 476629

E-mail: elliot@cena.demon.co.uk

Website: http://www.hyperstore.co.uk/rose/

Opening hours: by appointment between March and October.

Visitors welcome: yes, by appointment.

Catalogue: free.

Payment: cash, cheque or postal order.

Mail order: yes.

Post and packing: £5.50 for orders up to £30, £7.50 for orders £31 to £60, free thereafter.

Delivery: normally 14 days but allow 28.

Availability: plants are normally despatched from March to October. Some are in limited supply.

Refund/replacement: yes, if notified within 7 days.

GARDENERS' RECOMMENDATIONS: *"A specialist in drought-tolerant plants, knowledgeable and friendly."* Mr and Mrs T F Clarke.

See map page 390.

Spinners Garden
The garden itself slopes towards the River Lymington and has acid soil on which grow azaleas, rhododendrons, magnolias and camellias. It holds the national collection of trilliums. The nursery reflects this with an excellent list of magnolias and some camellias along with choice rhododendrons. There are also many hostas, irises, pulmonaria and ferns.

> **Spinners Garden**, School Lane, Boldre, Lymington, Hampshire SO41 5QE
> **Tel:** 01590 673347
> **Opening hours:** 10.00–17.00 Tuesday to Saturday and by appointment on Sunday and Monday.
> **Visitors welcome:** yes.
> **Catalogue:** 50p at nursery or send 3 first class stamps.
> **Payment:** cash or cheque.
> **Mail order:** no.
> **Availability:** all year round.
> **Refund/replacement:** by arrangement.
> **Special services:** advice on setting up wildlife and woodland gardens. Lectures and garden tours.

GARDENERS' RECOMMENDATIONS: ✿ *"Nursery specialises in less common and rare hardy shrubs and plants. Great knowledge – excellent advice!"* ✿ *"The first nursery I go to for unusual plants and shrubs."* Mr David Dampney. ✿ *"Rare and special plants, shrubs and trees. Garden containing many of those for sale, especially unusual rhododendrons and acers. A garden for the cognoscenti."* Mr and Mrs O Ziegler. ✿ *"We cannot recommend this beautiful nursery too highly – set in highly individual woodland, gardened with the utmost knowledge and a feeling for appropriate plant communities. Expert advice to hand."* ✿ *"An exceptional range of very rare shrubs."* Mr and Mrs E G Millais, Millais Nursery.

See map page 390.

Water Meadow Nursery and Herb Farm

Roy and Sandy Worth's nursery specialises in cottage garden plants, water plants and herbs. They have recently applied for the national collection of Papaver orientale, of which they have 94 different cultivars and varieties, some never seen in Britain. Their water lily list is excellent and the herbs are chosen for interest as much as culinary use.

Water Meadow Nursery and Herb Farm, Cheriton, nr Alresford, Hampshire SO24 0QB
Tel/fax: 01962 771895
E-mail: watermeadowplants@msn.com
Opening hours: 9.00–17.00 Wednesday to Saturday.
Visitors welcome: yes.
Catalogue: send 4 first class stamps.
Payment: cheque.
Mail order: yes.
Post and packing: £4.50 by first class post, £10.50 by 24-hour courier.
Delivery: 24 hours if available.
Availability: generally all year round.
Refund/replacement: yes.
Special services: pond advice, planting plans, design and landscaping.

GARDENERS' RECOMMENDATIONS: ✪ *"A small nursery set within their own garden with its large pond, specialising in water plants, shade plants and scented shrubs. Friendly and relaxed service."* Mr and Mrs T F Clarke. ✪ *"Consistently good and very knowledgeable. Good selection of water lilies."* The Hon Mr and Mrs Robin Borwick, Neptune House Gardens.

See map page 390.

Whitewater Nursery and Plant Centre

A true plant centre, say the owners, where, in 10 acres, skilled plantsmen can "appreciate the needs of both the trade and public alike." They have a no frills policy but a vast range of over 250,000 plants which is constantly expanding in order to keep up customers' interest.

Whitewater Nursery and Plant Centre, Hound Green, Hook, Hampshire RG27 8LQ
Tel: 0118 932 6487   **Fax:** 0118 932 6115

Opening hours: 9.00–17.30 (16.30 in winter) daily.

Visitors welcome: yes.

Catalogue: none.

Payment: cash, cheque, major credit cards, National Garden Tokens.

Mail order: no.

Availability: most stock is available all year round, but bare-rooted or rootballed stock is seasonal.

Refund/replacement: yes, if justified.

GARDENERS' RECOMMENDATIONS: ❀ *"This nursery was started by the Selfe brothers and has over 250,000 plants and trees in stock. Many are unusual, most grown at the nursery. It has an excellent reputation for personal service from experts. Quality plants at reasonable prices. They only sell plants, shrubs and trees and their own special compost."* Mr and Mrs J K Oldale.

See map page 390.

See also: Mrs Mitchell's Kitchen and Garden, page 358.

HEREFORDSHIRE

Abbey Dore Court Garden   Charis Ward has a rambling six-acre garden with a small nursery attached specialising in unusual herbaceous perennials. She doesn't do mail order and has no catalogue but she's "always here to speak to people." The plants she grows are the ones she sells. A bonus is a restaurant in the stables with wine licence.

Abbey Dore Court Garden, Abbey Dore, Herefordshire HR2 0AD
Tel/fax: 01981 240419
Opening hours: 11.00–18.00 daily except Mondays (excluding bank holidays) and Wednesdays from April to September.
Visitors welcome: yes.
Catalogue: none.

Payment: cash or cheque.

Mail order: no.

Availability: supplies can be limited and some plants are available only at certain times of year.

Refund/replacement: depends on circumstances.

GARDENERS' RECOMMENDATIONS: *"Wide range hemerocallis."* Mrs Jane Gladstone. ❀ *"Mainly herbaceous, wonderful river setting."* Mr and Mrs G Gough.

See map page 394.

The Arrow Cottage Garden

A small firm which specialises in climbers, including clematis, alpines, interesting perennials and shrubs. They are particularly good with advice, design and sourcing plants.

The Arrow Cottage Garden, Weobley, Herefordshire HR4 8RN

Tel: 01544 318468　**Fax:** 01544 318468

Opening hours: 14.00–17.00 Wednesday to Saturday from March to October.

Visitors welcome: yes.

Catalogue: none.

Payment: cheque.

Mail order: yes, if required.

Post and packing: at cost.

Delivery: allow 1 week.

Availability: supplies can be limited and some plants are available only at certain times of year.

Refund/replacement: yes.

Special services: garden design, plant sourcing.

GARDENERS' RECOMMENDATIONS: *"Wonderful garden, many unusual plants for sale."* Mr and Mrs G Gough.

See map page 394.

Aulden Farm

The nursery at Aulden has only been going since 1997 but, specialising in hardy herbaceous perennials, especially those which are tried and trusted, the firm have been able to get a good list together which it now sells through plant fairs and it opens two afternoons a week in summer.

Aulden Farm, Aulden, nr Leominster, Herefordshire HR6 0JT
Tel: 01568 720129
Opening hours: 12.00–17.00 Tuesday and Thursday from 1 April to 30 September.
Visitors welcome: yes, during opening hours or by appointment.
Catalogue: send sae.
Payment: cash or cheque.
Mail order: no.
Availability: limited quantities are propagated and these are available, subject to crop, until sold out.
Refund/replacement: by arrangement.

GARDENERS' RECOMMENDATIONS: ❀ *"Superb quality plants. Some unusual varieties rarely seen in other nurseries. Helpful and knowledgeable, friendly people. Will always try to trace and obtain hard to get or obscure plants. Very competitively priced. Absolutely ten out of ten for quality."* Miss A Barber.

See map page 394.

Kingstone Cottage Plants
There is a two-acre garden open to the public with a formal area devoted to old dianthus, of which the firm holds the national collection. It is happy to try to identify customers' plants in this area and act as a reference source for students.

Kingstone Cottage Plants, Weston-under-Penyard, Ross-on-Wye, Herefordshire HR9 7PH
Tel: 01989 565267
E-mail: kingstone@wyenet.co.uk
Opening hours: 9.00–16.00 Monday to Friday, in May and June. By appointment at other times.
Visitors welcome: yes, as shown in the yellow book (usually early May to early July) and by appointment.
Catalogue: send 2 first class stamps.
Payment: cheque.
Mail order: yes.
Post and packing: £4 for 4 plants, £6.60 for 12.
Availability: plants are normally despatched in spring.
Refund/replacement: yes.

Special services: as holders of the national collection of old-fashioned dianthus the nursery can often identify plants.

GARDENERS' RECOMMENDATIONS: *"National collection of old dianthus (140+ varieties). Nursery part of interesting cottage garden."* Mr and Mrs M Hughes.

See map page 394.

Ornamental Tree Nurseries

Offers what it says with everything from the native black poplar (once rare but now featuring on good tree lists) to exotic eucalyptus. There are also conifers and fruit trees and useful tree accessories such as stakes and rabbit guards.

Ornamental Tree Nurseries, Cobnash, Kingsland, Herefordshire HR6 9QZ

Tel: 01568 708016 **Fax:** 01568 709022

E-mail: enquires@ornamental-trees.co.uk

Website: http://www. ornamental-trees.co.uk

Opening hours: 9.00–17.00 Monday to Saturday.

Visitors welcome: yes.

Catalogue: send two 19p stamps.

Payment: cash, cheque, major credit cards.

Mail order: yes.

Post and packing: by quotation.

Delivery: by 24-hour carrier.

Availability: bare-root trees despatched from November to March. Small container trees available all your round.

Refund/replacement: container trees are guaranteed for 6 months. A refund is given for bare-root trees if they are genuinely unacceptable on arrival.

GARDENERS' RECOMMENDATIONS: *Recommended by* Mr Clive Richards.

See map page 394.

Rushfields of Ledbury

A small nursery which does not do mail order but they will take orders for their specialist herbaceous perennials at the flower shows they attend.

Jenny Holmwood-

Rushfields of Ledbury, Ross Road, Ledbury, Herefordshire HR8 2LP
Tel: 01531 632004 **Fax:** 01531 633454
Opening hours: 11.00–17.00 Wednesday to Saturday.
Visitors welcome: yes.
Catalogue: £1 plus A5 sae.
Payment: cheque, Visa, Mastercard.
Mail order: no.
Delivery: by arrangement for orders over £60.
Availability: seasonal.
Refund/replacement: yes.
Special services: orders can be collected from flower shows.

GARDENERS' RECOMMENDATIONS: ✿ *"Very helpful, excellent for hellebores, hostas and euphorbia in particular."* Col and Mrs J G T Polley.

See map page 394.

See also: Overcourt Garden Nursery, page 359.

HERTFORDSHIRE

Aylett Nurseries   The RHS gave Roger Aylett the Gold Veitch Memorial Medal for his contribution to horticulture and his nursery concentrates on the showier flowers available. There are bedding plants, flowers ideal for arranging and house plants. The business, still family run, was started in 1955.

Aylett Nurseries Ltd, North Orbital Road, London Colney,
St Albans, Hertfordshire AL2 1DH
Tel: 01727 822255 **Fax:** 01727 823024
E-mail: aylett-nurseries@compuserve.co
Website: http://www.martex.co.uk/hta/aylett
Opening hours: 8.30–17.30 Monday to Friday, 8.30–17.00 Saturday, 10.30–16.00 Sunday.
Visitors welcome: yes.

Catalogue: free.

Payment: cash, cheque, major credit cards.

Mail order: no.

Delivery: next-day delivery within a 20-mile radius of St Albans from £1.95 to £18.75.

Availability: dahlias mid-April to mid-June, fuchsias from March to June.

Refund/replacement: yes.

Special services: coffee shop.

GARDENERS' RECOMMENDATIONS: *"Excellent selection of plants. Specialises in unusual dahlias. Has special events and trips. Friendly service. All plants first class."* Mrs R M Rees. *"RHS gold medal dahlias. Also garden centre."* Mrs Carol Lee.

See map page 392.

Hopleys

One satisfied client is Lord Carrington whose gardens contain hundreds of varieties of plants. Other gardeners say that, though their plants can be small, they are always in extremely good condition and grow well. The nursery, now over 30 years old, grows 80% of the 1,200 varieties of shrubs and perennials itself. Few chemicals are used.

Hopleys Plants, High Street, Much Hadham, Hertfordshire SG10 6BU

Tel: 01279 842509 **Fax:** 01279 843784

E-mail: hopleys@compuserve.com

Opening hours: 9.00–17.00 Monday and Wednesday to Saturday, 14.00–17.00 Sunday. Closed Tuesday and from Christmas to March.

Visitors welcome: yes.

Payment: cheque, Visa, Access, Switch.

Mail order: yes, during autumn.

Post and packing: from £5.80 to £13.

Delivery: October/November. Collect from the nursery if possible.

Availability: around 90% of the plants in the catalogue should be available at any given time.

Refund/replacement: yes, if failure not due to neglect or adverse winter weather.

Special services: display garden and refreshments.
Use of WC, umbrellas, wheelchair, reference books and
picnic tables.

GARDENERS' RECOMMENDATIONS: ✾ *"Excellent plants, well
grown. In the forefront of new plants (I tend to buy one for
propagation!) Excellent catalogue – very helpful (no nonsense). Nice
illustrations of some plants."* Mrs A Conville. ✾ *"Wide range of
hardy and half-hardy shrubs and perennials. Plant sale in autumn.
Nursery set in lovely gardens."* Mrs R M Rees ✾ *"Good range of
rare herbaceous and good display gardens also."* Mr and Mrs E G
Millais, Millais Nursery.

See map page 393.

ISLE OF WIGHT

A la Carte Daylilies   Hemerocallis are easy plants to grow,
multiply well and are extremely showy. They fill sunny corners to
perfection and, if the flowers last only a few hours, they are profuse
and the leaves are elegant. This nursery sells nothing else and is
passionate about the plant.

A la Carte Daylilies, Little Hermitage, St Catherine's Down,
nr Ventnor, Isle of Wight PO38 2PU

Tel: 01983 730512

Opening hours: by appointment only.

Visitors welcome: yes, by appointment.

Payment: cheque or postal order.

Mail order: yes.

Post and packing: £3.50 for up to 5 plants, £4.50 for 6–10,
25p for each additional plant.

Delivery: dependent on weather and season.

Availability: plants are sent out from April to November.

Refund/replacement: yes.

Special services: helpful advice.

GARDENERS' RECOMMENDATIONS: *"A quite wonderful collection of hemerocallis and always fantastic quality plants."* Mrs Susan Beck.

See map page 390.

Ventnor Botanic Gardens

No catalogue because the stock changes so frequently. They propagate from the garden with its mild climate so plants include many from the southern hemisphere and Mediterranean plus sub-tropical palms, agapanthus, cordylines and cannas. The website gives an idea of what's on offer.

> **Ventnor Botanic Gardens**, Plant Sales Dept, Ventnor, Isle of Wight PO38 1UL
>
> **Tel:** 01983 855397 **Fax:** 01983 856154
>
> **E-mail:** simon@vbgl.demon.co.uk
>
> **Website:** http://www.botanic.co.uk
>
> **Opening hours:** 10.00–17.00 daily from March to October, 11.00–16.00 Saturday and Sunday from November to February.
>
> **Visitors welcome:** yes.
>
> **Catalogue:** none.
>
> **Payment:** cash, cheque, Visa, Mastercard, Access.
>
> **Mail order:** no.
>
> **Availability:** stocks vary throughout the year and are limited.
>
> **Refund/replacement:** yes.
>
> **Special services:** plants are all raised from own stock and can be seen growing in the Botanic Garden.

GARDENERS' RECOMMENDATIONS: *"Exceptionally high quality and unusual plants."* Mr and Mrs C Pain. *Also recommended by* Lady Scott, Rotherfield Park.

See map page 390.

Kent

J Bradshaw & Son   The nursery specialises in climbers, especially honeysuckles (of which it holds the national collection) and clematis, with other climbers added to the list. The clematis are helpfully divided into large flowered, small flowered and species. There's a good selection of climbing roses, ivies and passion-flowers and a section of shrubs which like being against a wall.

J Bradshaw & Son, Busheyfields Nursery, Herne Common, Herne Bay, Kent CT6 7LJ

Tel/fax: 01227 375415

Opening hours: 10.00–17.00 Tuesday to Saturday from 1 March to 31 October and bank holiday Mondays. By appointment at other times.

Visitors welcome: yes.

Catalogue: send 2 first class stamps plus A5 sae.

Payment: cash or cheque.

Mail order: yes. Minimum order 2 plants.

Post and packing: from £9 for 2 plants to £12.60 for 12 by Securicor.

Delivery: plants normally despatched within 1 week of receipt of payment.

Availability: not normally limited.

Refund/replacement: each case considered on merit.

GARDENERS' RECOMMENDATIONS: ✿ *"Excellent."* Mr and Mrs J Talbot.

See map page 392.

Capel Cottage Garden Nursery   The firm specialises in hardy herbaceous perennials and also has a good range of seasonal bedding, young shrubs and cottage garden plants. If they don't have what you want, they'll try to find it for you.

Capel Cottage Garden Nursery, Maidstone Road, Whetsted, nr Tonbridge, Kent TN12 6R

Tel: 01732 870314

Opening hours: 9.30–17.30 (dusk in winter) Tuesday to Sunday. Closed in January.

Visitors welcome: yes.

Catalogue: none.

Payment: cash or cheque.

Mail order: no.

Availability: seasonal.

Refund/replacement: yes.

Special services: plant finding service.

See map page 392.

Church Hill Cottage Gardens

A list of interesting perennials, grasses and shrubs which tend to be chosen for their stylish growth and leaves. There are ferns and hostas, crocosmia, dianthus and alpines.

Church Hill Cottage Gardens, Church Hill, Charing Heath, Ashford, Kent TN27 0BU

Tel/fax: 01233 712522

Opening hours: 10.00–17.00. Closed on Mondays except bank holidays and in December and January.

Visitors welcome: yes.

Catalogue: £1 or send 4 first class stamps.

Payment: cheque.

Mail order: yes. Minimum order £10.

Post and packing: postage at cost.

Delivery: minimum 3 days by Parcel Force.

Availability: supplies can be limited and some plants are available only at certain times of year.

Refund/replacement: they have never had a dissatisfied customer.

GARDENERS' RECOMMENDATIONS: ✸ *"An idyllic cottage garden from which the owners propagate most of their nursery stock, so you can see the plant in position. Unusual plants, beautiful colour and texture planting. A delightful couple, too!"* Mr and Mrs Loudon. ✸ *"Michael and Margaret Metianu with their son, Jeremy, grow many unusual and interesting herbaceous plants to an exceptionally high and reliable standard. The nursery beside their own house and much-visited cottage garden have a international reputation, well deserved."* Mrs Mills, Mr Richmond-Watson and Mr Rolla ✸ *" I regularly patronise this nursery because the plants are well grown and healthy at a reasonable price. I cannot recommend it too highly. There is a delightful garden attached to the nursery which is always worth seeing."* *"A first class nursery garden. Mr and Mrs Metianu, the owners, are very welcoming, very knowledgeable. Well worth a visit."* Mr and Mrs D Mure. *"All home grown plants. Excellent value."* Mr and Mrs R de Garston. *Also recommended by* Mrs R Alexander, The English Gardening School at the Chelsea Physic Garden.

See map page 392.

Copton Ash Gardens

The garden was started in 1978 in an old cherry orchard and has over 3,000 plant species. Many come from exotic places and look it. Tim Ingram is constantly testing new arrivals for hardiness and other attributes and, unusually, he welcomes advice from others at the sharp end of plant introduction. In autumn and winter, he'll give lectures on plants.

> **Copton Ash Specialist Nursery**, 105 Ashford Road, Faversham, Kent ME13 8XW
> **Tel:** 01795 535919
> **Opening hours:** 14.00–18.00 Tuesday to Sunday. Occasionally closed for shows, so ring before travelling.
> **Visitors welcome:** yes.
> **Catalogue:** send 4 first class stamps.
> **Payment:** cash or cheque.
> **Mail order:** no.
> **Availability:** many unusual plants are grown.
> **Refund/replacement:** yes, within reason.
> **Special services:** lectures on a range of gardening topics.

GARDENERS' RECOMMENDATIONS: *"Excellent."* Mr and Mrs J Talbot. *"Excellent plants are home produced."* Mr and Mrs G Smith. *Also recommended by* Christopher Lloyd, Great Dixter *and* Mr and Mrs M Metianu, Church Hill Cottage Gardens.

See map page 392.

P de Jager

The firm has specialised in flowering bulbs since 1868 and many long-established gardens owe their displays of narcissi to its list. It has a huge selection, very well illustrated, which comes out in spring and autumn. Deliveries can be made in 48 hours.

P de Jager and Sons Ltd, Staplehurst Road, Marden, Kent
TN12 9BP

Tel: 01622 831235 **Fax:** 01622 832416

Opening hours: 8.30–17.00 Monday to Friday.

Visitors welcome: yes.

Catalogue: send 2 first class stamps.

Payment: cheque, postal order, Visa, Access.

Mail order: yes, in spring and autumn. Minimum order £15.

Post and packing: £3.25, free for orders over £50.

Delivery: by 48-hour guaranteed delivery.

Availability: orders from the autumn catalogue are despatched from early September to December and spring orders are despatched from February to late April subject to weather conditions.

Refund/replacement: yes.

GARDENERS' RECOMMENDATIONS: ❀ *"Used over several years for lily bulbs and the quality has been excellent."* Mrs Susan Beck. *Also recommended by* Mrs M Linklater *and* Dr and Mrs Gallagher.

See map page 392.

Downderry Nursery Lavender specialist nursery which is set in a Victorian walled garden and boasts the largest range of the plants in Britain (and holds the national collection of lavenders.) There is a surprisingly large choice with, says Dr Simon Charlesworth, everything from Seal Lavender, raised nearby to the species aristibracteata found in the Surudi Hills of Northern Somalia. The nursery produces a twice yearly newsletter for lavender fans appropriately called The Lavender Bag.

Downderry Nursery, Pillar Box Lane, Hadlow, Tonbridge, Kent
TN11 9SW

Tel: 01732 810081 **Fax:** 01732 811398

E-mail: simon@downderry.demon.co.uk

Opening hours: 10.00–17.00 Wednesday to Saturday,
11.00–17.00 Sundays and bank holidays.

Visitors welcome: yes.

Catalogue: send 3 first class stamps.

Payment: cash, cheque, postal order, major credit/debit cards.
Mail order: yes.
Post and packing: £3 to £17 by first class post.
Delivery: 1 week to 3 months depending on time of year.
Availability: mail order plants from May to October.
Refund/replacement: within reason.

GARDENERS' RECOMMENDATIONS: *"I recently used this nursery when I needed to replace a double walk of lavender and found Dr Charlesworth most helpful."* Mrs P Styles. ❀ *"They specialise in lavenders only. They have a really good catalogue and the service was speedy."* Callum Johnston, Tan-y-Lyn Nurseries. ❀ *"Downderry Nursery is run by a dedicated owner who specialises in lavender and rosemary. The collection is well presented and, more importantly, well grown. The range of plants is slowly expanding but all within a Mediterranean orbit."* Viscountess De L'Isle.

See map page 392.

High Banks Nurseries

A general nursery list, from hedging and hedging conifers through herbs, conservatory plants and fruit trees. It has been sensibly chosen to provide interesting varieties rather than run-of-the-mill.

High Banks Nursery, Slip Mill Road, Hawkhurst, Kent TN18 5AD
Tel: 01580 754492/754450 **Fax:** 01580 753031
Opening hours: 8.30–17.00 Monday to Friday, 9.00–17.00 Saturday, 10.00–17.00 Sunday.
Visitors welcome: yes.
Catalogue: £1.
Payment: cash, cheque, Visa, Mastercard, Switch, Delta.
Mail order: no.
Delivery: only locally.
Refund/replacement: each case is treated individually.

GARDENERS' RECOMMENDATIONS: ❀ *"Good plants, sensibly priced. Being medalists at RHS shows has not gone to their heads!"* Lynda Shepherd, head gardener Finchcocks. ❀ *"Good general."* Mr D G W Barham.

See map page 391.

Iden Croft Herbs   A really comprehensive list of herbs here — 11 basils, 13 rosemarys, 37 mints, for instance — along with lesser known herbs like arnica, weld and asphodel. They hold the national collections for mint and origanum. Plants both cultivated and by seed.

Iden Croft Herbs, Frittenden Road, Staplehurst, Kent TN12 0DH

Tel: 01580 891432   **Fax:** 01580 892416

E-mail: idencroft.herbs@dial.pipex.com

Website: http://www.oxalis.co/ic.htm

Opening hours: 9.00–17.00 (dusk in winter) Monday to Saturday, 11.00–17.00 Sunday and bank holidays – phone first in depths of winter.

Visitors welcome: yes.

Catalogue: send 4 first class stamps.

Payment: cheque, major credit cards, Switch.

Mail order: yes.

Post and packing: seeds 50p, plants by carrier £9 for up to 20. Smaller quantities assessed by weight.

Delivery: 1-2 weeks unless very large or "grown to order" item.

Availability: seeds are despatched all year, plants from November to April/May. Limited supply of half-hardy plants in winter.

Refund/replacement: yes, within 2 weeks of receipt or for genuine reason.

Special services: advice, range of leaflets available, tours, courses, open days for national collections, common names in European languages.

GARDENERS' RECOMMENDATIONS: ✿ *"Plants very reasonably priced and a simply wonderful range of herbs. As a garden designer I find their list of plants using the common names rather than the botanic names very hard to use as I don't always know the common names."* Mr Frankie Warren. ✿ *"Although Iden Croft is a well-known and much visited nursery, the enthusiasm and imagination of the owners, David and Rosemary, have managed to convey an almost cottage garden atmosphere in their display garden. Banks of perfumed loveliness lead eyes and nose on an aromatic journey into a world of natural beauty and fascinating surprises, while the relaxing hum of bees and the song of birds delight the ears."* Mrs Z Grant.

See map page 391.

Madrona Nursery   Derek Jarman, of the shingle garden on Dungeness, called this "the most charming nursery in England" and it stocks just the kind of plants he liked. Some may be quite ordinary, such as clematis montana, or unusual varieties of ordinary plants, such as the tiny-leaved ivy, Hedera 'Spetchley' and the incised-leaf walnut, some are new, such as the Vitis coignetiae 'Claret Cloak' with deeply cut leaves turning purply. Whatever their status, all the plants are chosen for quality.

Madrona Nursery, Pluckley Road, Bethersden, Ashford, Kent TN26 3DD

Tel: 01233 820100 **Fax:** 01233 820091

Opening hours: 10.00–17.00 Saturday to Tuesday 20 March to 2 November. Closed 6-30 August.

Visitors welcome: yes.

Catalogue: free.

Payment: cash, cheque, major credit cards, Switch.

Mail order: yes.

Post and packing: £12 for next day delivery.

Delivery: allow 2-4 weeks.

Availability: all year round.

Refund/replacement: yes.

GARDENERS' RECOMMENDATIONS: ✸ *"Top choice. The man is an artist in the way he displays his stock. Excellent."* Major and Mrs R H Blizard. ✸ *"Uncommon trees and shrubs and herbaceous plants; helpful advice. Well grown examples in an unusual setting."* Mr and Mrs K H Wallis. ✸ *"Plants and shrubs of excellent quality in perfect condition."* Mr and Mrs J Eker. ✸ *"Unusual, interesting and rare plants."* Mr and Mrs S Jempson.

See map page 391.

Oakover Nurseries   This is a nursery which grows everything it sells and you can therefore be sure that each plant is in good condition. It specialises in hedges, from native hawthorn to neat cut yew and hornbeam, and it stocks all the standard stuff that every gardener needs.

Oakover Nurseries, Maidstone Road, Hothfield, Ashford, Kent TN26 1AR

Tel: 01233 712424 **Fax:** 01233 713991

Opening hours: 9.00–16.00 Monday to Saturday.
Visitors welcome: yes, to plant centre only.
Catalogue: free.
Payment: cash, cheque, major credit cards.
Mail order: no.
Delivery: can be arranged for large orders.
Availability: supplies can be limited.
Refund/replacement: dependent on circumstances.

GARDENERS' RECOMMENDATIONS: ✿ *"Excellent for trees"* Mr and Mrs J Talbot.

See map page 391.

The Old Walled Garden The policy here is to grow as wide a range of weird and unusual plants as the owners can find. They collect plants from Australia and recently have been given the NCCPG collection of callistemon. Many of the plants are intended for the conservatory — which would be a better place if planted in this way.

The Old Walled Garden, Oxonhoath, Hadlow, Tonbridge, Kent TN11 9SS
Tel/fax: 01732 810012
E-mail: amyrtle@aol.com
Opening hours: 9.00–17.00 Monday to Friday. By appointment at weekends.
Visitors welcome: yes.
Catalogue: send 2 first class stamps.
Payment: cash or cheque.
Mail order: no.
Availability: supplies can be limited and some plants are available only at certain times of year.
Refund/replacement: if notified within 7 days.

GARDENERS' RECOMMENDATIONS:
✿ *"The Old Walled Garden at Oxonhoath is a perfect example of a well run specialist nursery maintained by a father and daughter team for whom it is a labour of love. The range of plants is constantly expanding and includes a national collection of callistemons."*

Viscountess De L'Isle. *Also recommended by* Christopher Lloyd, Great Dixter.

See map page 392.

Pine Cove Nursery   Quite a general nursery with garden sundries, planted pots and hanging baskets along with a range of shrubs, trees, roses and alpines, often unusual. There is always someone to give advice and there's a hanging basket service in both summer and winter along with holly wreaths at Christmas.

Pine Cove Nursery, Appledore Road, Tenterden, Kent TN30 7DJ
Tel: 01580 765429
Opening hours: 8.45–17.15 Monday to Saturday, 9.00–16.00 Sunday.
Visitors welcome: yes.
Catalogue: none.
Payment: cash, cheque, major credit cards.
Mail order: no.
Availability: supplies can be limited and some plants are available only at certain times of year.
Refund/replacement: yes.

GARDENERS' RECOMMENDATIONS: ❀ *"Small, friendly and consistently good value family-run nursery."* Mr and Mrs S Jempson.

See map page 391.

Roger Platts Nurseries   The owner of the nursery is a garden designer and thus his plants are chosen to back up his designs. He has a good range of most trees, shrubs and perennials, many of them the less common varieties which he thinks worth growing. Obviously, he offers a garden design service.

Roger Platts Garden Design and Nurseries, Stick Hill, Edenbridge, Kent TN8 5NH
Tel/fax: 01732 863318
E-mail: plattsgdn@aol.com
Opening hours: 9.00–17.00 daily.
Visitors welcome: yes.
Catalogue: none.
Payment: cheque, Visa, Access, American Express, Switch.

Mail order: no.

Availability: some plants are seasonal, e.g. bedding.

Refund/replacement: yes – with some helpful advice where appropriate.

GARDENERS' RECOMMENDATIONS: ❀ *"Roger Platts has reasonably priced and unusual plants. It is a new nursery and I feel he has not got it well organised as yet. I think it has potential."* Mr and Mrs B Gough.

See map page 391.

Plaxtol Nurseries

The family-run nursery specialises in plants and shrubs which will enthuse flower arrangers and those who pine for Japanese gardens. Obviously, there are ferns, grasses and bamboos, herbaceous plants such as many geraniums, hemerocallis and aquilegia. There's an interesting list of conifers, trees and shrubs. The Japanese plant list has six wisteria, 13 camellias and seven Acer platanum.

Plaxtol Nurseries, Plaxtol, Sevenoaks, Kent TN15 0QR

Tel/fax: 01732 810550

Opening hours: 10.00–17.00 daily including bank holidays.

Visitors welcome: yes, preferred.

Catalogue: sjend 2 first class stamps.

Payment: cash, cheque, major credit cards if customer present.

Mail order: yes, from November to March.

Post and packing: from £10.

Delivery: 7 days.

Availability: supplies can be limited and some plants are available only at certain times of year.

Refund/replacement: yes.

Special services: talks to clubs and societies, plants for flower arrangers, Japanese garden ornaments.

GARDENERS' RECOMMENDATIONS: ❀ *"Small family nursery – plants nicely kept and presented. Knowledgeable and willing to help. Also marvellous free horse manure if you take your own sack."* Mrs P Hadrill. ❀ *"Excellent quality, wide range of hardy plants."* ❀ *"Well managed – knowledgeable owner."* Mr and Mrs Cosier.

See map page 392.

The Potted Garden Nursery I don't go along with the idea that hanging baskets are naff. They are great for difficult corners, houses with walls but no gardens and basements. I also love Christopher Lloyd's habit of arraying plants in pots around his front door according to season. This nursery offers hardy container plants for all these purposes.

> **The Potted Garden Nursery**, Ashford Road, Bearsted, Maidstone, Kent ME14 4NH
>
> **Tel/fax:** 01622 737801 (ring first for fax).
>
> **Opening hours:** 9.00–17.30.
>
> **Visitors welcome:** yes.
>
> **Catalogue:** none.
>
> **Payment:** cash, cheque, Visa, Switch, Delta.
>
> **Mail order:** no.
>
> **Availability:** supplies can be limited.
>
> **Refund/replacement:** yes, depending on circumstances.
>
> **Special services:** fruit trees with specific rootstocks.

GARDENERS' RECOMMENDATIONS: ✧ *"Every plant/shrub purchased from them has thrived."* Mr and Mrs J G Jackson.

See map page 392.

Rock Farm Nursery A small nursery attached to a garden which is regularly open. They sell hardy and half-hardy perennials, unusual shrubs and climbers. They will advise and help plan gardens.

> **Rock Farm Nursery**, Gibbs Hill, Nettlestead, nr Maidstone, Kent ME18 5HT
>
> **Tel:** 01622 812244
>
> **Opening hours:** 10.00–17.00 Wednesday to Saturday and bank holidays, 14.00–17.00 Sunday, from March to November.
>
> **Visitors welcome:** yes.
>
> **Catalogue:** none.
>
> **Mail order:** no.
>
> **Refund/replacement:** yes.
>
> **Special services:** advice and garden planning.

GARDENERS' RECOMMENDATIONS: ✧ *"The nursery is in a delightful setting with its own most attractive gardens. It stocks a wide but not enormous range of plants – all very plantable. The owner Mrs Sue Corfe is warm, friendly and knowledgeable. It is always a pleasure to go there."* Mr and Mrs R Fawssett. *Also recommended by* Mr and Mrs M Metianu, Church Hill Cottage Gardens.

See map page 392.

Rosewood Daylilies

Chris Searle has a good choice of over a hundred daylily hybrids, including some of the very latest from America, in his catalogue plus over 400 in the nursery where they are trialled for garden value. Some of those not listed may still be for sale. He also offers advice on planting and suggestions for companion planting.

> **Rosewood Daylilies**, 70 Deansway Avenue, Sturry, Canterbury, Kent CT2 0NN
> **Tel:** 01227 711071
> **Opening hours:** by appointment.
> **Visitors welcome:** yes, by appointment.
> **Catalogue:** send 2 first class stamps.
> **Payment:** cash or cheque.
> **Mail order:** yes.
> **Post and packing:** from £4.50 for up to 5 plants to £6 for 20.
> **Delivery:** plants sent from March to May and in September/October.
> **Availability:** supplies can be limited.
> **Refund/replacement:** yes.

GARDENERS' RECOMMENDATIONS: ⊛ *"Healthy plants, helpful advice, many recent American introductions at very reasonable prices. Small family business – good personal service. Plants true to name."* Mr Duncan Skene. ⊛ *"Very helpful. Good selection."*

See map page 392.

Starborough Nursery & G Reuthe Ltd

G Reuthe specialises in lime-hating rhododendrons and azaleas with both species and hybrids, while Starborough has a good mix of shrubs such as camellia, acers and and magnolia. They also stock good climbers.

> **Starborough Nursery & G Reuthe Ltd**, Starborough Road, Marsh Green, Edenbridge, Kent TN8 5RB

Tel: 01732 865614 **Fax:** 01732 862166

Opening hours: 10.00–16.30 Monday, Tuesday and Thursday to Saturday. Closed on Wednesdays as well as in January and July/August.

Visitors welcome: yes.

Catalogue: £2 (loose stamps or postal order).

Payment: cash, cheque, Visa, Access.

Mail order: yes. Minimum order £25.

Post and packing: £12.50 for orders up to £50, £17.50 for orders up to £100, negotiable thereafter.

Delivery: 2-3 weeks in season.

Availability: rhododendrons available all year, other plants only in season.

Refund/replacement: yes.

GARDENERS' RECOMMENDATIONS: ✺ *"Excellent, well grown, wide range of shrubs."* Mr P J Oliver-Smith. ✺ *"Excellent nursery for shrubs and trees: helpful and expert advice."* Mr and Mrs K H Wallis ✺ *"Small but excellent selection of high quality shrubs and trees."*

See map page 391.

Tile Barn Nursery Liz and Peter Moore specialise in cyclamen which, they say, are not nearly as temperamental as we think (shop-bought tubers are notoriously unreliable and a sure way of killing the plant is overwatering.) Plants here are raised from seed and the nursery has a helpful list of varieties, not all of which are for sale.

Tile Barn Nursery, Standen Street, Iden Green, Benenden, Kent TN17 4LB

Tel/fax: 01582 40221

Opening hours: 9.00–16.00 Wednesday to Saturday.

Visitors welcome: yes.

Catalogue: send sae.

Payment: cash or cheque.

Mail order: yes.

Post and packing: at cost.

Delivery: 7 days.

Availability: all year round.

Refund/replacement: yes.

GARDENERS' RECOMMENDATIONS: *"Good specialist nursery with a wide range."* Mr and Mrs R A Cunningham. *"Wonderful range of cyclamen."* Mr and Mrs E W Dyer.

See map page 391.

Wallace and Barr

Bulb specialists selling everything from daffodils to arum lilies, fancy tulips, fritillary and cyclamen. Helpfully illustrated catalogue.

Wallace and Barr, The Nurseries, Marden, Kent TN12 9BP
Tel: 01622 831235 **Fax:** 01622 832416
E-mail: pdejag@aol.com
Opening hours: 9.00–17.00 Monday to Friday.
Visitors welcome: yes.
Catalogue: send 2 first class stamps.
Payment: cheque, postal order, Visa, Mastercard.
Mail order: yes. Minimum order £15.
Post and packing: £3.25 for orders up to £50, free thereafter.
Delivery: autumn orders despatched in rotation from September to December, spring orders from early Feburary to late April, depending on weather conditons.
Availability: from September to December and February to April, subject to weather conditions.
Refund/replacement: yes, or credit note.

GARDENERS' RECOMMENDATIONS: *"Good quality bulbs."* Mrs F Denby. *"Very good plants, service, delivery."* Mrs Craig. *"We always get our bulbs from them."* Mr and Mrs W N Bolt.

See map page 392.

Wildflower Nursery

It does what it says: offers wildflower plants and seed. Some of our native plants can be surprisingly difficult to establish and, in small areas, it's an idea to plant little plugs rather than rely on seeds. Wildflowers also help our birds and bees.

Johanna Westgate produces four different collections: cornfield annuals, meadow flora, woodland flora and cottage garden biennials and perennials.

Wildflower Nursery, 62 Lower Sands, Dymchurch, Romney Marsh, Kent TN29 0NF

Tel: 01303 873052

Opening hours: generally from 10.30 from March to October. By appointment at other times.

Visitors welcome: yes, but advisable to telephone first.

Catalogue: free.

Payment: cash or cheque.

Mail order: yes, for seeds and Johanna Westgate's book *Creating Habitats for Garden Wildlife*.

Post and packing: 50p.

Delivery: within a week.

Availability: all year round.

Refund/replacement: yes.

See map page 391.

Wood Cottage Nursery   Roger King's hobby of gardening turned, as so many do, into his business but he prides himself on running a friendly, casual nursery. He sells about 2,000 varieties of hardy perennials plus shrubs, climbers and 65 varieties of clematis. Like so many hobbyists turned businessmen, his advice is free and should be sought.

Wood Cottage Nursery, Maidstone Road, Nettlestead Green, Kent ME18 5HJ

Tel/fax: 01622 813311

Opening hours: 10.00-dusk daily.

Visitors welcome: yes.

Catalogue: none.

Payment: cash or cheque.

Mail order: no.

Availability: a good range available all year.

Refund/replacement: yes.

Special services: help and advice on any gardening problems.

GARDENERS' RECOMMENDATIONS: ✿ *"A small nursery growing a wide range of hardy plants and shrubs. I wish we had found him years ago. The plants and shrubs are beautifully produced and are mature.*

The added bonus is he charges only about half of other nurseries. We haven't had a failure yet, and if we did it does not cost and arm and leg to replace." Mr and Mrs Fyson.

See map page 392.

See also: Edenbridge House, page 354; **Sue Hartfree,** page 355; **Mr and Mrs D Jolley, Maycotts,** page 357.

Lancashire

Barkers Garden Centre and Florist   The nursery divides its list into five separate catalogues: trees, rhododendrons (with azaleas), roses, fruit and perennials. This means that the plant descriptions are good and full and that planting and pruning advice is included. The selection is not huge.

> **Barkers Garden Centre and Florist**, Primrose Nurseries, Whalley Road, Clitheroe, Lancashire BB7 1HT
>
> **Tel:** 01200 423521 **Fax:** 01200 428160
>
> **E-mail:** sales@bgc-uk.com
>
> **Website:** http://www.bgc-uk.com
>
> **Opening hours:** 8.30–17.30 Monday to Saturday, 10.00–17.00 Sunday.
>
> **Visitors welcome:** yes.
>
> **Catalogue:** 5 separate catalogues at 20p each.
>
> **Payment:** cash, cheque, credit/debit cards.
>
> **Mail order:** sundries only by e-mail.
>
> **Post and packing:** by quotation according to weight.
>
> **Delivery:** 1 week.
>
> **Availability:** supplies can be limited and some plants are available only at certain times of year.
>
> **Refund/replacement:** yes.

GARDENERS' RECOMMENDATIONS: ❀ *"Not a mere plant super-market with dreary clutters of non-horticultural products to distract and irritate, Barkers has knowledge and flair and offer a fine range of plants, many outside the usual run of "safe" varieties. Staff helpful and knowledgeable – an unusual combination."* Mr and Mrs J Bowker. *"Good shrub nursery."* Dr and Mrs R L Belsey.

See map page 395.

Catforth Gardens

Holders of the national collection of geraniums and hence a huge list of these (with others unlisted but for sale when available.) Also good list of plants like campanula and euphorbia which, somehow, fit in with geraniums. There are three gardens here of about three acres open at the same time as the nursery.

Catforth Gardens and Nursery, Roots Lane, Catforth, Preston, Lancashire PR4 0JB

Tel: 01772 690561/690269

Opening hours: 10.30–17.00 from mid-March to mid-September.

Visitors welcome: yes.

Catalogue: send 5 first class stamps.

Payment: cash or cheque.

Mail order: no.

Availability: rare plants are usually available early in the season. Ring to check before travelling.

Refund/replacement: yes.

GARDENERS' RECOMMENDATIONS: *"Hardy geranium specialist. Excellent gardens for geranium freaks and others."* Mr and Mrs R L Jefferson.

See map page 395.

The Hawthornes Nursery and Gardens

The nursery grows its own plants and, among many interesting perennials and shrubs, picks out clematis for special treatment along with a few honeysuckles and good roses. The garden will show what can be done with the plants.

The Hawthornes Nursery and Gardens, Marsh Road, Hesketh Bank, Preston, Lancashire PR4 6XT

Tel: 01772 812379

Opening hours: 9.00–18.00 from 1 March to 30 June, 9.00–18.00 Thursday to Sunday from July to October.

Visitors welcome: yes.

Catalogue: £1 or 5 first class stamps.
Payment: cash or cheque.
Mail order: no.
Availability: most plants are available most of the season.
Refund/replacement: yes.
Special services: Gardens open from May to October displaying plants propagated in the nursery (admission £1).

GARDENERS' RECOMMENDATIONS: ❀ *"Family run, very good value for money, wide choice of plants of which they are very knowledgeable."* Mr and Mrs T Iddon. ❀ *"Small nursery run by husband and wife, Richard and Irene Hodson, with a large variety of plants and many clematis to choose from. The nursery is alongside their very beautiful garden. A plantsman's garden …well worth a visit."* Mrs Brenda Hale.

See map page 395.

Holden Clough Nursery

The nursery was started by the plantsman, Richard Milne-Redhead, in 1927 and is still going strong, selling alpines and other unusual plants. It also continues to win medals at shows, including awards at Courson, near Paris. It has a most interesting list, including hardy ferns, dianthus and heathers. Worth a voyage.

Holden Clough Nursery, Bolton by Bowland, Clitheroe, Lancashire BB7 4PF
Tel/fax: 01200 447615
Opening hours: 9.00–17.00 Monday to Saturday, 13.30–16.30 on occasional Sundays in spring.
Visitors welcome: yes.
Catalogue: £1.40.
Payment: cash, cheque, postal order.
Post and packing: from £5.60 per parcel.
Delivery: 7-28 days.
Availability: most plants available all year round.
Refund/replacement: yes.
Special services: garden advisory visits locally. Nursery event days.

GARDENERS' RECOMMENDATIONS: ❀ *"Very good alpines, small shrubs and trees."* Dr and Mrs R L Belsey.

See map page 395.

Stoney Leach Nursery The firm has been growing perennials and alpines for nearly 30 years — nearly 99 per cent come from the nursery itself via cuttings, seed or root stock. Like many older nurseries, they make their own compost. Plants include alpines, perennials, unusual shrubs and climbers. "We try to do our best for our plants and our customers."

Stoney Leach Nursery, 40 Toogood Lane, Wrightington, Wigan, Lancashire WN6 9PL (Car park entrance in Tunley Lane.)
Tel: 01257 253105
Opening hours: 9.00–16.30 daily from 1 March to 30 September, and at other times by appointment.
Visitors welcome: yes.
Catalogue: none.
Payment: cash or cheque.
Mail order: no.
Availability: a good selection of unusual and popular varieties always available from March to September.
Refund/replacement: yes.

GARDENERS' RECOMMENDATIONS: ✿ *"This is a larger nursery with a good selection of healthy plants, pleasant surroundings and a relaxed and friendly atmosphere."* Mrs Brenda Hale.

See map page 395.

LEICESTERSHIRE & RUTLAND

Goscote Nurseries A collection particularly strong on acid-loving plants with heathers, rhododendrons and azaleas and hydrangeas but this is also a very good general list of trees, shrubs and climbers with a section on fruit trees and bushes from apples and mulberry to rhubarb, blueberries and even worcestershireberries.

Goscote Nurseries, Syston Road, Cossington, Leicestershire
LE7 4UZ
Tel: 01509 812121 **Fax:** 01509 814231

Opening hours: daily.

Visitors welcome: yes.

Catalogue: send 5 first class stamps.

Payment: cheque, major credit cards.

Mail order: yes.

Post and packing: £10 for up to 10 kg.

Delivery: next day.

Availability: all year round, with a few exceptions.

Refund/replacement: replacement.

Special services: landscape and design service, show garden.

GARDENERS' RECOMMENDATIONS: ✿ *"Very helpful and not over-priced. They have very interesting material."* Mr and Mrs M Taylor. ✿ *"A friendly nursery with a rather wider selection of shrubs and small trees than is usually found."* Mr and Mrs J Buchanan. ✿ *"An excellent nursery with a wide and interesting range of trees, shrubs and hardy plants, 1,600 of which are raised on the site. There is an attractive show ground and professional advice is readily available."*

See map page 393.

The Herb Nursery

The Herb Nursery The catalogue sensibly puts together the culinary and medicinal herbs along with wild flowers, cottage garden flowers and scented leaf geraniums because so many interlap. Geraniums are herbs and can be eaten, herbs are used in cottage gardens and many are virtually wild. The list is comprehensive.

The Herb Nursery, Main Street, Thistleton, Oakham, Rutland LE15 7RE

Tel: 01572 767658 **Fax:** 01572 768021

Opening hours: 9.00–18.00 daily.

Visitors welcome: yes.

Catalogue: send A5 sae.

Payment: cash or cheque.

Mail order: no.

Availability: perennials normally available all year, other plants are seasonal.

Refund/replacement: yes.

Special services: group visits by appointment.

GARDENERS' RECOMMENDATIONS: ✿ *"Grow their own plants."* Mr and Mrs J L Cookson. ✿ *"An excellent family-run nursery with a wonderful range of unusual plants/scented geraniums in a fantastic rural setting."* Mr C McAlpine. ✿ *"Each visit to this nursery is a wonderful experience of discovery."* Mr and Mrs A R B Wadd.

See map page 393.

Kayes Garden Nursery

Kayes Garden Nursery Like many good nurseries, this has a garden attached where plants can be seen in their maturity and where the older plants can be used for propagation. The specialities are hardy herbaceous, climbing and aquatic plants and there is a good selection of choice varieties. Grasses and clematis are in particularly good supply.

> **Kayes Garden Nursery**, 1700 Melton Road, Rearsby, Leicester, Leicestershire LE7 4YR
>
> **Tel:** 01664 424578
>
> **Opening hours:** 10.00–17.00 Tuesday to Saturday and bank holiday Mondays, 10.00–12.00 Sunday.
>
> **Visitors welcome:** yes.
>
> **Catalogue:** send 50p or 2 first class stamps.
>
> **Payment:** cash or cheque.
>
> **Mail order:** no.
>
> **Availability:** good stocks of most plants, but some may not be available all season and some are in very short supply.
>
> **Refund/replacement:** by arrangement.
>
> **Special services:** garden open at the same time as the nursery, slide talks, RHS speaker.

GARDENERS' RECOMMENDATIONS: ✿ *"Very helpful, friendly nursery. Super garden open also under NGS yellow book – made new from a field site, many of the plants displayed in suitable planting environments."* Mrs Sally Knight, Pasture Farm. ✿ *"A small nursery within a charming garden where all the plants can be seen in the borders. A wide range of clematis. Hazel and all her staff are very knowledgeable and helpful."* Mr and Mrs P Bland. ✿ *"Mrs Hazel Kaye's nursery has a wonderful selection of unusual herbaceous perennials, climbers and water plants. The garden at the side of the nursery (about 1.5 acres) is fully stocked and has a stream and wildlife pond. Well worth a visit."* Mr and Mrs W D Hall.

See map page 393.

Mozart House Nursery Garden

Des Martin likes his leaves so he sells plants which emphasise texture, form and foliage with especially good selections of hosta, bamboo and other grasses. He has two chusquea bamboos and the wonderful thamnocalamus. He is very keen on giving personal service — though by appointment — and wants to build up his collection through swapping.

Mozart House Nursery Garden, Mozart House, 84 Central Avenue, Wigston Magna, Wigston, Leicestershire LE18 2AA

Tel: 0116 288 9548

Opening hours: by appointment.

Visitors welcome: yes, by appointment.

Catalogue: send 5 second class stamps.

Payment: cash or cheque.

Mail order: yes. Minimum order £15 plus p&p.

Post and packing: £6 to £12 depending on order value; 10% for orders over £150.

Delivery: next day despatch if possible (plants are not sent from Thursday to Saturday to avoid postal delays).

Availability: supplies of certain plants can be limited and a waiting list operates where appropriate. Some plants are available only at certain times of year.

Refund/replacement: the nursery should be notified of any problems within 7 days and will endeavour to reach an agreement.

Special services: plant association and cultivation hints. Local delivery service by arrangement.

See map page 393.

Anita and Andrew Thorp

In a small nursery, Anita and Andrew Thorp concentrate on unusual hardy plants and alpines and do their best to seek out the best forms of each. There are hardy geraniums, corydalis, Anemone nemerosa, cyclamen and campanulas. They are always ready to talk plants and recommend them and, they say, "are always honest about plants — if we don't like a plant we say so."

Anita and Andrew Thorp, Bungalow no 5, Main Street, Theddingworth, Leicestershire LE17 6QZ

Tel: 01858 880496

Opening hours: 10.00–17.00.

Visitors welcome: yes.

Catalogue: 50p plus sae.

Payment: cash or cheque.

Mail order: no.

Availability: most plants are seasonal and supplies can be limited.

Refund/replacement: yes.

GARDENERS' RECOMMENDATIONS: *"Exciting bulbs and unusual plants."*

See map page 393.

Ulverscroft Grange Nursery
The nursery is for personal callers only and sells a range of hardy perennials along with interesting and fashionable grasses and bamboos and some shrubs.

Ulverscroft Grange Nursery, Priory Lane, Ulverscroft, nr Markfield, Leicestershire LE67 9PB

Tel: 01530 243635

Opening hours: 10.00–17.00 Tuesday to Sunday from March to October.

Visitors welcome: yes.

Catalogue: none.

Payment: cash or cheque.

Mail order: no.

Availability: supplies can be limited and some plants are available only at certain times of year.

Refund/replacement: yes.

GARDENERS' RECOMMENDATIONS: *"Exceptionally good and has display area."*

See map page 393.

Warren Hills Nursery
A nice list of hardy perennials — geraniums, foxglove, heuchera and penstemon, for instance — and soon, they hope, the national collection of astrantias. The gardens are being planted in different areas such as woodland, scree and herbaceous borders.

Warren Hills Nursery, Warren Hills Cottage, Warren Hills Road, Coalville, Leicestershire LE67 4UY

Tel: 01530 812350

Opening hours: by appointment.

Visitors welcome: very much.

Catalogue: send 2 first class stamps.

Payment: cash or cheque.

Mail order: no.

Availability: most plants available all year, however supplies of new and rare items are usually limited.

Refund/replacement: yes.

GARDENERS' RECOMMENDATIONS: ❁ *"Specialising in astrantias and hardy perennials."*

See map page 393.

Wingwell Nursery

Over 600 varieties of plants, mostly herbaceous perennials, grasses, bamboos and ferns, with a few shrubs and climbers are offered here, along with the chance to see their performance in open-ground beds and in the gardens, which are being developed, by appointment. Customers can also ask for help in choosing their plants and the nursery offers a design service too.

Wingwell Nursery, 5 Top Street, Wing, Oakham, Rutland LE15 8SE

Tel: 01572 737727   **Fax:** 01572 737788

Opening hours: 10.00–17.00 Wednesday to Sunday and bank holiday Mondays (excluding Easter Day) from March to December.

Visitors welcome: yes.

Catalogue: £1.

Payment: cash or cheque.

Mail order: yes.

Post and packing: from £5.35 for up to 6 plants to £9.10 for 36.

Delivery: 2 weeks if ordered between October and March.

Availability: mail order from October to March only.

Refund/replacement: yes.

GARDENERS' RECOMMENDATIONS: ❁ *"Run by Rose de Jardin, her own name! …grows her own plants."* Mr and Mrs J L Cookson. ❁ *"Very helpful and not over-priced. They have especially interesting material."* Mr and Mrs M Taylor. ❁ *"Unusual shrubs and perennial plants. Small but well stocked. (Not always open!)"* ❁ *"A large range of perennials, shrubs, grasses grown in a field. Plant sales area attractively set out and plants of good quality. Very knowledgeable proprietor."* Mr and Mrs N J Henson.

See map page 393.

LINCOLNSHIRE

Asterby Nurseries   A list of shrubs, clematis and herbaceous perennials which includes many of those awarded certificates of garden merit by the RHS (helpfully signalled with a little cup.)

> **Asterby Nurseries**, Dairy Farm, Church Lane, Asterby, Louth, Lincolnshire LN11 9UF
>
> **Tel:** 01507 343549
>
> **E-mail:** nursery@asterby.freeserve.co.uk
>
> **Website:** http://www.asterby.freeserve.co.uk
>
> **Opening hours:** 10.00–18.00 most days, but ring first if making a special journey.
>
> **Visitors welcome:** yes.
>
> **Catalogue:** send first class stamp, free if collected from nursery.
>
> **Payment:** cash, cheque, major credit cards.
>
> **Mail order:** no.
>
> **Refund/replacement:** yes.

GARDENERS' RECOMMENDATIONS: ✿ *"Good source of home-grown plants."*

See map page 396.

Choice Plants   Joan Gunson specialises in hardy geraniums but she has also a good list of the choicer hardy perennials and other border plants such as iris, crocosmia, sea holly and salvias. The helpful catalogue has been mostly written from her own observation.

> **Choice Plants**, 83 Halton Road, Spilsby, Lincolnshire PE23 5LD
>
> **Tel:** 01790 752361 or 07887 913704

Opening hours: 10.00–17.00 Wednesday to Sunday and bank holiday Mondays or by appointment at other times.

Visitors welcome: yes.

Catalogue: send 2 first class stamps, free if collected from nursery.

Payment: cash or cheque.

Mail order: possibly in the future.

Availability: supplies can be limited and some plants are available only at certain times of year.

Refund/replacement: yes.

See map page 396.

The Contented Gardener Nursery

This nursery specialises in perennials which are more for the wildish garden than for the herbaceous border. It sells plants which like the prairie and the steppe — that is without much shade and not too lush a soil — and for the woodland edge, part-shaded and often damp. This is a place to go if you have problem areas in your garden.

The Contented Gardener Nursery, The Garden House, 42 Wragby Road, Bardney, Lincolnshire LN3 5XL

Tel: 01526 397307 **Fax:** 01526 397280

Opening hours: by appointment.

Visitors welcome: yes, please telephone first.

Catalogue: send A4 sae and 2 first class stamps.

Payment: cheque.

Mail order: yes. Minimum order £15.

Post and packing: £9.50 for orders up to £25, £14 for orders from £25-£50.

Delivery: allow up to 10 days.

Availability: as this is a small nursery supplies can be limited.

Refund/replacement: yes, for plants damaged in transit if notified within 48 hours. No responsibility taken for plants lost through neglect or mistreatment.

Special services: garden design service.

See map page 396.

The Fern Nursery

Ferns only by mail order but other plants may be sold from the nursery. The fern catalogue is short and to the point and the owners will offer advice on them — they do not behave as normal plants and are quite difficult to get accustomed to. But worth it.

The Fern Nursery, Aldre, Grimsby Road, Binbrook, Lincolnshire LN3 6DH

Tel: 01472 398092

Opening hours: 9.00–17.00 Saturday and Sunday from April to October and by appointment.

Visitors welcome: yes, much preferred to mail order.

Catalogue: send 2 first class stamps.

Payment: cheque.

Mail order: yes (ferns only).

Post and packing: 20% of order value.

Delivery: allow 2 weeks between April and October. Orders received during the winter will be delivered in spring.

Availability: ferns available between April and October. As the nursery is small supplies are limited and it is best to check if ordering more than two of a kind.

Refund/replacement: yes.

Special services: talks to gardening clubs and other groups.

GARDENERS' RECOMMENDATIONS: ✿ *"Exceptionally good and has display area."*

See map page 396.

Groom Brothers Ltd Bulb specialists with everything from amaryllis to lily of the valley. The list is pretty much middle of the road — no unusual species, for instance — but within popular varieties, quite comprehensive. There is a short list of border plants such as hemerocallis, hellebores and delphiniums. The firm will offer advice.

Groom Brothers Ltd, Pecks Drove Nurseries, Clay Lake, Spalding, Lincolnshire PE12 6BJ

Tel: 01775 722421 **Fax:** 01775 712252

Opening hours: 8.30–16.30.

Visitors welcome: not as a rule, but could be arranged.

Catalogue: free.

Payment: cheque, major credit cards.

Mail order: yes.

Post and packing: £2.50 for orders under £20.

Delivery: in rotation from 1 September. Spring orders delivered by late March.

Availability: bulbs are despatched in autumn.

Refund/replacement: yes.

GARDENERS' RECOMMENDATIONS: *"Bulk order bulbs of fairly common varieties."*

See map page 393.

Mendle Nursery

Mrs Earnshaw specialises in alpines of which she has an excellent list but what really interests me is her list of sempervivum species and hybrids. Tiny and entirely undemanding, these are at home in roof gardens, troughs, plant pots and creeping over gravel. You can get bitten by the bug.

Mendle Nursery, Holme, Scunthorpe, Lincolnshire DN16 3RF

Tel: 01724 850864

Opening hours: 10.00–16.00.

Visitors welcome: yes.

Catalogue: send 3 second class stamps.

Payment: cheque.

Mail order: yes.

Post and packing: from £3.50 for up to 3 plants to £9 for 30.

Delivery: about 2 weeks.

Availability: supplies can be limited.

Refund/replacement: yes.

GARDENERS' RECOMMENDATIONS: *"Good source of home-grown plants."*

See map page 396.

Kathleen Muncaster Fuchsias

The nursery holds the national collection of hardy fuchsias and. during the summer, these can be seen flowering in the garden. There is also a good list of species fuchsias.

Kathleen Muncaster Fuchsias, 18 Field Lane, Morton, Gainsborough, Lincolnshire DN21 3BY

Tel: 01427 612329

E-mail: jim@smuncaster.co.uk

Website: http://www.kathleenmuncasterfuchsias.co.uk

Opening hours: 10.00 to dusk Thursday to Monday from February to mid-July. By appointment at other times.

Visitors welcome: yes.

Catalogue: send 2 first class stamps.

Payment: cheque.

Mail order: yes.

Post and packing: 50p per plant, minimum £2.50.

Delivery: normally as requested, or within a week.

Availability: mail order plants from February to May.

Refund/replacement: replacement.

See map page 396.

Martin Nest Nurseries
The firm holds the national collection for alpine primulas and auriculas and also specialises in cyclamen, saxifrages, some alpines and conifers. The auriculas, in particular, are in great variety, some rare.

Martin Nest Nurseries, Grange Cottage, Harpswell Lane, Hemswell, Gainsborough, Lincolnshire DN21 5UP

Tel: 01427 668369   **Fax:** 01427 668080

E-mail: mary@martin-nest.demon.co.uk

Website: http://www.martin-nest.demon.co.uk

Opening hours: 10.00–16.30 daily except for two weeks at Christmas/New Year.

Visitors welcome: yes.

Catalogue: send 3 second class stamps.

Payment: cheque, postal order, major credit cards.

Mail order: yes.

Post and packing: £3.95 by carrier in UK. At cost elsewhere.

Delivery: 7–14 days, or up to 28 days during summer months.

Availability: all year round.

Refund/replacement: yes.

See map page 396.

The Palm Farm   Palms are not as delicate as their exotic appearance indicates. The palm farmers of South Humberside talk about planting a Chusan palm during a winter when the Humber was full of ice floes. It survived. So do several other palms along with cordyline, tree ferns and the Japanese banana, which needs some protection. Big-leaved plants are fashionable for "rain forest" gardens and this nursery can supply both hardy and tender exotics along with advice.

> **The Palm Farm,** Station Road, Thornton Curtis, nr Ulceby, Lincolnshire DN39 6XF
> **Tel/fax:** 01469 531232
> **Opening hours:** 14.00–17.00 daily. Telephone first in winter.
> **Visitors welcome:** yes.
> **Catalogue:** send first class stamp.
> **Payment:** cash, cheque, postal order.
> **Mail order:** yes. Minimum order £11.
> **Post and packing:** £7.25 by post, £9.85 by carrier.
> **Delivery:** allow up to 4 weeks, usually sooner.
> **Availability:** certain items are seasonal.
> **Refund/replacement:** yes.
> **Special services:** specialist advice, demonstration palm garden.

GARDENERS' RECOMMENDATIONS: ✵ *"Exceptionally good and has display area."*

See map page 396.

Potterton and Martin   With a string of gold medals to its name, the nursery has a fine list of dwarf bulbs — crocus, allium, cyclamen, narcissus and tulips among others. A second list concentrates on dwarf shrubs, from dianthus to thymes. This would clearly be an excellent place for those with small gardens, town plots and even window boxes.

> **Potterton and Martin,** Moortown Road, Nettleton, Caistor, Lincolnshire LN7 6HX
> **Tel:** 01472 851714 **Fax:** 01472 852580
> **E-mail:** pottin01@globalnet.co.uk
> **Website:** http://www.users.globalnet.co.uk/~pottin01
> **Opening hours:** 9.00–17.00. Display garden open all year.
> **Visitors welcome:** yes.

Catalogue: send 50p in stamps.

Payment: cash, cheque, postal order, major credit cards.

Mail order: yes.

Post and packing: see catalogue.

Delivery: generally 2-3 weeks, unless otherwise specified in catalogue.

Availability: some items are seasonal, eg: bulbs are despatched in the autumn.

Refund/replacement: yes.

GARDENERS' RECOMMENDATIONS: ❀ *"They propagate and sell their own plants and are very helpful and reasonably priced."* Mr and Mrs G Grantham. ❀ *"Their lists are by far the best we see. They are wide ranging, contain many unusual plants, seeds and bulbs and have great depth of offer. Prices and service are excellent, we have not visited but the service by post is very good and we have used them for many years."* D S Taylor. ❀ *"Superb alpines at reasonable prices."* Mr and Mrs E W Dyer.

See map page 396.

Rasells' Nurseries

The family-run nursery has good lists of the more unusual trees, roses, shrubs and herbaceous perennials along with some half-hardy plants. Good on sorbus, rose species, camellias, hydrangeas and hollies with helpful comments.

Rasells' Nurseries, Station Road, Little Bytham, Grantham, Lincolnshire NG33 4QY

Tel: 01780 410345 **Fax:** 01780 410475

Opening hours: 9.00–17.00 Monday to Saturday, 10.00–16.00 Sunday.

Visitors welcome: yes.

Catalogue: free.

Payment: cash, cheque, Visa, Switch.

Mail order: no.

Post and packing: at cost, when used.

Delivery: locally within 7 days.

Availability: supplies can be limited and some plants are available only at certain times of year.

Refund/replacement: yes, depending on circumstances.

Special services: individual advice at customer's property from £30.

GARDENERS' RECOMMENDATIONS: *"Very helpful and not over-priced. They have very interesting material."* Mr and Mrs M Taylor. *"Excellent family-run nursery."* *"Family firm. Healthy shrubs. Wonderful helpful staff."* Mr and Mrs S D Pettifer. *"Wide range of shrubs, good service and advice from Tim Rasell."*

See map page 393.

Walkers Bulbs   The firm holds the Royal Warrant for both the Queen and the Queen Mother and has a gigantic selection of daffodils and narcissi, with new cultivars regularly appearing. More than half the catalogue is given over to this with a good list of snowdrops, scillas, fritillaries and alliums jammed in the back. The prices are excellent for bulk buying. A second catalogue is entirely for lilies, both species and hybrid.

J Walker Bulbs, Washway House Farm, Holbeach, Spalding, Lincolnshire PE12 7PP

Tel: 01406 426216   **Fax:** 01406 425468

E-mail: walkers@taylors-bulbs.com

Opening hours: not open to the public.

Visitors welcome: no.

Catalogue: send 2 first class stamps.

Payment: cheque, major credit cards.

Mail order: yes.

Post and packing: £2.95 for up to 10 bulbs, £3.70 for 11-30, £4.30 for 31-70, free thereafter.

Delivery: orders are despatched in rotation in season.

Availability: supplies of certain varieties are limited.

Refund/replacement: only if the bulb was obviously at fault.

GARDENERS' RECOMMENDATIONS: 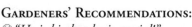 *"He is big but he is special!"*

LONDON

Camden Garden Centre   Unusual for central London, this is a complete garden centre with a wide range of plants and accessories. It is also unusual in that it is a charity and makes no profits — funds instead go to the Southern Task Educational Trust — and they offer training to the disadvantaged. For the London gardener, this is a good place for general stocking-up.

> **Camden Garden Centre**, 2 Barker Drive, London NW1 0JW
> **Tel:** 020 7485 8468 **Fax:** 020 7383 7018
> **E-mail:** sales@camdengardencentre.freeserve.co.uk
> **Opening hours:** 9.00–17.30 Monday to Saturday, 11.00–17.00 Sunday in summer (BST), 9.00–17.00 Monday to Saturday, 10.00–16.00 Sunday in winter (GMT)
> **Visitors welcome:** yes.
> **Catalogue:** none.
> **Payment:** cash, cheque, major credit cards.
> **Mail order:** no.
> **Refund/replacement:** yes.

GARDENERS' RECOMMENDATIONS: ❀ *"Good range of plants and shrubs, variety of pots and containers, garden furniture, trellis etc. Most staff can give expert advice."* Mr and Mrs J Wardroper. ❀ *"Very pleasant and helpful."* Mr and Mrs M Leman. ❀ *"Will get any plant for you even exotic things not normally stocked."* Mrs K Herbert.

See map page 392.

Clifton Nurseries   One of London's most stylish nurseries situated in smart Little Venice. It has a good range of shrubs, trees and herbaceous plants along with large plants and topiary, all suitable for London gardens. There is an interesting and good collection of statuary and containers along with lush tropical plants grown in their greenhouse. They will design gardens for homes and offices.

> **Clifton Nurseries**, Clifton Villas, Little Venice, London W9 2PH
> **Tel:** 020 7289 6851 **Fax:** 020 7286 4215

E-mail: @clifton.co.uk

Website: http://www.clifton.uk

Opening hours: 8.30–18.00 Monday to Saturday, 10.30–16.30 Sunday from March to September. 8.30–17.30 Monday to Saturday, 10.00–16.00 Sunday from October to February.

Visitors welcome: yes.

Catalogue: none.

Payment: cash, cheque, major credit cards.

Mail order: no.

Delivery: within London area only. Allow 1 or 2 days.

Availability: most shrubs and trees available all year round. Some plants are seasonal.

Refund/replacement: plants are guaranteed for 1 year, provided they are given adequate care.

Special services: landscape design, maintenance and construction. Interior landscaping on site.

GARDENERS' RECOMMENDATIONS: ❀ *"Very pleasant and helpful."* Mr and Mrs M Leman. ❀ *"Although not a true nursery, I am addicted to trips to Clifton just because everything is well presented and the buildings and display areas are so well designed."* Diana Yakeley. ❀ *"This nursery is very good with helpful assistants. Unfortunately, because of its small size it is, of necessity, limited in what it can supply. Its bedding plants are of good quality and it has a fair selection of house plants and shrubs. The fact that it is in central London would, I feel, make it worthy of inclusion."* Lady Barbirolli. ❀ *"Excellent plants and good advice but very expensive."* Mrs K Herbert.

See map page 392.

Croxted Road Garden Centre

A good general centre for London which has been selling for over 30 years. Unlike many garden centres — but sensibly in view of the London microclimate — tree ferns, outdoor palms and bamboos are all on sale.

Croxted Road Garden Centre, Croxted Road, London SE24

Tel/fax: 020 8674 4366

Opening hours: 9.30–18.00 Wednesday to Sunday; daily during May, June and December.

Visitors welcome: yes.

Catalogue: none.

Payment: cash, cheque, major credit cards.

Mail order: no.

Delivery: 48-hour delivery available locally.

Availability: some plants are seasonal, but good stock all year round.

Refund/replacement: yes.

GARDENERS' RECOMMENDATIONS: *"The size of a garden shed but holds everything. Lovely pots and vases. Very reasonable. Will order anything as has uncle with large nurseries in the Midlands. Knowledgeable and helpful."* Mr and Mrs J Nieboer.

See map page 392.

Fulham Palace Garden Centre

An excellent nursery in Central London whose profits go to the charity Fairbridge which supports the youth of inner cities. The nursery sells a wide variety of both plants and hardwear ideal for London. There are window boxes and plants for them, herbs for tiny patios, fountains, statues, garden furniture, trellises and obelisks as well as indoor and outdoor plants.

Fulham Palace Garden Centre, Bishop's Avenue, London SW6 6EE

Tel: 020 7736 2640/9820 **Fax:** 020 7371 8468

Opening hours: 9.30–17.30 Monday to Thursday, 9.30 –18.00 Friday and Saturday, 10.00–17.00 Sunday and bank holidays.

Visitors welcome: yes.

Catalogue: none.

Payment: cash, cheque, major credit cards, garden gift vouchers.

Mail order: no.

Delivery: only locally.

Availability: seasonal.

Refund/replacement: yes.

Special services: window box/hanging baskets planted. Christmas wreaths and table decorations.

GARDENERS' RECOMMENDATIONS: *"Excellent plants, good staff and a good ambience, tasteful pots etc. Not the usual garish garden centre!"*

See map page 392.

N Payne of Payne's Japanese Irises Mr Payne really likes people to come to see his irises, especially in June when they are flowering. He sells them in six-inch pots. But, if you really can't visit him in London, he'll post them bare-rooted — and you should suggest a substitute in case he can't fulfil the order.

> **Payne's Japanese Irises**, 84 Whatley Avenue, Merton Park, London SW20 9NU
>
> **Tel:** 020 8540 4794
>
> **Opening hours:** by appointment.
>
> **Visitors welcome:** yes, at bloom time.
>
> **Catalogue:** free.
>
> **Payment:** cash or cheque.
>
> **Mail order:** yes.
>
> **Post and packing:** 50p per plant.
>
> **Delivery:** bare-root plants posted late August.
>
> **Availability:** potted plants all year round. Limited supplies of some varieties.
>
> **Refund/replacement:** yes.

GARDENERS' RECOMMENDATIONS: ✿ *Recommended by* Dr and Mrs R L Belsey.

See map page 392.

MANCHESTER

Peter Nyssen Ltd As soon as I'd looked through this catalogue, I found I had spent over £200 and ordered well over a thousand bulbs. It has that effect on you: a hundred Crocosmia lucifer for £13, ten Bishop of Llandaff dahlia bulbs for £9, tulips galore, wood anemones, fritillaries, the list is addictive. If you adore colour in blocks, this is the catalogue.

> **Peter Nyssen Ltd**, 124 Flixton Road, Urmston, Manchester M41 5BG
>
> **Tel:** 0161 747 4000 **Fax:** 0161 748 6319
>
> **E-mail:** peternyssenltd@btinternet.com

Opening hours: 9.00–17.00 Monday to Friday.

Visitors welcome: no.

Catalogue: free.

Payment: cheque, Visa, Mastercard, Switch, Delta, Electron, Solo.

Mail order: yes.

Post and packing: £4.70 for orders up to £50, £7.05 for orders between £50 and £100, free thereafter.

Delivery: 2-3 weeks depending on time of order. Bulbs despatched from end August to end April.

Availability: autumn bulbs – August to October; spring bulbs and plants – November to May.

Refund/replacement: yes.

Special services: will try to locate items not listed in catalogue.

GARDENERS' RECOMMENDATIONS: ✤ *"For a new large garden this mail order firm is very useful for large orders of bulbs including lilies and perennials, all good quality and not too expensive."* ✤ *"Quality bulbs in bulk."* Mr and Mrs S J Gude.

MERSEYSIDE

Lady Green Nursery The nursery began as a ploughed field in 1985 with a garden design business attached. It is now halfway between a garden centre and nursery and thus has no catalogue. There is, however, a garden based on the owners' ideas of how best to use the plants.

Lady Green Nursery and Garden Centre, Lady Green Lane, Ince Blundell, Merseyside L38 1QD

Tel: 0151 929 3635 **Fax:** 0151 929 3778

Opening hours: 9.00–17.30 Monday to Saturday, 10.30–16.30 Sunday.

Visitors welcome: yes.

Catalogue: none.

Payment: cash, cheque, major credit cards.

Mail order: local deliveries or carrier by arrangement.

Post and packing: by quotation.

Delivery: allow 7 days if in stock.

Availability: some items are seasonal.

Refund/replacement: yes.

Special services: coffee shop with home-cooked food.

GARDENERS' RECOMMENDATIONS: *"Good range of quality plants. Owner, Philip Allison, is very knowledgeable and helpful. Display gardens. Excellent coffee shop."* Mr and Mrs D Cheetham.

See map page 395.

NORFOLK

Peter Beales Roses   One of the major rose nurseries of Britain with virtually every variety you could want. The bias is towards old and shrubby roses rather than hybrid tea and floribunda. There are many coloured illustrations in the catalogue — for this is a complex area — along with helpful descriptions, advice and suggested gardens to visit to see roses at their best. The nursery has some unique roses and a design service.

Peter Beales Roses, London Road, Attleborough, Norfolk NR17 1AY

Tel: 01953 454707 **Fax:** 01953 456845

E-mail: sales@classicroses.co.uk

Website: http://www.classicroses.co.uk

Opening hours: 9.00–17.00 Monday to Friday, 9.00–16.30 Saturday, 10.00–16.00 Sunday and bank holidays.

Visitors welcome: yes.

Catalogue: £2.

Payment: cash, cheque, postal order, major credit/debit cards.

Mail order: yes.

Post and packing: £3.95 for up to 3 plants to £5.95 for more than 10.

Delivery: despatched between end October and end March.

Availability: supplies can be limited and some plants are available only at certain times of year.

Refund/replacement: yes.

GARDENERS' RECOMMENDATIONS: *"A wonderful collection of roses (once you have Peter Beale's book you can't stop buying). The quality has always been excellent, and I have always found them so obliging when I have rung up to add an extra rose on my order."* Mrs Susan Beck. *"Wonderful catalogue – well illustrated and very well thought out with lots of useful information. Good plants, well-packed and usually available."* Mr Frankie Warren. *"They are efficient and they have beautiful healthy stock."* Anne, Lady Elton.

See map page 393.

Creake Plant Centre

The centre is especially proud of its unusual list of shrubs, climbers and herbaceous perennials. It also has interesting conservatory and house plant selections.

> **Creake Plant Centre**, Nursery View, South Creake, Fakenham, Norfolk NR21 9PW
>
> **Tel:** 01328 823018
>
> **Opening hours:** 10.00–17.30 daily except Christmas and Boxing Day.
>
> **Visitors welcome:** yes.
>
> **Catalogue:** none.
>
> **Payment:** cash or cheque.
>
> **Mail order:** no.
>
> **Availability:** a good range all year round.
>
> **Refund/replacement:** yes.

GARDENERS' RECOMMENDATIONS: *"Excellent with a mass of unusual plants."* The Marchioness of Cholmondeley. *"No garden but very good plants."* Mrs Jane Alhusen.

See map page 393.

Four Seasons

I'd just been round a brilliantly coloured garden when I discovered this nursery. It had everything I yearned for — apricot achilleas, scarlet hemerocallis, sapphire irises and green red hot pokers. Wonderful.

> **Four Seasons**, Forncett St Mary, Norwich, Norfolk NR16 1JT
>
> **Tel:** 01508 488344 **Fax:** 01508 488478
>
> **E-mail:** contact@fsperennials.co.uk

Website: http://www.fsperennials.co.uk
Visitors welcome: no, mail order only.
Catalogue: free.
Payment: cheque, Visa, Mastercard, Switch.
Mail order: yes.
Post and packing: £8.50 in mainland UK.
Delivery: during autumn and spring.
Availability: autumn and spring only.
Refund/replacement: depends on circumstances.

GARDENERS' RECOMMENDATIONS: *"This is a wonderful catalogue which seems to get better every year and the quality of the plants has been quite excellent."* Mrs Susan Beck. *"Many unusual hardy plants produced by a very artistic and knowledgeable grower who has a reputation for introducing interesting new varieties. Informative catalogue."* Mr and Mrs K H Wallis. *"Good selection of plants, with good rootball."* *"For good herbaceous plants."* The Hon Julian and Mrs Darling.

See map page 393.

See map page 393.

Hickling Heath Nursery

Here there's a wide range of shrubs and herbaceous plants with emphasis on unusual varieties.

Hickling Heath Nursery, Sutton Road, Hickling, Norwich, Norfolk NR12 0AS
Tel: 01692 598513
Opening hours: 9.30–17.00 Tuesday to Sunday and bank holiday Mondays.
Visitors welcome: yes.
Catalogue: none.

Payment: cash, Visa, Mastercard, Delta.

Mail order: no.

Availability: some plants in limited supply.

Refund/replacement: yes.

Special services: garden design and planting service.

GARDENERS' RECOMMENDATIONS: *"Only small, but the owners are exceedingly knowledgeable and their plants are very good indeed."* Mrs N N Green.

See map page 393.

Hoecroft Plants

Hoecroft Plants Not everyone likes flowers. Some of us like leaves and this is a good place to start looking at what leaves can do. First there are grasses, rushes and bamboos, then the creepers like thymes and lamiums and, of course, hostas, ivies and lavenders.

Hoecroft Plants, Severals Grange, Holt Road, Wood Norton, Dereham, Norfolk NR20 5BL

Tel: 01362 684206

Opening hours: 10.00–16.00 Thursday to Sunday from 1 April to 30 September.

Visitors welcome: yes.

Catalogue: £1 or 5 second class stamps.

Payment: cheque.

Mail order: yes.

Post and packing: from £5.

Delivery: orders sent in strict rotation in spring and autumn.

Refund/replacement: yes.

Special services: advice on ornamental grasses.

GARDENERS' RECOMMENDATIONS: *"Extremely helpful painstaking proprietor. Very wide range of grasses and they are on view growing in a lovely sunny garden."* Mr and Mrs K H Wallis.

See map page 393.

Holkham Nursery Gardens The gardens are attached to the Norfolk house and sell a wide range with only perennials by post. There are good plants for seaside areas and also the Dunwich rose, R. pimpinellifolia.

Holkham Nursery Gardens, Holkham Park, Wells next the Sea, Norfolk NR23 1AB

Tel: 01328 711636

Opening hours: 10.00–17.00 daily.

Visitors welcome: yes.

Catalogue: send 3 first class stamps.

Payment: cash, cheque, major credit cards except American Express, Switch.

Mail order: no.

Availability: supplies can be limited and some plants are available only at certain times of year.

Refund/replacement: yes.

GARDENERS' RECOMMENDATIONS: ✿ *"All in the old walled garden, huge, well planted up including walls."* Mrs Jane Alhusen.

See map page 393.

Hythe Alpines

Asked if they replace plants to dissatisfied customers, this nursery replies confidently "we do not have dissatisfied customers." What they do have is a well-written, large catalogue with constant arrivals of new plants. The range is wide but specialised and full of rarities.

Hythe Alpines, Methwold Hythe, Thetford, Norfolk IP26 4QH

Tel/fax: 01366 728543

Opening hours: 10.00–17.00 Tuesday and Wednesday from March to October.

Visitors welcome: yes, during opening hours or by appointment.

Catalogue: send 6 first class stamps or 4 IRCs.

Payment: cheque.

Mail order: yes.

Post and packing: 72-hour guaranteed delivery from £5.80 for 5 plants to £8.80 for 24.

Delivery: normally within 3 weeks but allow up to 6 weeks in early spring.

Availability: demand for specialist items always exceeds supply.

Refund/replacement: never had a dissatisfied customer.

GARDENERS' RECOMMENDATIONS: ✿ *"An oasis in the middle of bleak fenland and very difficult to find. The nursery and garden are tucked round two sides of a bungalow and are a haven for alpine lovers. Mike Smith, the owner, always seems to be working in his propagating shed and answers visitors' questions and queries with great enthusiasm and deep knowledge. The visitor is free to wander quietly through the alpine houses full of jewel-like treasure and the garden where a lot of the plants are growing and seeding happily in unexpected places. This is one of my favourite nurseries where you can forget everything except the beauty and fascination of these diverse and small plants from all over the world."* *"Many rare and unusual alpines. Some prices a little high."* Mr and Mrs E W Dyer.

See map page 393.

Magpies

Patricia Cooper offers a good selection of hardy perennials and grasses, some quite rare. The nursery is next to her garden, which customers can visit. She produces everything single-handed and will be happy to give advice on any of them.

Magpies, 4 Green Lane, Mundford, Norfolk IP26 5HS
Tel: 01842 878496
Opening hours: 9.00–17.00 weekdays (closed Wednesday), 12.00–17.00 weekends.
Visitors welcome: yes.
Catalogue: free.
Payment: cash or cheque.
Mail order: no.
Availability: supplies can be limited as a wide range is produced.
Refund/replacement: yes.

GARDENERS' RECOMMENDATIONS: *"Informal cottage-style garden intensively planted and displaying the perennials, grasses and cottage garden plants that are for sale. Strong, well-presented plants. Expert advice."* Mrs A Hoellering.

See map page 393.

Norfolk Lavender

From being a firm which produced lavender to make scented products — soaps, candles, lotions — it is now branching out into scented plants in general as well as lavender. It sells plants for lavender hedges and certain named varieties plus philadelphus, honeysuckle and jasmine among others. This is not a nursery for advanced gardeners but for those keen to bring scent into their lives.

Norfolk Lavender, Caley Mill, Heacham, Norfolk PE31 7JE
Tel: 01485 570384 Helpline: 01485 572383 **Fax:** 01485 571176
E-mail: admin@norfolk-lavender.co.uk
Website: http://www.norfolk-lavender.co.uk
Opening hours: 8.30–17.30 daily.
Visitors welcome: yes.
Catalogue: free.
Payment: cheque, postal order, major credit/debit cards.
Mail order: yes.
Post and packing: £1.95 for up to 2 items, £3.45 thereafter.
Delivery: 10 days.
Availability: bare-root lavenders available until mid-April, plug and 9cm pot plants all year round.

Refund/replacement: yes.

GARDENERS' RECOMMENDATIONS: ⊛ *"Lavender – very good plants, service, delivery."* Mrs Craig.

See map page 393.

P W Plants

Paul Whittaker is a bamboo enthusiast. He grows them in the garden attached to the nursery and will enthuse about each one to anyone who visits. His enthusiasm is highly infectious: you will leave with a boot packed with beautiful stems, eccentric leaves and arching habits. He also has other plants grown for their leaves, not flowers. Highly recommended.

P W Plants, Sunnyside, Heath Road, Kenninghall, Norfolk NR16 2DS
Tel/fax: 01953 888212
Opening hours: 9.00–17.00 every Friday and last Saturday of the month and by appointment.
Visitors welcome: yes.
Catalogue: send 5 first class stamps
Payment: cheque, major credit cards.
Mail order: yes.
Post and packing: £7.50 for orders up to £50, £10 for orders up to £100, £12.50 for orders up to £150, £15 for orders up to £200, 5% of order value thereafter.
Delivery: February to April and September to December. Next day delivery available.
Availability: supplies can be limited.

Refund/replacement: yes.

Special services: free delivery to shows around the country.

GARDENERS' RECOMMENDATIONS: ❀ *"Mr and Mrs Whittaker have a superb collection of unusual shrubs and particularly bamboos. The range of bamboos is mouth-watering and many of the species and varieties offered can be seen beautifully displayed in their garden. Both the owners and staff are experts and freely offer advice and guidance in choosing plants for particular locations. The bamboo king and queen of Britain!"* Mr and Mrs R Vernon, Bluebell Nursery. ❀ *"Enormous range of bamboos, also grasses and shrubs."* Mr P J Oliver-Smith. ❀ *"List is varied and different. Plants arrived in good condition and established well."* Mrs Danae Johnston. ❀ *"Specialise in bamboos and grasses, and other shrubs. Gold medal winners at RHS shows."* Mrs Patricia Lombe Taylor.

See map page 393.

Reads The firm has been going for over a century and is excellent for the more exotic fruit trees such as figs, citrus fruits and olives as well as orchard and greenhouse fruit trees. Another speciality is for conservatory and greenhouse plants such as bougainvillea, datura and oleander. A lovely nursery to visit.

> **Reads Nursery**, Hales Hall, Loddon, Norfolk NR14 6QW
> **Tel:** 01508 548395 **Fax:** 01508 548040
> **E-mail:** plants@readsnursery.co.uk
> **Website:** http://www.readsnursery.co.uk
> **Opening hours:** 10.00–17.00 (or dusk if earlier) Tuesday to Saturday, and 11.00–16.00 on Sunday from May to October and bank holiday Mondays. Closed from 25 December to 5 January and on Good Friday.
> **Visitors welcome:** yes.
> **Catalogue:** send 4 first class stamps for catalogue.
> **Payment:** cash, cheque, Visa, Mastercard, Access, Switch, Delta/Connect.
> **Mail order:** yes.
> **Post and packing:** from £8 for box holding 2-3 plants 3ft high.

GARDENERS' RECOMMENDATIONS: ❀ *"Specialists in conservatory plants, citrus, figs and vines. Knowledgeable and helpful, both on the telephone and when visited."* Mr and Mrs H Morley-Fletcher.

❀ *"A proper nursery where you will always find an exciting unusual or rare plant that makes you pounce – a rare occurrence today"* Mr Gray and Mr Robeson. ❀ *"The best place for conservatory plants and reliable for mail order."* Mr and Mrs J D Sword. ❀ *"Conservatory plants, garden fruits (citrus, vines, figs). Wonderful medieval barn."* ❀*Also recommended by* Christopher Lloyd, Great Dixter.

See map page 393.

The Romantic Garden Nursery
Specialists in all forms of topiary which are ideal for small gardens, town gardens, patios and other formal sites. The plants are not only box and yew but rosemary, lavender and citrus trees. Also very good for interesting leaves.

> **The Romantic Garden Nursery**, Swanington, Norwich, Norfolk NR9 5NW
>
> **Tel:** 01603 261488   **Fax:** 01603 864231
>
> **E-mail:** enquiries@romantic-garden.demon.co.uk
>
> **Website:** http://www.romantic-garden.demon.co.uk
>
> **Opening hours:** 10.00–17.00 Wednesday, Friday, Saturday and bank holiday Monday.
>
> **Visitors welcome:** yes.
>
> **Catalogue:** send 4 first class stamps.
>
> **Payment:** cash, cheque, major credit cards.
>
> **Mail order:** yes.
>
> **Post and packing:** standing charge of £8 plus weight-related supplement.
>
> **Delivery:** within a few days if in stock.
>
> **Availability:** some topiary shapes are in limited supply.
>
> **Refund/replacement:** yes.
>
> **Special services:** plant hire.

GARDENERS' RECOMMENDATIONS: ❀ *"Large selection of topiary and ornamental standards. Wonderful things for London gardens, to remind one of summers abroad, and they are friendly and helpful."* Diana Yakeley. ❀ *"Very obliging."*

See map page 393.

Thorncroft Clematis Nursery The nursery, which offers all the various complicated forms of clematis and nothing else, has a garden with over 300 of them on show. They are traditionally grown up walls and pergolas and also with roses (from Peter Beales qv), scrambling through heather and up trees. A new idea is to use the climber without walls. The nursery gives pruning demonstrations and advice.

Thorncroft Clematis Nursery, The Lings, Reymerston, Norwich, Norfolk NR9 4QG

Tel: 01953 850407 **Fax:** 01953 851788

Opening hours: 10.00–16.30 daily except Wednesday.

Visitors welcome: yes.

Catalogue: £1.

Payment: cash, cheque, Visa, Mastercard, Switch, Delta, Solo.

Mail order: yes.

Post and packing: £6.50 per parcel (about 3 plants).

Delivery: depends on availability, minimum 10 days.

Availability: mostly all year round, although supplies of certain varieties can be limited at times.

Refund/replacement: yes.

Gardeners' Recommendations: ✵ *"One of the top clematis nurseries. Propagate all their own stock and win medals at the RHS shows."* Mrs Patricia Lombe Taylor. ✵ *"A brilliant nursery with a huge range of clematis and a splendid garden to demonstrate how they can be grown. All good value and well grown."* ✵ *"Extremely good clean plants, efficiently run business, well set out sales area."* Mr and Mrs Elliot, Old Hall Plants. ✵ *"Excellent plants and friendly knowledgeable service. They will not let you take a plant that they do not think is ready to go. Enormous variety, well presented and also grown in adjoining garden. They give free pruning demonstrations in spring. I cannot recommend the Gooch family more highly."* Mrs J Foulkes.

See map page 393.

Van Tubergen A big bulb merchant offering plants for all the seasons and for growing indoors. The catalogue is in full colour and very helpful. The range is huge, from the common to the choice and you can get huge quantities cheaply, too. A hundred and twenty

Fritillaria meleagris at £12.95, for instance or 60 Queen of the Night tulips for £9.95.

Van Tubergen UK Ltd, Bressingham, Diss, Norfolk IP22 2AB
Tel: 01379 688282 **Fax:** 01379 687227
E-mail: vantubergen@tesco.net
Website: http://www.vantubergen.co.uk
Opening hours: 24-hour orderline as above.
Visitors welcome: no, mail order only.
Catalogue: free.
Payment: cheque, postal order, major credit cards.
Mail order: yes.
Post and packing: £2.25 for orders under £25, free thereafter.
Delivery: spring and autumn despatch.
Availability: spring and autumn only.
Refund/replacement: yes.

GARDENERS' RECOMMENDATIONS: *"Good quality bulbs."* Mrs F Denby.

West Acre Gardens

A selection of alpines, herbaceous and shrubs with a good list of grasses (currently very fashionable). Euphorbia, penstemon and geraniums are also well represented.

West Acre Gardens, West Acre, Kings Lynn, Norfolk PE32 1UJ
Tel: 01760 755562 **Fax:** 01760 755989
Opening hours: 10.00–17.00 from 15 February to 15 November.
Visitors welcome: yes.
Catalogue: send 4 first class stamps.
Payment: cheque.
Mail order: yes.
Post and packing: £5 for 1-4 plants, £10 for 5-30, £17.30 for 31-60. Larger quantities by quotation.
Delivery: approx 14 days.
Availability: supplies may be limited in mid-winter and possibly in mid-summer.
Refund/replacement: yes.

GARDENERS' RECOMMENDATIONS: *"In the walled garden. Getting better all the time."* Mrs Jane Alhusen.

See map page 393.

See also: Congham Hall Herb Gardens, page 351.

NORTHAMPTONSHIRE

Coton Manor Garden   Like many nurseries, this started as a garden and, such was the demand, started to sell what it grew. Staff are happy to be dragged about the garden and asked to identify plants and find ones for sale. And, like many interesting gardens, the plants on sale are interesting also.

> **Coton Manor Garden**, Coton, Northamptonshire NN6 8RQ
> **Tel:** 01604 740219 **Fax:** 01604 740838
> **Opening hours:** 12.00–17.30 Wednesday to Sunday from Easter to end September.
> **Visitors welcome:** yes, during opening hours.
> **Catalogue:** £1.
> **Payment:** cash, cheque, major credit cards.
> **Mail order:** no.
> **Availability:** supplies can be limited and some plants are available only at certain times of year.
> **Refund/replacement:** probably.

GARDENERS' RECOMMENDATIONS: *"Beautiful garden – getting better and better. Ian and Susie Pasley-Tyler are not only knowledgeable and enthusiastic but also very patient with one's queries."* Mr and Mrs Anthony Hopkinson. *"Lovely place to visit. The gardens are beautiful."* *"Very good."* Mr and Mrs J Gale.

See map page 393.

E L F Plants Asked if they offer any special services, the nursery says "a friendly ear." An elf-like one, presumably. The firm specialises in hardy dwarf and slow-growing conifers and shrubs and has a good balanced list. And a lot of patience.

> **E L F Plants**, Cramden Nursery, Harborough Road North, Kingsthorpe, Northampton, Northamptonshire NN2 8LU
>
> **Tel:** 01604 846246
>
> **Opening hours:** 10.00–17.00 Thursday to Saturday. Closed from 1 November to end January.
>
> **Visitors welcome:** yes, very much.
>
> **Catalogue:** send 3 first class stamps.
>
> **Payment:** cash or cheque.
>
> **Mail order:** no.
>
> **Availability:** from February to October.
>
> **Refund/replacement:** usually.

GARDENERS' RECOMMENDATIONS: ✿ *"We have purchased many excellent plants from this nursery and can recommend highly both stock and owners."* Mr and Mrs J Leatherland. ✿ *"Good range of small plants and we found Syringa protolaciniata there, also Exochorda Wilsonii."* Mr and Mrs E Harper.

See map page 393.

The Plant Nursery A supremely practical nursery shoe-horned between garages and a paper recycling plant, avoiding all tea areas, loos and bags of compost but, sensibly, with the ground covered against mud. It has a fine list of alpines, geraniums, grasses and sempervivums. Good reasonable prices, too.

> **The Plant Nursery**, Sandy Hill Lane, off Overstone Road, Moulton, Northamptonshire NN3 7JB
>
> **Tel:** 01604 491941 after 7 pm.
>
> **Opening hours:** 10.00–17.00 Friday to Sunday and bank holidays.
>
> **Visitors welcome:** yes.
>
> **Catalogue:** 75p, or send 3 first class stamps.
>
> **Payment:** cheque.
>
> **Mail order:** sempervivums only.
>
> **Post and packing:** included for sempervivums.
>
> **Delivery:** 10 days.

Availability: limited as plants are propagated in small numbers.

Refund/replacement: yes.

GARDENERS' RECOMMENDATIONS: *"We have purchased many excellent plants from this nursery and can recommend highly both stock and owners."* Mr and Mrs J Leatherland.

See map page 393.

Podington Garden Centre

There are over 7,000 plant varieties available here with, luckily, a team of ten to help you sort them out. The staff are specially chosen for their knowledge and helpfulness.

Podington Garden Centre, High Street, Podington, Wellingborough, Northamptonshire NN29 7HS

Tel: 01933 353656 **Fax:** 01933 410332

E-mail: jread@podington.co.uk

Website: http://www.podington.co.uk

Opening hours: 9.00–18.30 Monday to Saturday (9.00–20.00 Thursday), 10.30–16.30 Sunday.

Visitors welcome: yes.

Catalogue: none.

Payment: cash, cheque, Visa, Mastercard, Switch, Delta, Electron, Solo.

Mail order: no.

Availability: supplies can be limited and some plants are available only at certain times of year.

Refund/replacement: yes.

GARDENERS' RECOMMENDATIONS: *"Although Podingtons is a garden centre they have expert gardeners and plantspeople employed."*

See map page 393.

Ravensthorpe Nursery

The nursery has a wide range of shrubs, herbaceous and bedding plants along with fruit trees and hedging plants to order. Indeed, they will take special orders in winter and search out unusual plants if work is not too pressing.

Ravensthorpe Nursery, 6 East Haddon Road, Ravensthorpe, Northamptonshire NN6 8ES

Tel/fax: 01604 770548

Opening hours: 10.00–18.00 or dusk Tuesday to Sunday and bank holiday Mondays.

Visitors welcome: yes.

Catalogue: send 4 first class stamps.

Payment: cash, cheque, major credit cards.

Mail order: yes.

Post and packing: at cost plus VAT. Next day delivery generally £10 including VAT.

Delivery: rarely more than a week if in stock.

Availability: supplies are sometimes limited.

Refund/replacement: in case of justified complaint.

Special services: search and delivery service in winter months for large orders.

GARDENERS' RECOMMENDATIONS: ❀ *"Very good."* Mr and Mrs J Gale.

See map page 393.

———————————— ⚘ ————————————

See also: Geddington Gardens, page 354.

NORTHUMBERLAND

Chipchase Castle Nursery   "We specialise in less readily available hardy herbaceous perennials — we are particularly fond of erodium, eryngium, geranium, penstemon and viola," say the owners. They're pretty good also on primula, campanula and pulmonaria. A very interesting selection.

Chipchase Castle Nursery, Wark, Hexham, Northumberland NE48 3NT

Tel: 01434 230083

Opening hours: 10.00–17.00 Thursday to Sunday and bank holidays from 1 April (or Easter) to mid-October.

Visitors welcome: yes.

Catalogue: send A5 sae.

Payment: cash or cheque.

Mail order: by arrangement.

Post and packing: at cost.

Delivery: approx 3 days.

Availability: certain plants are only propagated in small quantities.

Refund/replacement: yes.

GARDENERS' RECOMMENDATIONS: ❀ *"Another walled garden, another real enthusiasts' operation. The garden needs another couple of years to be mature (they've only been in operation for 4 years or so and have worked wonders in the time) but is already a pleasure. The range of plants – essentially herbaceous – is already astonishingly wide. Ditto the number of rarities on offer. It's always worthwhile asking what's coming on and not yet in the catalogue: these are adventurous propagators, willing to have a go at almost anything if seed turns up or a plant takes their eye."* Mr Tim Longville. ❀ *"Unusual perennials and 'cottage garden' plants."*

See map page 397.

Ford Nursery   This is a good general list of choice plants from perennials to alpines, grasses and trees. They will happily design garden areas and also deliver plants within a range of 150 miles. The catalogue is always innovative and helpful in its descriptions.

Ford Nursery, Castle Gardens, Ford, Berwick-upon-Tweed, Northumberland TD15 2PZ

Tel: 01890 820379 **Fax:** 01890 820594

Opening hours: 10.00–18.00 daily from March to October, 10.00–16.30 weekdays only from November to February.

Visitors welcome: yes.

Catalogue: £1.

Payment: cash, cheque, major credit cards.

Mail order: yes.

Post and packing: by quotation.

Delivery: large orders can be delivered within a 150-mile radius.

Availability: supplies can be limited and some plants are available only at certain times of year.

Refund/replacement: by arrangement.

Special services: garden design.

See map page 398.

GARDENERS' RECOMMENDATIONS: *"This nursery used to be known as Northumbria Nurseries but has changed ownership in the last two years. It has evolved in the old neglected walled garden of Ford Castle. There is a small area of garden where many of the available plants are growing. There is a large selection of plants, home propagated, and the emphasis is on plants suitable for growing in the north and also near the seaside."*

See map page 398.

Halls of Heddon

Halls of Heddon   Though the firm stocks a wide range of trees, shrubs, herbaceous plants and roses, its main interest is in dahlias, chrysanthemums and bedding plants. They offer many new introductions as well as old favourites. The family nursery, started in 1921, now exports to 11 different countries around the world.

Halls of Heddon, West Heddon Nurseries, Heddon-on-the-Wall, Newcastle-upon-Tyne, Northumberland NE15 0JS

Tel: 01661 852445

Opening hours: 9.00–17.00 Monday to Saturday. 10.00–17.00 Sunday.

Visitors welcome: yes.

Catalogue: send 3 second class stamps.

Payment: cheque.

Mail order: yes, for dahlias, chrysanthemums and bedding.

Post and packing: from £2.75.

Delivery: about 6 weeks, depending on time of ordering.

Availability: supplies can be limited and some plants are available only at certain times of year.

Refund/replacement: yes.

GARDENERS' RECOMMENDATIONS: *"Dahlias – nicely rooted plugs."* *Also recommended by* Christopher Lloyd, Great Dixter.

See map page 397.

Heighley Gate Nursery Garden Centre

Heighley Gate Nursery Garden Centre   The nursery offers a large range of conifers and prides itself on its large-size trees and shrubs. Their leaflet suggests that "gardening is the purest pleasure known to man" and the firm seems extremely enthusiastic in all it does. The range of prices — 25p to £899 — says it all.

Heighley Gate Nursery Garden Centre, Wooler Road (A697), Morpeth, Northumberland NE61 3DA

Tel: 01670 513416 **Fax:** 01670 510013

Opening hours: 9.00–17.30 Monday to Friday, 9.00–17.00 Saturday, 10.30–16.30 Sunday.

Visitors welcome: yes.

Catalogue: none.

Payment: cash, cheque, major credit cards.

Mail order: no.

Delivery: local delivery within 3 working days.

Availability: seasonal variations, but most stock available all year round.

Refund/replacement: yes, 2-year plant guarantee.

GARDENERS' RECOMMENDATIONS: ❀ *"An excellent range of plants, always well grown at reasonable prices."* Colonel S J Furness.

See map page 397.

Hexham Herbs

The nursery holds the national collections for thyme and marjoram and also shows off its plants in a knot garden, a Roman herb garden (suitable for Hexham) and woodland walks for its wild flowers. It has become a TV star and is chosen by many top gardeners.

Hexham Herbs, Chesters Walled Garden, Chollerford, Hexham, Northumberland NE46 4BQ

Tel: 01434 681483

Opening hours: 10.00–17.00 daily from Easter to 31 October. Phone for winter opening details.

Visitors welcome: yes.

Catalogue: none.

Payment: cash or cheque.

Mail order: no.

Refund/replacement: no.

GARDENERS' RECOMMENDATIONS: ❀ *"National collections of thymes and oregano."* Mrs Margaret Easter. *"Wonderful."* Mr and Mrs R L Jefferson.

See map page 397.

Ryal Nursery   The nursery, which specialises in alpine and woodland plants, offers good value collections of plants for the beginner or those less able to make up their minds. These include a trough collection, sun-loving collection and woodland collection — and they will make a customised collection to order.

Ryal Nursery, East Farm Cottage, Ryal, Northumberland NE20 0SA
Tel: 01661 886562 **Fax:** 01661 886918
E-mail: alpines@ryal.freeserve.co.uk
Opening hours: 13.00–16.00 Monday and Tuesday, 10.00–16.00 Sunday from March to July. By appointment at other times.
Visitors welcome: yes.
Catalogue: send sae.
Payment: cheque or postal order.
Mail order: yes. Minimum order £5.
Post and packing: £5.60 for 1–10 plants, £6 for 11-20, £6.50 for 21 or more.
Delivery: 2-3 weeks.
Availability: all year round.
Refund/replacement: yes.

GARDENERS' RECOMMENDATIONS: ❀ *"Back garden nursery – excellent."* Mrs Margaret Easter.

See map page 397.

NOTTINGHAMSHIRE

Brockings Exotics A nursery selling up-to-the-minute plants for the exotic garden. These include cannas, coleus, half-hardy perennials and such plants as plumbago, gazania, heliotropes and osteospermum. These are the smart plants for town gardens, conservatories and seaside plantings.

Brockings Exotics, Rosedene, Nottingham Road, Woodborough, Nottinghamshire NG14 6EH
Tel: 0115 847 9359/07970 866832
E-mail: ian.cooke@brockings.freeserve.co.uk

Website: http://www.brockings.freeserve.co.uk

Opening hours: by appointment.

Visitors welcome: yes, by appointment.

Catalogue: send 3 first class stamps.

Payment: cheque.

Mail order: yes. Minimum order £15.

Post and packing: £10.50.

Delivery: allow 28 days.

Availability: limited supplies of specialist plants eg: cannas available May to August.

Refund/replacement: yes.

Special services: canna and coleus identification.

GARDENERS' RECOMMENDATIONS: ❀ *"Good source of home-grown plants."*

See map page 393.

Trevor Edwards Mr Edwards runs his small nursery from his home where he has a small front garden and back garden only nine yards by 25 yards. The plants are grown on a piece of land at the back and the sales area is but seven by eight yards. He's very adaptable and, if you phone in advance, can make appointments outside the working day. "There's been a lot of love put into my garden and I like to think that I give a warm and friendly welcome to visitors." He has no catalogue — "too many odds and ends" — but grows his own perennials and some shrubs. I wish more nurseries were as small and friendly.

Trevor Edwards, 81 Huthwaite Road, Sutton-in-Ashfield, Nottinghamshire NG17 2GS

Tel: 01623 468138

Opening hours: by appointment.

Visitors welcome: yes.

Catalogue: none.

Payment: cash or cheque.

Mail order: no.

Availability: supplies can be limited and some plants are available only at certain times of year.

Refund/replacement: yes.

See map page 396.

Felley Priory   The house itself dates from the 16th century and is now surrounded by gardens created from 1976 onwards with herbaceous borders, pergolas, knot gardens and a medieval garden. The nursery sells plants which are grown in the garden. Many are old-fashioned and unusual and, says the Hon Mrs. Chaworth Musters, "fairly tender — but all of them have survived in this garden at 600ft above sea level."

Felley Priory, Underwood, Nottinghamshire NG16 5FL
Tel: 01773 810230   **Fax:** 01773 580440
Opening hours: 9.00–12.30 Tuesday, Wednesday and Friday all year round. 9.00–16.00 every second and fourth Wednesday and 11.00–16.00 every third Sunday from March to October.
Visitors welcome: yes, during opening hours.
Catalogue: none.
Payment: cash or cheque.
Mail order: no.
Availability: small nursery so supplies can be limited.
Refund/replacement: yes, within the same season.

GARDENERS' RECOMMENDATIONS: ✿ *"A lovely garden to visit at any time of year with a nursery of healthy unusual plants."*

See map page 396.

Field House Nurseries   Doug Lochhead and Val Woolley hold no less than three national collections — those for European primulas, Primula allionni hybrids and cultivars and show and alpine auriculas. The list is huge and quite difficult for a beginner — though thrilling for an aficionado. However, the catalogue does its best to explain and the owners will also help. There is a great deal of interest in all these plants.

Field House Nurseries, Leake Road, Gotham, Nottingham, Nottinghamshire NG11 0JN
Tel: 0115 983 0278   **Fax:** 0115 983 1486
Opening hours: 9.00–17.00 Friday to Wednesday.
Visitors welcome: yes, advisable to telephone first if travelling far.
Catalogue: Send 4 first class stamps.
Payment: cash, cheque, Visa, Mastercard.
Mail order: yes. Minimum order 4 plants.

Post and packing: from £4 for up to 10 plants to £6 for up to 40.

Delivery: within 21 days.

Availability: availability lists issued throughout the season.

Refund/replacement: yes.

GARDENERS' RECOMMENDATIONS: *"Exceptionally good and has display area."*

See map page 393.

Granby Gardens
Offers herbaceous perennials, often both rare and unusual, along with an interesting range of shrubs and climbers plus some small trees. The only service is "friendly, honest advice" which sounds just right.

Granby Gardens, Granby House, 8 Long Acre, Bingham, Nottinghamshire NG13 8BG

Tel/fax: 01949 837696

Opening hours: 9.30–17.30 Monday to Wednesday and at other times by appointment.

Visitors welcome: yes.

Catalogue: send 2 second class stamps for plant list.

Payment: cash or cheque.

Mail order: no.

Delivery: free locally.

Refund/replacement: yes.

GARDENERS' RECOMMENDATIONS: *"Good source of home-grown plants."*

See map page 393.

Mill Hill Plants
Specialists in bearded irises with a splendid list which, helpfully, lists the colours of both falls and beard along with the main flower head. Massed irises, whether of one variety, one or two colours or the whole shebang, are a splendid sight in early summer and their leaves pretty effective for the rest of the year. The nursery also has some alpines, herbaceous perennials and shrubs.

Mill Hill Plants, Elston Lane, East Stoke, Newark, Nottinghamshire NG23 5QJ

Tel: 01636 525460

E-mail: millhill@talk21.com

Opening hours: 10.00–18.00 Wednesday to Sunday from March to September and Friday to Sunday in October.

Visitors welcome: yes.

Catalogue: send large sae for iris list.

Payment: cash or cheque.

Mail order: iris only.

Post and packing: at cost.

Delivery: irises despatched from August to October only.

Availability: plants are available in small numbers only depending on crop.

Refund/replacement: yes.

Special services: maintenance leaflet for iris. Group visits by appointment.

GARDENERS' RECOMMENDATIONS: ✿ *"An excellent specialist nursery built around superb gardens which have featured on the TV. Always good advice available from a very friendly husband and wife. The epitome of a good nursery!"* Dr A Ward, Norwell Nurseries.

See map page 393.

Millfield Nurseries
Hostas are a vast a complex area with new varieties appearing constantly: the leaves get more glaucous, variegated, twisted and curvaceous by the moment. Millfield has over a hundred to choose from.

Millfield Nurseries, Mill Lane, South Leverton, nr Retford, Nottinghamshire DN22 0DA

Tel/fax: 01427 880422

Opening hours: by appointment.

Visitors welcome: yes.

Catalogue: £1 discounted against order.

Payment: cash or cheque. Euro cheques accepted at current rate of exchange.

Mail order: yes. Minimum order: UK £10 plus p&p; EFTA and EEC £25 plus p&p.

Post and packing: £3.50.

Delivery: 28 days.

Availability: mail order plants despatched during dormant season only.

Refund/replacement: yes.

GARDENERS' RECOMMENDATIONS: *"Good source of home-grown plants."*

See map page 396.

Dr Andrew Ward at Norwell Nurseries   Dr Ward specialises

in penstemons, hardy geraniums, geums, summer bulbs and grasses. The nursery has its own display gardens including a new daisy bed and woodland and Mediterranean areas. He tries to make his catalogue fun — and swears people take it to bed. Gardening is the new sex, indeed.

Dr Andrew Ward at Norwell Nurseries, Woodhouse Road, Norwell, nr Newark, Nottinghamshire NG23 6JX

Tel: 01636 636337

E-mail: wardha@aol.com

Opening hours: 10.00–17.00 daily except Saturday and Tuesday. May and June closed Tuesday only. August and from 20 October to 1 March by appointment.

Visitors welcome: yes.

Catalogue: 90p or 3 first class stamps.

Payment: cash or cheque.

Mail order: yes. Minimum order £10.

Post and packing: at cost.

Delivery: 2-5 weeks depending on time of year.

Availability: plants despatched by mail order preferably in the autumn or early spring. Supplies of some rare plants are limited to a few each year.

Refund/replacement: yes.

Special services: plant selection advice and lectures given. Coach parties welcome by appointment.

See map page 396.

OXFORDSHIRE

Acacia Nurseries   No catalogue and a large selection of plants make this nursery hard to describe but Geoffrey Hellman prides himself on growing all his own plants and for the good value he offers.

> **Acacia Nurseries**, Beagles Close, Water Eaton Lane, Kidlington, Oxford, Oxfordshire OX5 2QJ
>
> **Tel:** 01865 372452
>
> **Opening hours:** 9.00–13.00, 14.00–17.00 Tuesday, Friday and Saturday.
>
> **Visitors welcome:** yes.
>
> **Catalogue:** none.
>
> **Payment:** cash or cheque.
>
> **Mail order:** no.
>
> **Availability:** all plants are grown at the nursery so supplies are limited to what can be produced.
>
> **Refund/replacement:** by arrangement.

GARDENERS' RECOMMENDATIONS: ❀ *"One-man concern offering the best quality shrubs at the cheapest price of any nursery I have come across. An incredible man who makes a living by customer satisfaction."* Mr and Mrs M J Clist.

See map page 393.

Mattocks Roses   A good list of all roses from little patio plants to old-fashioned shrub roses and the fully-illustrated catalogue is very helpful. The firm also sells its own introductions.

> **Mattocks Roses**, Nuneham Courtenay, Oxford, Oxfordshire OX44 9PY
>
> **Tel:** 0345 585652   **Fax:** 01865 343166
>
> **E-mail:** roses@mattocks.co.uk
>
> **Website:** http://www.mattocks.co.uk
>
> **Opening hours:** 9.00–18.00 Monday to Saturday, 10.30–16.30 Sunday.
>
> **Visitors welcome:** yes.
>
> **Catalogue:** free.
>
> **Payment:** cash, cheque, major credit cards.

Mail order: yes.

Post and packing: £4.50.

Delivery: plants despatched from November to March.

Availability: November to March.

Refund/replacement: yes.

GARDENERS' RECOMMENDATIONS:
⌖ *Recommended by* Mr and Mrs E Harper.

See map page 390.

The Nursery Further Afield
The nursery holds the NCCPG national collection of hemerocallis, the daylily, which is a delightful plant to grow and in increasingly exciting colours. There are open days with conducted tours of both their geraniums and hemerocallis to show the plants at their best.

The Nursery Further Afield, Evenley Road, Mixbury, Brackley, NN13 5YR

Tel: 01280 848808 (day), 848539 (evenings) **Fax:** 01280 848864

E-mail: sinclair@nurseryfurtherafield.freeserve.co.uk

Opening hours: 10.00–13.00, 14.00–17.00 Wednesday to Saturday from April to early October (closed last two weeks of August).

Visitors welcome: yes.

Catalogue: send sae for list of hemerocallis.

Payment: cheque.

Mail order: hemerocallis only. Minimum order £15.

Post and packing: £5 for up to 10 plants, 25p per plant thereafter.

Delivery: despatch during spring and autumn.

Availability: the selection varies according to season. All stocks are limited though some varieties can be produced in large quantities to order.

Refund/replacement: problems should be reported within 7 days of receipt.

GARDENERS' RECOMMENDATIONS: ⌖ *"Gerald Sinclair is a great plantsman and enthusiast. His cranesbill geraniums and daylilies are without peer and he is an enchanting person to deal with."* Mr and Mrs H Morley-Fletcher. ⌖ *"A small one-man nursery offering an interesting range of less common herbaceous perennials. Specialises in hardy geraniums. The owner is always helpful and*

informative and willing to spend time offering advice." Mr and Mrs
G Metcalfe.

See map page 393.

The Plantation
Pauline Gattley doesn't have a catalogue but her
intention is to sell the most beautiful and unusual plants at the lowest
prices — an aim which couldn't be bettered in my view. The nursery
is in a garden and has plants for deep shade, ground cover, hot sunny
areas and containers. She's very happy to help out with advice.

> **The Plantation**, Hilbre House, Somerton, nr Bicester, Oxfordshire
> OX6 4NF
> **Tel/fax:** 01869 346654
> **E-mail:** sales-gfgb.ranik@virgin.net
> **Opening hours:** 10.00–17.00 Tuesday and Wednesday, 10.00-
> 20.00 Thursday to Saturday, 10.00–16.00 Sunday in season.
> **Visitors welcome:** yes.
> **Catalogue:** none.
> **Payment:** cash or cheque.
> **Mail order:** no.
> **Availability:** varies according to demand.
> **Refund/replacement:** yes.

GARDENERS' RECOMMENDATIONS: ❀*"A big display of plants in
owner's garden. Still a bit underdeveloped. Prices low."* Mrs G C Royle.

See map page 393.

Sheards Garden Centre
The firm specialises in old fashioned
roses along with the more unusual perennials and basket plants. It
will make up colour-themed hanging baskets designed by florists.

> **Sheards Garden Centre**, High Road, Brightwell-cum-Sotwell,
> Wallingford, Oxfordshire OX10 0PT
> **Tel:** 01491 836277 **Fax:** 01491 824151
> **Opening hours:** 9.00–17.00 daily.
> **Visitors welcome:** yes.
> **Catalogue:** none.
> **Payment:** cash, cheque, major credit/debit cards.
> **Mail order:** no.

Delivery: within 4-mile radius.
Availability: all year round.
Refund/replacement: yes.

GARDENERS' RECOMMENDATIONS: *"Rather untidy mass of very good plants but superb choice of magnificent David Austin New English Roses in pots and many of the finest old roses and fine climbing sorts. For lovers of classic roses absolutely irresistible."* Mr F S Tordoff.

See map page 390.

Swallows Nursery

A wide range of shrubs, climbers, heathers, ferns, grasses, roses and trees here but always with an interesting twist. Also a small collection of fruit trees. They will try to find plants which are not stocked.

Swallows Nursery, Mixbury, nr Brackley, NN13 5RR
Tel: 01280 847721 **Fax:** 01280 848611
Opening hours: 9.00–13.00, 14.00–16.30 Monday to Friday. Also at weekends in April, May, June and September: 10.00–13.00 Saturday, 14.30–16.30 Sunday. Phone at any time.
Visitors welcome: yes.
Catalogue: free.
Payment: cash or cheque.
Mail order: can be arranged.
Post and packing: typically £5 to £15.
Delivery: usually 3 weeks.
Availability: trees, hedging etc from November to March. Other plants, including containerised trees, all year round.
Refund/replacement: plants are guaranteed to be OK at time of sale.

GARDENERS' RECOMMENDATIONS: *"Very nice guy. Good basic shrubs for background planting – can get anything."* Mr and Mrs N R Wilson.

See map page 393.

Waterperry Gardens

This is both a famous garden and a famous nursery whose catalogue comes in three sections: alpines, herbaceous and trees, shrubs and conifers. There are almost a hundred yards of herbaceous border in the garden, flowering between mid-May and October plus the national collection of porophyllum saxifrages in the alpine nursery along with a formal knot garden with medicinal and culinary herbs.

Waterperry Gardens, nr Wheatley, Oxfordshire OX33 1JZ
Tel: 01844 339254 **Fax:** 01844 339883
Opening hours: 9.00–17.00.
Visitors welcome: yes.
Catalogue: 75p.
Payment: cheque.
Mail order: yes.
Post and packing: at cost.
Delivery: allow 21 days in season.
Availability: supplies can be limited and some plants are available only at certain times of year.
Refund/replacement: yes.
Special services: tea room.

GARDENERS' RECOMMENDATIONS: ✤ *"Really helpful and knowledgeable staff and most of plants on offer are home grown rather than mass-produced imports."* Mr and Mrs R H Bradbury. ✤ *"Wide range of plants. Beautifully situated in country estate and park surrounding. Restaurant."* Mr F S Tordoff.

See map page 390.

S West & Sons "If we haven't got it, we'll try to get it" says the firm
helpfully. It stocks most normal garden centre products, however, along with trees, shrubs, herbaceous plants and composts.

S West & Sons, 74 Windmill Road, Headington, Oxford, Oxfordshire OX3 7BZ
Tel: 01865 763556
Opening hours: 8.30–17.30 Monday to Saturday.
Visitors welcome: yes.
Catalogue: none.
Payment: cash, cheque, Visa, Mastercard, Switch.
Mail order: no, although local telephone orders are accepted.
Post and packing: local deliveries only. £3 for up to 5 miles, free for orders over £50 or for pensioners spending over £15.

Delivery: 2-3 days.

Availability: some items are seasonal.

Refund/replacement: yes, subject to good care by gardener.

GARDENERS' RECOMMENDATIONS: *"Very useful smallish garden centre within the Oxford city area."* Mr F S Tordoff. ❀ *"Small family run centre which can be well recommended."* Mr E Townsend-Coles.

See map page 393.

Whitehill Farm Nursery

Paul and Anne Youngson have been going for only a few years, propagating their own plants from bought-in stock. They specialise in perennials, grasses, bamboos, shrubs and herbs and, judging by their list, have an eye for contemporary garden design with black grass, dwarf bamboo, grey-leaved cardoons and plenty of ivies.

Whitehill Farm Nursery, Burford, Oxfordshire OX18 4DT

Tel: 01993 823218 **Fax:** 01993 822894

Opening hours: 9.00–18.00, or dusk if earlier, daily.

Visitors welcome: yes.

Catalogue: free.

Payment: cash or cheque.

Mail order: yes.

Post and packing: £10.50 for first 10 kg.

Delivery: 48 hours.

Availability: supplies can be limited and some plants are available only at certain times of year.

Refund/replacement: yes.

GARDENERS' RECOMMENDATIONS: ❀ *"All plants propagated from own seed or stock grown by traditional methods and in normal environment so suitable for most gardens particularly local ones. 200 varieties shrubs, 150 perennials, grasses, bamboos and trees developing. Long opening times with owners available to give advice."* Anthea Gibson.

See map page 393.

SHROPSHIRE

Hall Farm Nursery   Sells interesting herbaceous plants with a bias towards leaves rather than flowers. Arum italicum Marmoratum, aeoniums and euphorbias feature, as do hostas and grasses. Everything is grown on site and it's worth phoning to check availability in advance.

> **Hall Farm Nursery**, Vicarage Lane, Kinnerley, nr Oswestry, Shropshire SY10 8DH
>
> **Tel:** 01691 682135
>
> **Opening hours:** 10.00–17.00 Tuesday to Saturday from March to end September.
>
> **Visitors welcome:** yes.
>
> **Catalogue:** £1.50 or send 6 first class stamps.
>
> **Payment:** cash or cheque.
>
> **Mail order:** no.
>
> **Refund/replacement:** no.

GARDENERS' RECOMMENDATIONS: ❀ *"A continually growing interesting and unusual collection of mainly perennials and an extensive collection of grasses. Always worth a visit. Owner usually available for advice and information."* Mr and Mrs B P Kavanagh. ❀ *"They propagate and sell their own plants and are very helpful and reasonably priced."* Mr and Mrs G Grantham. ❀ *"Apart from the excellent quality of the herbaceous perennial plants on offer, many unusual, the nursery is situated in such a peaceful, lovely area with many attractive areas planted up showing the flair and design that has won Hall Farm Nursery many gold medals in shows."* Mr and Mrs S Lewis-Dale, The Mead Nursery. ❀ *"A visit to the owner's garden is possible to see many of the same plants growing."* Mr and Mrs P Bean.

See map page 394.

Hillview Hardy Plants   Well-chosen list of mostly herbaceous plants with ferns, grasses and lots of cottage garden flowers such as phlox, auricula and hosta. Stock beds and a charming garden are designed to help buyers see what plants look like out of the pot.

Hillview Hardy Plants, Worfield, nr Bridgnorth, Shropshire
WV15 5NT

Tel/fax: 01746 716454

E-mail: hillview.hardy.plants@compuserve.com

Opening hours: 9.00–17.00 Monday to Saturday from March
to mid-October.

Visitors welcome: yes.

Catalogue: send 4 second class stamps.

Payment: cash or cheque.

Mail order: yes.

Post and packing: from £5.50 for 5 plants to £8.50 for 20. At
cost thereafter.

Delivery: normally 2 weeks, weather permitting.

Availability: all plants should be available during March and
April, then stocks reduce during the season.

Refund/replacement: the nursery likes to inspect plants before
giving a refund in order to help the customer.

GARDENERS' RECOMMENDATIONS: ❀ *"Interesting collection of
hardy perennials and alpines. Very good on primulas."* Tessa King-
Farlow. ❀ *"Herbaceous, penstemon, rudbeckia, primula auricula,
aquilegia – excellent plants, service, delivery."* Mrs Craig.

See map page 394.

Lingen Nursery and Garden
This is an old-fashioned nursery
which specialises in alpine and herbaceous plants — a fully working
business where gardeners can see the plants being nurtured. The
penstemons, show auriculas and irises are particularly good. With a
group booking the owners will show you round personally.

Lingen Nursery and Garden, Lingen, nr Bucknell, Shropshire
SY7 0DY

Tel/fax: 01544 267720 (ring first for fax)

E-mail: kim&maggie@lingen.freeserve.co.uk

Opening hours: 10.00–17.00.

Visitors welcome: yes.

Payment: cheque.

Mail order: yes. Minimum order 5 plants.

Post and packing: £7 for 48-hour delivery.

Delivery: allow 1–3 weeks.

Availability: supplies may be limited, and some plants are
available at certain times of year only.

Refund/replacement: yes.
Special services: group bookings including personal tour.
Tea room

GARDENERS' RECOMMENDATIONS: *"Has a good choice of alpines and irises."* Mrs A Turnbull.

See map page 394.

Priors Lea Plants

This is a small but growing nursery selling aquilegia, artemisia, erysimum, hemerocallis, geraniums and many silver plants. Rarer plants come from seeds collected all over the world. There are also gardens designed to show off the plants on sale.

Priors Lea Plants, 5 Bank Farm Road, Shrewsbury, Shropshire
SY3 9DH
Tel: 01743 231452
Opening hours: by appointment from May to October.
Visitors welcome: yes, by appointment.
Catalogue: none.
Payment: cash or cheque.
Mail order: no.
Availability: May to October. Special orders can be propagated or divided by demand.
Refund/replacement: possibly.
Special services: some seeds available. Garden design service. Cup of tea for visitors if required.

GARDENERS' RECOMMENDATIONS: *"Interesting plants, many grown from wild-collected seed."* Callum Johnston, Tan-y-Lyn Nurseries.

See map page 394.

Sandstones Cottage Garden Plants

The nursery has a charming list of plants for the old-fashioned garden or ones which respond well to the new avant garde perennial planting. There's a good selection of foxgloves, geraniums, heuchera and salvia, among others.

Sandstones Cottage Garden Plants, 58 Bolas Heath, Great Bolas, Shropshire TF6 6PS
Tel: 01952 541657 **Fax:** 01952 541958

E-mail: pbrelsforth@mcmail.com

Website: http://www.sandstonesplants.mcmail.com

Opening hours: by appointment.

Visitors welcome: yes, by appointment.

Catalogue: £1, refundable with order.

Payment: cash or cheque.

Mail order: yes.

Post and packing: £6.50 for orders under £10, £9 for orders £10 to £40, at cost thereafter.

Delivery: 4-6 weeks.

Availability: supplies can be limited and some plants are available only at certain times of year.

Refund/replacement: yes.

GARDENERS' RECOMMENDATIONS: ✪ *"Some unusual plants and always helpful. Delphinium – 'Alice Artindale'. Very good geranium selection."* Mr and Mrs R Hall.

See map page 395.

SOMERSET

Avon Bulbs This is a very good list of bulbs of all sorts — from snowdrops to species paeonies to lilies and nerines. The nursery seems to like its plants to be species rather than too fussed about (a charming species Gladiolus papilio for example) and the care notes are extremely helpful. A recent innovation is a five-year gardener's diary to record planting, growth, weather etc.

Avon Bulbs, Burnt House Farm, Mid-Lambrook, South Petherton, Somerset TA13 5HE

Tel: 01460 242177 **Fax:** 01460 242177

Opening hours: 9.00–13.00, 14.00–16.30 Thursday to Saturday from mid-September to end October and mid-February to end March.

Visitors welcome: orders may be collected by prior arrangement.

Catalogue: send 4 second class stamps.

Payment: cheque, postal order, Visa, Access.

Mail order: yes.

Post and packing: £3.40 to £6.

Delivery: by post or Parcel Force in season.

Availability: bulbs are despatched depending on weather conditions from August to November and February to March .

Refund/replacement: yes, in case of error.

Special services: gift vouchers. Orders can be collected from shows.

GARDENERS' RECOMMENDATIONS: ❀ *"Fine range of good quality bulbs."* ❀ *"Excellent bulbs."* Mrs P Tham. ❀ *"I order faithfully from their catalogues twice a year."* Hon Peter and Mrs Dickinson. ❀ *"Always reliable."* ❀ *"Wiser to lose your Access card before you open the catalogue."* Simone Nelson. ❀ *Also recommended by* Lady Barbirolli *and* Christopher Lloyd, Great Dixter.

See map page 389.

Broadleigh Gardens

The nursery specialises in small bulbs and has a generous catalogue. The cyclamen list is huge, as is the lily list. Two catalogues come out each year, one for autumn and one for spring.

Broadleigh Gardens, Bishops Hull, Taunton, Somerset TA4 1AE

Tel: 01823 286231 **Fax:** 01823 323646

Opening hours: 9.00–16.00 Monday to Friday.

Visitors welcome: yes, for viewing only or collection of pre-booked orders.

Catalogue: send 2 first class stamps.

Payment: cash, cheque, Visa, Access.

Mail order: yes.

Post and packing: £3.50 or £5 by datapost.

Delivery: orders despatched in rotation. 24-hour delivery available at extra cost.

Availability: orders despatched from February to April and from August to November.

Refund/replacement: yes.

Special services: unusual and rare plants.

GARDENERS' RECOMMENDATIONS: ❀ *"Bulbs and herbaceous rarities, slightly expensive for some things but very good."* Mr and Mrs T F Clarke. ❀ *"The range of bulbs is very good, the catalogue is easy and interesting to use. They usually have what you want in stock and it is well packed."* Mr Frankie Warren. *"Interesting bulbs, reliable quality, excellent service by mail order. Value for money."* *"Bulbs of every kind, summer and winter."* Mrs Carol Lee. *"Dwarf bulbs, well displayed, growing in blocks in fields beside Christine Skelmersdale's lovely old house and garden."* Mr and Mrs J Southwell, Sherborne Garden. *"A wide range of small (and not so small) bulbs, together with a range of mostly small and mostly spring-flowering herbaceous plants. An excellent mail order service."* Mr P D Boyd.

See map page 389.

Cleeve Nursery
A general nursery offering everything from seeds to semi-mature plants: trees, shrubs, climbers, roses, conifers, herbs, fruit trees and bushes along with perennials, grasses and plants for the patio, conservatory and house.

Cleeve Nurseries, Main Road, Cleeve, nr Bristol BS49 4PW

Tel: 01934 832134 **Fax:** 01934 876498

Opening hours: 9.00–18.00 Monday to Saturday (9.00–17.00 in winter). 10.00–17.00 Sunday and bank holidays. Closed from Christmas to 2 January.

Visitors welcome: yes.

Catalogue: none.

Payment: cash, cheque, Eurocheque, Visa, Mastercard, Switch, Solo, National Garden and Interflora gift tokens.

Mail order: no.

Delivery: within a 15-mile radius. Allow up to 1 week.

Availability: seasonal.

Refund/replacement: yes. 1-year guarantee for hardy plants with proof of purchase.

Special services: border design service. Hanging baskets and containers planted.

GARDENERS' RECOMMENDATIONS: *"Knowledgeable and friendly and will always try to get in anything that they do not stock."* *"This is a small well-managed garden centre managed by the owners who seem to be extremely knowledgeable and helpful."*

See map page 390.

East Lambrook Manor Garden

This is where the great plantswoman, Margery Fish, created her famous garden and where the plants she loved are now propagated. The present owners, Robert and Marianne Williams, keep up the good work growing and selling the plants she pioneered; they also have the national collection of geraniums. They specialise in herbaceous perennials including euphorbia, artemisia and grey/silver plants. A place for a pilgrimage.

East Lambrook Manor Garden, East Lambrook, South Petherton, Somerset TA13 5HL

Tel: 01460 240328 **Fax:** 01460 242344

E-mail: elambrook@aol.com

Opening hours: 10.00–17.00 Monday to Saturday.

Visitors welcome: yes.

Catalogue: none.

Payment: cash or cheque.

Mail order: no.

Availability: supplies can be limited and some plants are available only at certain times of year.

Refund/replacement: yes.

GARDENERS' RECOMMENDATIONS: ❀ *National collection of geraniums (home grown)."* Major and Mrs Poe. ❀ *"Herbaceous and unusual."* Mrs Jane Gladstone.

See map page 389.

Elworthy Cottage Plants

Jenny Spiller's garden is set just within the Exmoor national park and is designed to fit in with that landscape. The good range of perennials is available at the small, attached nursery and includes penstemons, pulmonarias, violas, grasses and hardy geraniums. The garden provides inspiration of what and how to plant.

Elworthy Cottage Plants, Elworthy Cottage, Elworthy, nr Taunton, Somerset TA4 3PX

Tel: 01984 656427

Opening hours: 10.00–16.30 Tuesday, Thursday and Friday from mid-March to mid-October, also by appointment.

Visitors welcome: yes.

Catalogue: send 3 second class stamps.

Payment: cash or cheque.

Mail order: no.

Availability: some items are in limited supply.

Refund/replacement: yes.

Special services: the garden is open to visitors to the nursery.

GARDENERS' RECOMMENDATIONS: ✤ *"Concentrates on hardy plants, many unusual. Attached garden slightly chaotic but adds to the charm."* Mr and Mrs M R Everett. ✤ *"Jenny Spiller's small nursery within a garden overflowing with a vast selection of hardy geraniums, amongst other gems – always something of interest. Not easy to find, but well worth the journey."* Mrs Jessica Duncan. ✤ *"Excellent range (esp. hardy geraniums) of less common plants."* ✤ *"An excellent selection of herbaceous perennials, particularly hardy geraniums which are difficult to find elsewhere."* Mrs Gillian Baird. ✤ *Also recommended by* Mr and Mrs R Hubbard, Hill House Nursery.

See map page 389.

Hadspen Garden and Nursery
This is a famous garden and nursery run by Nori and Sandra Pope, authors of *Colour by Design*. Their plant list backs up their interest in colourist planting — visitors will find plants arranged by colour in the sales area — and they will help others to design their gardens along these lines. A must.

Hadspen Nursery, Hadspen House, Castle Cary, Somerset BA7 7NG

Tel/fax: 01749 813707

Opening hours: 10.00–17.00 Thursday to Sunday and bank holiday Mondays from March to October.

Visitors welcome: yes.

Catalogue: send 3 first class stamps.

Payment: cash or cheque.

Mail order: no.

Availability: supplies can be limited.

Refund/replacement: yes.

Special services: help with design and planting.

GARDENERS' RECOMMENDATIONS: ✤ *"Always a joy to visit – fabulous garden of such interesting and wonderful plants and colour associations and a nursery as well!"* Mr and Mrs H Lock. ✤ *"High quality plants selected for garden worthiness and beautifully arranged in colour themes. (The garden is managed on organic principles)"* Mrs Pam Lewis, Sticky Wicket. *"Excellent nursery; unusual varieties of largely hardy perennials, clematis, roses etc. presented in colour blocks. Superb oval walled garden with rainbow borders. Sandra and Nori Pope are very knowledgeable and helpful. A real joy to visit."* ❀ *"The Popes are both dedicated and inspirational."* Mrs Jessica Duncan.

See map page 389.

Kelways

A famous name among nurserymen, Kelways have been growing irises for more than 50 years and have a comprehensive catalogue of hundreds of different species and hybrids. They will even try to grow to order. Their other speciality is for paeonies and daylilies (hemerocallis) which come in a separate and equally helpful catalogue. The nursery itself also stocks many trees and shrubs, house plants and herbaceous varieties with orchids from McBeans.

Kelways Nursery and Plant Centre, Langport, Somerset TA10 9EZ
Tel: 01458 250521 **Fax:** 01458 253351
Opening hours: Monday to Friday 9.00–17.00, Saturday 10.00–17.00, Sunday 10.00–16.00.
Visitors welcome: yes, at plant centre.
Payment: cheque, Visa, Mastercard, Switch.
Mail order: yes. Minimum order £4.
Postage and packing: £4 for orders up to £25, £7.50 up to £49.99, free thereafter.
Delivery: minimum 3 days, maximum 8 months, depending on time of order.
Availability: seasonal. Iris despatched August–October, paeonia November–March. Early ordering recommended as popular varieties sell out quickly.
Refund/replacement: yes, problems are dealt with on an individual basis.

GARDENERS' RECOMMENDATIONS: ❀ *"Marvellous tree paeonies."* ❀ *"They seem to have recovered after a sticky patch? They are, I think, uniquely splendid for their irises and paeonies."* ❀ *"Great improvement in plant material and service from 10–15 years ago."*

See map page 389.

Kingsdon Nursery   Unusually for a small nursery, Patricia Marrow enjoys having bus parties and also suggests visitors eat lunch, tea or supper provided by the Women's Institute in the village hall at Kingsdon. She prides herself on selling only "good garden plants" which is helpful to the tyro. Her range is rock plants, herbaceous, shrubs, ornamental trees, box and yew.

Kingsdon Nursery, Kingsdon, Somerton, Somerset TA11 2LE
Tel: 01935 840232
Opening hours: 9.00–19.00 daily.
Visitors welcome: yes.
Catalogue: none.
Payment: cash or cheque.
Mail order: no.
Availability: all year round.
Refund/replacement: yes, if notified within 7 days.

GARDENERS' RECOMMENDATIONS: ⊗ *"Patricia Marrow runs this splendid nursery. It is an experience to go there. The plants are wide-ranging and well grown. She has supplied 80% of the plants for our garden over 15 years. She's a pleasure to deal with!"* Mr and Mrs Boileau. ⊗ *Also recommended by* Mr and Mrs R Hubbard, Hill House Nursery *and* Derry Watkins, Special Plants.

See map page 389.

Little Creek Nursery   Virtually all the plants, say Rhys and Julie Adams, are home grown. "We offer a very personal service." But the buyers of their cyclamen, hellebores and herbaceous perennials are worldwide. The general list has many geraniums, kaffir lilies and penstemon. The cyclamen are made into collections for various flowering times.

Little Creek Nursery, 39 Moor Road, Banwell, Somerset BS29 6EF
Tel/fax: 01934 823739

Opening hours: by appointment.

Visitors welcome: yes, by appointment.

Catalogue: send 3 first class stamps.

Payment: cheque.

Mail order: yes.

Post and packing: at cost.

Delivery: 7-28 days from receipt of payment depending on weather conditions.

Availability: supplies can be limited and some plants are available only at certain times of year.

Refund/replacement: yes.

GARDENERS' RECOMMENDATIONS: *"I have used this nursery for mail order plants. All arrived in good order, healthy plants, owners very helpful. Hellebore plants are excellent and good prices." "This nursery is concerned with propagating rare plants and I obtained the delphinium 'Alice Artindale' from them and several 'special' campanulas."*

See map page 390.

Long Acre Plants Snowdrops are a current obsession with many gardeners and this nursery has a nice selection. The firm is quite new with a clear idea of what it wants to sell — ferns, pulmonarias, unusual bulbs. It will make up special collections, especially of ferns, to suit your garden.

Long Acre Plants, South Marsh, Charlton Musgrove, Wincanton, Somerset BA9 8EX

Tel/fax: 01963 32802

Opening hours: on certain days listed in catalogue and by appointment.

Visitors welcome: by appointment.

Catalogue: send 3 first class stamps.

Payment: cheque.

Mail order: yes. Minimum order £10.

Post and packing: £4.50 to £10 depending on service required. Free for snowdrops only.

Delivery: orders despatched in rotation from mid-February to end April. (Cheques cashed at time of despatch).

Availability: woodland bulbs are only available in summer by mail order.

Refund/replacement: yes.

Special services: talks on woodland bulbs, plants and paeonia.

GARDENERS' RECOMMENDATIONS: *"Ferns and rarities."* Mrs Caroline Todhunter. *"Small nursery, ferns and unusual plants."* Mr and Mrs A W A Baker. *Also recommended by* Major and Mrs Arbuthnott, Stone House Cottage Gardens.

See map page 389.

Lower Severalls Nursery

This began life as a herb nursery in 1985 but gradually the range of plants widened. The herb list is still extremely comprehensive with a wide choice of thymes, lavender, basil and mint along with more abstruse herbs but now there are nearly four pages of geraniums in the catalogue, many salvias and some nice grasses. The garden opens under the NGS scheme. The owners offer a design service and are keen to give advice to nursery customers.

> **Lower Severalls Nursery**, Crewkerne, Somerset TA18 7NX
> **Tel:** 01460 73234   **Fax:** 01460 76105
> **Opening hours:** 10.00–17.00 daily except Thursdays and Sundays from 1 March to 20 October.
> **Visitors welcome:** yes.
> **Catalogue:** send 4 first class stamps.
> **Payment:** cash or cheque.
> **Mail order:** yes. Minimum order £10.
> **Post and packing:** minimum £15.
> **Delivery:** 1 month.
> **Availability:** all year round.
> **Refund/replacement:** yes.

GARDENERS' RECOMMENDATIONS: *"Good plant supports, herbs. Lovely garden."*

See map page 389.

Lynash Nurseries

Ashley and Lynn Wallis are hebe specialists who got into the business by growing and loving the plants themselves. They grow around a hundred and offer about 80 for sale. They are obviously full of knowledge about how to cultivate them — they especially hate bitterly cold winds.

> **Lynash Nurseries**, Culhaven, Wall Ditch Lane, Boozer Pit, Merriott, Somerset TA16 5PW

Tel: 01460 77764/76643 **Fax:** 01460 76643

Opening hours: 9.00–17.00 Thursday to Saturday, 10.00–16.00 Sunday and bank holidays.

Visitors welcome: yes, by appointment.

Catalogue: send 4 first class stamps.

Payment: cash, cheque, National Garden gift tokens, major credit cards except American Express.

Mail order: yes.

Post and packing: postage at cost, packing £2.

Delivery: 14 days from receipt of order.

Availability: supplies can be limited according to crop.

Refund/replacement: yes.

Special services: location service.

GARDENERS' RECOMMENDATIONS: ❀ *"Good plants and well packed."* Mrs P Tham. *"A fairly new nursery, owned and superbly cared for by a married couple. They specialise in hebes, but have a large range of mainly shrubby plants, but plenty of others too. Everything, including the plants, in the very pleasant surroundings, is immaculate and of the highest quality."* Lady Crossley.

See map page 389.

Mallet Court Nursery Sells rare varieties of trees and shrubs with a special leaning towards oaks, beech and maples.

Mallet Court Nursery, Curry Mallet, Taunton, Somerset TA3 6SY

Tel: 01823 480748 **Fax:** 01823 481009

Opening hours: 9.00–13.00, 14.00–17.00 Monday to Friday. Weekends by appointment.

Visitors welcome: yes.

Catalogue: send sae (31p).

Payment: cheque, Visa, Access.

Mail order: yes.

Post and packing: at cost. Minimum £4.

Delivery: depending on availability. Allow a minimum of 10 days.

Availability: mail order from October to March only.

Refund/replacement: yes, if notified within 7 days of purchase.

GARDENERS' RECOMMENDATIONS: ❀ *"Helpful nursery with excellent trees and shrubs. Many good species and varieties. Willing to find trees not on their list."* Mr and Mrs Gueterbock. ❀ *"Excellent selection of unusual trees, particularly acers. Easy to get lost en route!"* Mrs Jessica Duncan. *"Good range of trees, awful to visit, but mail order OK."* *"James Harris goes seed hunting so has a lot of rare trees etc. We now collect oaks (have 25) from him and hollies. He has vast tunnels and so many rows of trees one does not notice the weeds!"* Mr and Mrs J Southwell, Sherborne Garden. *"Best and widest range of trees we have found."* Mr and Mrs E W Dyer. *Also recommended by* Christopher Lloyd, Great Dixter.

See map page 389.

Meadows Nursery

This is a charming small nursery within a walled garden. It sells mainly herbaceous perennials of interesting varieties and these can be seen growing in the garden nearby. The owners are friendly and helpful and will grow plants to order.

Meadows Nursery, 5 Rectory Cottages, Selwood Street, Mells, Frome, Somerset BA11 3PN

Tel: 01373 813025

Opening hours: 10.00–18.00 Tuesday to Sunday.

Visitors welcome: yes.

Catalogue: send 4 first class stamps.

Payment: cash or cheque.

Mail order: no.

Availability: small numbers only of each plant so it is advisable to ring first.

Refund/replacement: yes.

GARDENERS' RECOMMENDATIONS: *"Specialises in long flowering perennials with many unusual plants available. Most are propagated by Mrs Lees and she is very knowledgeable and extremely helpful with guidance on their cultivation."* Mr and Mrs G B David. *Also recommended by* Derry Watkins, Special Plants.

See map page 389.

Mill Cottage Plants

Sally Gregson moved to Wookey a decade ago and started her garden and nursery from scratch, extending the two and a half-acre garden bit by bit. She propagates the plants which she grows and encourages customers to see how they look, mature, in her own garden. This hands-on approach nearly always makes for a good nursery. Visitors are advised to ring for directions.

Mill Cottage Plants, The Mill, Henley Lane, Wookey, Somerset BA5 1AP

Tel: 01749 676966

Opening hours: 10.00–18.00 on Wednesdays from March to September.

Visitors welcome: yes, by appointment.

Catalogue: send 4 first class stamps.

Payment: cheque.

Mail order: yes.

Post and packing: £6.50 by Parcel Force, sent on Mondays. £14 by Interlink 24-hour service.

Delivery: allow one week by Parcel Force, 24 hours by Interlink.

Availability: orders sent in rotation when plants are ready, from October to March, or by Interlink by arrangement at other times.

Refund/replacement: yes.

Special services: garden open to visitors on Wednesdays or to parties by arrangement. Talks on a variety of topics.

GARDENERS' RECOMMENDATIONS: ✿ *"Delightful small nursery (not a commercial garden centre) and gardens run by owners, Mr and Mrs Gregson, who every Wednesday from March to September stop what they are doing and spend time advising and showing you plants suitable for a cottage garden. They have traditional and unusual species and you always are tempted to buy more."* Professor and Mrs G H Arthur. ✿ *"Excellent for hardy perennials and true to name collection and mail order."* Mrs M Durston. ✿ *"I have not visited the nursery but I regularly buy plants from them at rare plant sales. Reasonably priced and unusual plants. The owner is very enthusiastic and keen to obtain plants you require."* Mrs S White. ✿ *Also recommended by* Derry Watkins, Special Plants.

See map page 389.

P M A Plant Specialities Many nurserymen are plagued by unexpected callers. We seem to think we can drop in any time. PMA goes strong on mail order and invites callers only by appointment. They are keen on Japanese maples with pages devoted to those they offer, along with many varieties of cornus and daphne.

P M A Plant Specialities, Junkers Nursery, Lower Mead, West Hatch, Taunton, Somerset TA3 5RN

Tel: 01823 480774 **Fax:** 01823 481046

Opening hours: strictly by appointment only.

Visitors welcome: by appointment only please.

Catalogue: send 5 second class stamps.

Payment: cheque with order.

Mail order: yes.

Post and packing: £10 per order.

Delivery: by return if available.

Availability: some rare/desirable plants need to be reserved for delivery when ready – usually September.

Refund/replacement: yes, where appropriate, and not as a result of damage by inclement weather.

Special services: gift vouchers and books.

GARDENERS' RECOMMENDATIONS: ✸ *"Specialises in rare and unusual trees and shrubs. Their own stock plants are collected from around the world. Very knowledgeable, enthusiastic and helpful owners."* Sir Walter and Lady Luttrell. ✸ *"Has a good range of daphnes. The Junkers are active plantspeople with good knowledge and a growing range of cornus, liquidamber and magnolias."* Mr and Mrs E Harper. ✸ *"First class trees (ornamental), beautifully packed and presented and have thrived."* Mr and Mrs Newman Burberry. ✸ *"An outstandingly excellent service provided by Karan and Nick Junker. The mail order catalogue is 'of the best' – informative in its detail and of real help to the gardener. The owners were eager to discuss my queries on specific plants, particularly the daphnes which would be best suited to my Yorkshire garden. The plants arrived in pristine condition. This is a nursery which can be whole-heartedly recommended."* Dr and Mrs A H Raper. ✸ *"An exceptional range of very rare shrubs."* Mr and Mrs E G Millais, Millais Nursery.

See map page 389.

Scotts Nurseries (Merriott) Ltd They describe themselves as a garden centre, but Scotts have a long and noble history as a nursery. One speciality is fruit trees with several pages of apples and pears (including cider and perry fruits), plums and gages, soft fruit plus cherries, grapes, mulberry, quince and figs. Roses are another major line with a good all-round list from hybrid teas to species. Other sections of the catalogue are trees and shrubs, climbers and herbaceous plants.

Scotts Nurseries (Merriott) Ltd, Merriot, Somerset TA16 5PL
Tel: 01460 72306 **Fax:** 01460 77433
Opening hours: 9.00–17.00 Monday to Saturday, 10.30–16.30 Sunday.
Visitors welcome: yes.
Catalogue: £1 (cash, cheque or loose stamps).
Payment: cash, cheque, major credit cards.
Mail order: yes.
Post and packing: from £4 to £20.
Delivery: dependent on season.
Availability: supplies can be limited and some plants are available only at certain times of year.
Refund/replacement: yes.

GARDENERS' RECOMMENDATIONS: ✤ *"Have used them for roses and perennials and they have been quite excellent."* Mrs Susan Beck. ✤ *"They have a good selection of fruit trees and much more than is on show in the garden centre."* ✤ *"Good solid service and willingness to suggest an alternative supplier if they can't provide."* Sir Neville and Lady Bowman-Shaw. ✤ *"Now a garden centre but still has fields of trees, roses, fruit and herbaceous plants and is well run and tidy."* Mr and Mrs J Southwell, Sherborne Garden. ✤ *"Huge heavenly catalogues. They answer questions. Both mail order and cash and carry are excellent."*

See map page 389.

Sue Strickland Plants Sue Strickland has a nice, smallish list of cottage garden plants such as phlox, campanula and foxgloves but her main area of speciality is in nepetas (over 30), salvias (more than 100), monarda and helianthus. She will propagate to order.

Sue Strickland Plants, The Poplars, Isle Brewers, Taunton, Somerset TA3 6QN
Tel: 01460 281454 **Fax:** 01460 281808
Opening hours: 9.30–14.30 Monday to Wednesday from April to July and during September. By appointment at other times.
Visitors welcome: yes.
Catalogue: send 2 first class stamps.

Payment: cash or cheque.

Mail order: yes.

Post and packing: at cost plus £1 for packing.

Delivery: allow 28 days though usually sooner.

Availability: plants are propagated in small numbers and may not always be available.

Refund/replacement: yes.

GARDENERS' RECOMMENDATIONS: *"Unusual perennials."* Mr and Mrs M Adams.

See map page 389.

Triscombe Nurseries

The nursery has no catalogue because it finds it impossible to list everything it grows but herbaceous perennials are the central part. There are also roses, fruit trees, soft fruit, alpines and climbers. The whole is sited in a Victorian walled kitchen garden (many old walled gardens have found new life as nurseries) and has been going since the 1950s.

Triscombe Nurseries, West Bagborough, nr Taunton, Somerset TA4 3HG

Tel: 01984 618267

Opening hours: 9.00–13.00, 14.00–17.30 Monday to Saturday, 14.00–17.30 Sunday.

Visitors welcome: yes.

Catalogue: none.

Payment: cash or cheque.

Mail order: no.

Delivery: available locally. Allow 5 days.

Availability: generally all year round.

Refund/replacement: depending on circumstances.

GARDENERS' RECOMMENDATIONS: *"A small nursery with good stock of healthy plants. Well-informed owner with helpful staff. Very popular locally."* Sir Walter and Lady Luttrell. *"For shrubs and herbaceous."* Mrs Caroline Todhunter.

See map page 389.

STAFFORDSHIRE

Country Lady Nursery   A selection of about 650 choice perennials, especially geraniums, penstemons and grasses with an acre of show garden alongside plus plenty of personal advice on planting and growing. The varieties are carefully chosen.

Country Lady Nursery, Lilac Cottage, Chapel Lane, Gentleshaw, nr Rugeley, Staffordshire WS15 4ND

Tel/fax: 01543 675520

Opening hours: 10.00–17.00 Wednesday to Sunday and bank holidays from beginning of March to end October.

Visitors welcome: yes, during opening hours or by appointment.

Catalogue: send A5 sae plus 2 first class stamps.

Payment: cash or cheque.

Mail order: no.

Availability: majority of plants available in March, then at intervals through the season, when ready for sale.

Refund/replacement: yes.

Special services: cream teas on open day (normally second Sunday in July).

GARDENERS' RECOMMENDATIONS: ❀ *"A visit to Country Lady Nursery and the personal service of Sylvia Nunn is the highlight of a gardener's day. Her knowledge and love of plants helps the most discerning gardener. Her enthusiasm for perennials opens a whole new learning curve for the new gardener that could last a lifetime."* Tom and Margaret Adams. ❀ *"A specialist nursery with attractive gardens, selling a good choice of hardy perennials, many unusual. Good quality plants at reasonable prices."* Mr and Mrs M Harvey. ❀ *"The only 'nursery' as far as I know around this area but it is excellent for picking up something a bit unusual."* Mr and Mrs T Atkins.

See map page 394

SUFFOLK

Gardiner's Hall Plants Raymond Mayes and Joe Smart specialise in herbaceous perennials and now stock 3,000 varieties of plants which are hard to find in more general garden centres. They have a good selection of fashionable cranesbills, variegated lamiums and interesting foxgloves. There are also grasses and rushes.

> **Gardiner's Hall Plants**, Gardiner's Hall, Braiseworth, Eye, Suffolk IP23 7DZ
> **Tel:** 01379 678285 **Fax:** 01379 678192
> **Opening hours:** 10.00–18.00 Wednesday to Saturday from April to October.
> **Visitors welcome:** yes.
> **Catalogue:** send 5 first class stamps.
> **Payment:** cheque.
> **Mail order:** yes. Minimum order £20.
> **Post and packing:** £10 for orders up to £100, 10% of order value thereafter.
> **Delivery:** 1-4 weeks.
> **Availability:** plants by mail order from October to April.
> **Refund/replacement:** yes.

GARDENERS' RECOMMENDATIONS: ❀ *"Small private garden."* Mrs Jane Alhusen.

See map page 393.

Goldbrook Plants A major hosta nursery with Chelsea gold medals in a straight run since 1988. Some of these are very rare, ordered months in advance and limited to one plant per customer. Sandra Bond may even refuse to sell a plant if she thinks a buyer will fail with it. The nursery also has many hemerocallis and a selection of other plants — mostly those which look well with her specialities.

> **Goldbrook Plants**, Hoxne, Eye, Suffolk IP21 5AN
> **Tel/fax:** 01379 668770
> **Opening hours:** 10.00–17.00 Thursday to Sunday from April to September. 10.00–17.00 at weekends from October to March

and by appointment. Closed in January and during Chelsea and Hampton Court Shows.

Visitors welcome: yes.

Catalogue: send 4 first class stamps.

Payment: cash, cheque, Eurocheque, credit transfer.

Mail order: yes. Minimum order £15 plus p&p.

Post and packing: £5 for orders up to £40, £8 for orders from £41 to £99, free thereafter.

Delivery: orders despatched October/November and March/April.

Availability: plants supplied during correct planting season.

Refund/replacement: yes.

GARDENERS' RECOMMENDATIONS: ❀ *"Herbaceous, hosta, hemerocallis – very good plants, service, delivery."* Mrs Craig. *"For hostas."* Mrs Caroline Todhunter.

See map page 393.

Goldsmith Trees, Crown Nursery
If you want good quality hedging plants or parkland trees this is your nursery. The plants are always good quality and cheap at the price. Though this is their speciality, they have plenty of shrubs and perennials plus good fruit trees, always sold in excellent condition. The firm will also help move large trees — they get plenty of practice.

Goldsmith Trees, Crown Nursery, High Street, Ufford, Woodbridge, Suffolk IP13 6EL

Tel: 01394 460755 **Fax:** 01394 460142

Opening hours: 9.00–17.00 Monday to Saturday. Closed bank holiday weekends.

Visitors welcome: yes.

Catalogue: free.

Payment: cash, cheque, major credit/debit cards.

Mail order: yes.

Post and packing: varies according to size of order, eg £7.50 for 9 to 12 perennials.

Delivery: normally 7 days.

Availability: supplies can be limited and some plants are available only at certain times of year.

Refund/replacement: yes, depending on circumstances.

Special services: landscape design.

GARDENERS' RECOMMENDATIONS: *"Trees, hedging – very good plants, service, delivery."* Mrs Craig.

See map page 393.

Harvey's Garden Plants

Specialists in eryngiums, epimediums, monardas and anemones plus the hellebores they breed — all woodland plants. Helleborus Ashwood Garden hybrid is offered in a range of colours and, soon, Helleborus Bradfield hybrids will be on sale. Double versions are also coming up.

Harvey's Garden Plants, Mulberry Cottage, Bradfield St George, nr Bury St Edmunds, Suffolk IP30 0AY

Tel/fax: 01284 386777

Opening hours: by appointment 10.00–17.00 Friday and Saturday from January to end June and from 1 September to 31 October.

Visitors welcome: yes.

Catalogue: send 4 first class stamps.

Payment: cheque.

Mail order: yes. Minimum order £15.

Post and packing: £8.60 for 6 plants, £1 per plant thereafter. Large orders by quotation.

Delivery: 14 days.

Availability: plants are available from the nursery all year round. Mail order service from October to April.

Refund/replacement: yes.

GARDENERS' RECOMMENDATIONS: *"Small, excellent and specialised nursery – hellebores particularly."* *"Very small nursery, brilliant tunnel of hellebores really well grown."*

See map page 393.

Hill Cottage Nursery

This is a small nursery where the owner lives on site in an old timber-framed cottage. The plants are generally cottage garden plants, especially perennials and shrub roses. The nursery takes up about a quarter acre of land around the cottage and the containerised plants are arranged to give the feel of a real garden. The plants are bred for conditions in East Anglia — cold winters and often dry summers.

Hill Cottage Nursery, 4 Ashes Corner, Walsham-le-Willows, Suffolk
IP31 3BS

Tel: 01359 259358

Opening hours: 9.30–17.00 Wednesday to Sunday and bank
holiday Mondays. Closed in January.

Visitors welcome: yes.

Catalogue: none.

Payment: cash or cheque.

Mail order: no.

Availability: supplies can be limited and some plants are
available only at certain times of year.

Refund/replacement: depends on circumstances.

GARDENERS' RECOMMENDATIONS: ❀ *"Highly recommended."*
❀ *"Small nursery with good stock, run by owner (Miss Matheson)
with young manager, who writes good monthly garden articles in the
village magazine. Very pleasant service and enthusiasm."* Dr and Mrs
A J Russell.

See map page 393.

Home and Garden at Winter Flora   The firm has been
producing flowers for drying for 30 years but has only recently
moved into selling plants from their own garden. "I would hesitate
to call ourselves a nursery yet," says Jane Seppings modestly, "but I
have often been disappointed when visiting gardens open to the
public that their plant sales seldom include unusual plants featured
in the garden." She aims to change this.

Home and Garden at Winter Flora, Hall Farm, Weston, Beccles,
Suffolk NR34 8TT

Tel: 01502 716810 **Fax:** 01502 717139

E-mail: flowers@winterflora.co.uk

Website: http://www.flowerstyle.com

Opening hours: 10.00–17.00 Monday to Saturday, 11.00–17.00
Sunday.

Visitors welcome: yes.

Catalogue: none.

Payment: cash, cheque, major credit cards.

Mail order: no.

Availability: supplies can be limited and some plants are
available only at certain times of year.

Refund/replacement: yes.

Special services: plant finding service.

GARDENERS' RECOMMENDATIONS: *"Have a large garden and good quality plants for sale. Extremely friendly staff. They also have a large shop selling a large range of dried flowers and many other items. Also teas and light lunches are available."* Mr and Mrs M Elliot, Old Hall Plants.

See map page 393.

The Kitchen Garden

Francine Raymond, author of several books about keeping characterful hens in her garden, also sells the plants she grows for herself in a charming garden outhouse. She has stylish garden impedimenta and the sort of cottage garden plants it's hard to find in larger places. A walk round the garden, which has appeared in various glossy magazines, is a treat. There are aids for hens and, next year, bee-keeping, and she does delicious lunches.

> **The Kitchen Garden**, Church Cottage, Church Lane, Troston, Suffolk IP31 1EX
>
> **Tel/fax:** 01359 268322
>
> **E-mail:** francine@jfraymond.demon.co.uk
>
> **Opening hours:** 10.00–18.00 Friday and Saturday from May to July and September to October.
>
> **Visitors welcome:** by appointment.
>
> **Catalogue:** none.
>
> **Mail order:** no.
>
> **Availability:** plants are only available during opening season.
>
> **Refund/replacement:** by arrangement.
>
> **Special services:** teas and lunches. Products for hen and bee keepers.

GARDENERS' RECOMMENDATIONS: *"Serves tea and light meals. Very small."*

See map page 393.

Ladybird Nurseries

The nursery grows everything it sells. It specialises in geraniums, fuchsias and other plants for patios and hanging baskets. They also have plenty of bedding plants.

Ladybird Nurseries, Gromford Lane, Snape, Saxmundham, Suffolk
IP17 1RD

Tel: 01728 688289

Opening hours: 9.00–17.00 daily.

Visitors welcome: yes.

Catalogue: none.

Payment: cash, cheque, major credit/debit cards.

Mail order: no.

Availability: supplies can be limited.

Refund/replacement: yes.

Special services: baskets and containers filled.

GARDENERS' RECOMMENDATIONS: *"An excellent choice of plants, some unusual, of high quality and, on the whole, reasonably priced."* Lady Cave. ✿ *"Has a colossal range (largely bedding and tender plants) at amazingly low prices."*

See map page 393.

Mills Farm Plants   This friendly nursery, run by Sue and Peter Russell, has a splendid selection of pinks (including their own Mendlesham patio pinks), a nice collection of roses and plenty of other garden goodies. Their plants are always in extremely good condition.

Mills Farm Plants and Gardens, Norwich Road, Mendlesham, Suffolk IP14 5NQ

Tel/fax: 01449 766425

Opening hours: 9.00–17.30 daily except Tuesday. Closed from Christmas to mid-February.

Visitors welcome: yes.

Catalogue: send 5 second class stamps.

Payment: cash, cheque, Visa, Access, Switch, Solo, Electron.

Mail order: yes.

Post and packing: £5.95.

Delivery: usually within 2 weeks.

Availability: supplies can be limited and some plants are available only at certain times of year.

Refund/replacement: yes.

GARDENERS' RECOMMENDATIONS: *Recommended by* Mr and Mrs S Ingerson.

See map page 393.

North Green Snowdrops

North Green Snowdrops These shy little plants have a growing band of aficionados and John Morley is clearly one of them. He has not been diverted in any way. The catalogue lists nothing but galanthus — nearly 70 of them — but if you want to buy in bulk to create drifts, he asks you to go elsewhere. This, however, is the place for rarities.

> **North Green Snowdrops**, North Green Only, Stoven, Beccles, Suffolk NR34 8DG
> **E-mail:** snowdrops@compuserve.com
> **Opening hours:** mail order only.
> **Visitors welcome:** by appointment.
> **Catalogue:** £1.50.
> **Payment:** cheque, postal order.
> **Mail order:** yes. Minimum order £5.
> **Post and packing:** £3.50.
> **Delivery:** seasonal, one month from despatch of catalogue.
> **Availability:** supplies can be limited and some plants are available only at certain times of year.
> **Refund/replacement:** yes.

See map page 393.

Paradise Centre

Paradise Centre Hedy Stapel-Valk grew up in wartime Holland and she named her nursery after the contentment she found in Suffolk. The nursery specialises in bulbs, plants for shade and herbaceous perennials. The owners are extremely helpful and offer advice on planning, planting and choice. They will also give talks on their enthusiasms.

> **Paradise Centre**, Twinstead Road, Lamarsh, Bures, Suffolk CO8 5EX
> **Tel/fax:** 01787 269449
> **E-mail:** hedy@paradisecentre.com
> **Website:** http://www.paradisecentre.com

Opening hours: April to end October at weekends only.

Visitors welcome: yes.

Catalogue: send 5 first class stamps.

Payment: cheque, postal order, Visa.

Mail order: yes. Minimum order £7.50.

Post and packing: from £4 for up to 10 plants to £15 for over 40.

Delivery: despatched according to season. Bulbs from mid-August. Plants from February to mid-March and October to November.

Availability: some unusual plants are in short supply.

Refund/replacement: yes.

Special services: lectures, advice on planning and selections. Plants may be collected from shows.

GARDENERS' RECOMMENDATIONS: *"For bulbs and tubers."* Mrs Caroline Todhunter.

See map page 393.

Park Green Nurseries

Park Green Nurseries Recently, this firm won 14 medals at the 17 shows it attended, including Chelsea and Hampton Court. Hostas are a major interest, with 200 varieties stocked, along with ferns, grasses, astilbes and other hardy herbaceous perennials. The catalogue is for hostas only as the rest cannot be bought by mail order.

Park Green Nurseries, Wetheringsett, Stowmarket, Suffolk IP14 5QH

Tel: 01728 860139 **Fax:** 01728 861277

Opening hours: daily from March to September 10.00–17.00.

Visitors welcome: yes.

Catalogue: £1.

Payment: cheque, Visa, Mastercard, Switch, Delta.

Mail order: hostas only.

Post and packing: £2 for 1-2 plants, £4 for orders up to £40, free thereafter.

Delivery: plants despatched November and February to mid-April.

Availability: some varieties are grown in limited quantities.

Refund/replacement: yes.

Special services: happy to offer advice on all aspects of growing hostas and other hardy perennials.

GARDENERS' RECOMMENDATIONS: ❀ *"Wonderful collection of hostas, with excellent quality plants."* Mrs Susan Beck. ❀ *"This nursery has a comprehensive list of hostas and as part of my garden is 'bog' is very useful to me. They have a very informative catalogue which gives full details of all their stock. The nursery is run by Mary and Richard Force who have been successful exhibitors at Chelsea and Hampton Court shows."* Mrs Anna Wortham.

See map page 393.

The Place for Plants As they boast, the nursery has a huge range of both popular and rare plants — from grasses to bulbs, box topiary to species roses. There's also a 15-acre garden and arboretum attached.

The Place for Plants, East Bergholt Place, East Bergholt, Suffolk CO7 6UP

Tel: 01206 299224 **Fax:** 01206 299224

E-mail: placeforplants@martex.net

Opening hours: 10.00–17.00 (dusk if earlier) daily. Closed Easter Sunday and from Christmas Eve for two weeks.

Visitors welcome: yes.

Catalogue: free.

Payment: cash, cheque, major credit cards.

Mail order: no.

Availability: supplies are not generally limited.

Refund/replacement: yes, if justified.

GARDENERS' RECOMMENDATIONS: ❀ *"Owned by Rupert and Sarah Eley. Specialises in trees and shrubs. Very knowledgeable. Has excellent variety and quality of plants and large arboretum where trees and shrubs can be seen. Very helpful. Plenty of parking space."* Mr and Mrs J C Jenkinson. ❀ *"Run by young owners who are extremely obliging and willing to obtain the more unusual plants."* Dr and Mrs A J Russell. ❀ *"The Eleys are a delightful, enthusiastic young couple. Many really interesting trees and shrubs – very reasonable prices."* Mr and Mrs R Pilkington. ❀ *"Has a most beautiful garden adjoining the nursery, which is open to the public sometimes – a joy to visit."* Mrs N N Green. ❀ *"Clean, well laid out in walled garden, good labelling and description of usual and some unusual plants, especially shrubs, trees and climbers."* Mr and Mrs J Ineson.

See map page 393.

Plants of Distinction

Plants of Distinction Actually, the list is nearly all of seeds — but what seeds! For a few coins, you can get 15 arisaema seeds, 100 delphinium belladonna seeds or 15 martagon lily seeds. I am known to go mad with seed catalogues and, if you see this one, you'll understand the temptation.

> **Plants of Distinction**, Abacus House, Station Yard, Needham Market, Suffolk IP6 8AS
>
> **Tel:** 01449 721720 **Fax:** 01449 721722
>
> **E-mail:** sales@podseeds.co.uk
>
> **Opening hours:** 24-hour mail order service.
>
> **Visitors welcome:** no.
>
> **Catalogue:** free.
>
> **Payment:** cheque, major credit cards.
>
> **Mail order:** yes. Minimum order £10.
>
> **Post and packing:** 60p.
>
> **Delivery:** allow 7–14 days.
>
> **Availability:** seeds are available all year round, plants are despatched at the appropriate time as indicated in the catalogue.
>
> **Refund/replacement:** yes.
>
> **Special services:** gift vouchers, overseas service.

Rougham Hall Nurseries

Rougham Hall Nurseries A comprehensive list of hardy perennials including irises, daylilies and red hot pokers. The catalogue says firmly that plastic gnomes and barbecues are not on offer — it's the plants they care about.

> **Rougham Hall Nurseries**, Rougham, Bury St Edmunds, Suffolk IP30 9LZ
>
> **Tel:** 01359 270577 **Fax:** 01359 271149
>
> **E-mail:** kelvin-harbutt@msn.com
>
> **Opening hours:** 10.00–16.00 from Easter to October.
>
> **Visitors welcome:** yes.
>
> **Catalogue:** £1 or 5 first class stamps.
>
> **Payment:** cash, cheque, Visa, Mastercard.

Mail order: yes.

Post and packing: £7.50.

Delivery: orders are despatched in spring and autumn.

Availability: certain plants may occasionally be sold out.

Refund/replacement: depends on circumstances.

GARDENERS' RECOMMENDATIONS: *"Herbaceous– very good plants, service, delivery."* Mrs Craig.

See map page 393.

Siskin Plants
No fewer than three catalogues a year with, if you are feeling bereft, intermediary newsletters to keep you up to date. The firm specialises in dwarf hebes and holds the national collection but also sells other alpines and dwarf shrubs.

Siskin Plants, Davey Lane, Charsfield, Woodbridge, Suffolk IP13 7QG

Tel/fax: 01473 737567

E-mail: siskinplants@btinternet.com

Website: http://www.oxalis.co.uk

Opening hours: 10.00–17.00 Tuesday to Saturday from March to October. By appointment at other times.

Visitors welcome: yes.

Catalogue: send 4 first class stamps.

Payment: cheque, postal order, Visa, Mastercard.

Mail order: yes.

Post and packing: £2.90 for orders up to £7.50, £4.50 thereafter. Free for orders over £40.

Delivery: orders despatched the week following receipt. Next day delivery can be arranged.

Availability: all year round, weather permitting.

Refund/replacement: yes.

Special services: postal design service, free helpline, gift vouchers.

See map page 393.

Thompson and Morgan
This is a huge seed list, both for flowers and vegetables and one, what is more, that keeps up to date with fashionable plants. Among the vegetables are saladisi, Indian

corn and red onions; the flowers Eryngium Miss Wilmott's Ghost (a must-have today), black irises and the oregano-scented lavender. Growing from seed is addictive and, with this catalogue, you'll need a giant greenhouse.

Thompson and Morgan, Poplar Lane, Ipswich, Suffolk IP8 3BU
Tel: 01473 688821 **Fax:** 01473 680199
E-mail: tm-enquiries@thompson-morgan.com
Website: http://www.thompson-morgan.com
Opening hours: 24-hour credit card orderline: 01473 690869.
Visitors welcome: no. Open weekend in August. Ring 01473 688821 for details.
Catalogue: free.
Payment: cheque, postal order, major credit cards.
Mail order: yes.
Post and packing: 75p.
Delivery: 7 days.
Availability: order early to avoid disappointment.
Refund/replacement: yes.

GARDENERS' RECOMMENDATIONS: ❀ *Recommended by* Mrs M Linklater.

The Walled Garden Excellent (with all those walls) for climbers with good roses, clematis both viticella and species vines and parthenocissus. Also perennials, shrubs, grasses and bamboos. The garden, of two acres, was originally a kitchen garden for 19th century Benhall Lodge and its quarter mile of walls used, they say, 300,000 red bricks.

The Walled Garden, Park Road, Benhall, Saxmundham, Suffolk IP17 1JB
Tel/fax: 01728 602510
E-mail: jim@thewalledgarden.co.uk
Opening hours: 9.30–17.00 Tuesday to Sunday. Ring for winter opening hours.
Visitors welcome: yes.
Catalogue: send 2 first class stamps.
Payment: cash, cheque, major credit cards.
Mail order: no.
Availability: seasonal variations.
Refund/replacement: where applicable.

GARDENERS' RECOMMENDATIONS: *"Always helpful and knowledgeable."* Mr and Mrs D R Brightwell. ✿ *"Superb quality and good prices."* Mr and Mrs J Walker. ✿ *"An excellent choice of plants, some unusual, of high quality and, on the whole, reasonably priced."* Lady Cave. ✿ *"A wide range of perennials and shrubs always extremely well grown – also lovely selection of terracotta pots. Garden itself being developed."* Mrs Catherine Horwood.

See map page 393.

See map page 393.

Woottens Plants   There are four different — but all extremely witty and informative — catalogues; those for grasses, pelargoniums, penstemons and herbaceous plants. Some are beautifully illustrated and all tell you the derivation of the plants' names. Michael Loftus has strong views and delightful prejudices (I don't agree with all of them) and his comments make good bedside reading. Oh, yes, and his plants are interesting and well chosen, too. He also adds, and I wish others did, a list of local suppliers, nurseries and a place for lunch.

> **Woottens Plants**, Blackheath, Wenhaston, Halesworth, Suffolk IP19 9HD
> **Tel:** 01502 478258
> **Opening hours:** 9.30–17.00 daily.
> **Visitors welcome:** yes.
> **Catalogue:** £2.50.
> **Payment:** cheque, major credit cards, Switch.
> **Mail order:** no.
> **Refund/replacement:** all plants are guaranteed.

GARDENERS' RECOMMENDATIONS: ✤ *"Especially good for species pelargoniums and salvias. Beautiful catalogue."* Mrs Catherine Horwood. ✤ *"Has a huge range of plants, imaginatively chosen and excellent value for sizable plants."* ✤ *"An excellent choice of plants, some unusual, of high quality and, on the whole, reasonably priced."* Lady Cave. ✤ *"Excellent herbaceous plants."* Mrs G W Deterding.

See map page 393.

See also: Old Hall Plants, page 359.

SURREY

Rupert Bowlby Mr Bowlby sells bulbs of a most arcane nature: he's increasing his stock from South Africa while sticking with some wonderful alliums, 11 different fritillaries and a dozen tulip species. Don't look for boring daffies here but small scented gladiolus and showy eremurus.

> **Rupert Bowlby**, Gatton, Reigate, Surrey RH2 0TA
> **Tel/fax:** 01737 642221
> **Opening hours:** 10.00–17.00 Saturday, 14.00–17.00 Sunday in March, September and October only, or by appointment.
> **Visitors welcome:** during opening hours or by appointment.
> **Catalogue:** send 3 second class stamps.
> **Payment:** cash, cheque, postal order.
> **Mail order:** yes.
> **Post and packing:** £3.90 for orders under £40, free thereafter.
> **Delivery:** despatched in order from late August.
> **Availability:** bulbs only available in season.
> **Refund/replacement:** yes.

GARDENERS' RECOMMENDATIONS: ✤ *"For unusual bulbs and corms."* Mrs Caroline Todhunter.

See map page 392.

The Conservatory It's surprising how difficult it is to find good plants for conservatories — or, at least, if you want to share the space with them — but this nursery has done the selecting for you including citrus trees, the exotically scented datura and equally fragrant Genista fragrans. They sell coffee plants, Japanese bananas and European olives. Good also for roof terraces, town gardens and other confined spaces if there's somewhere to overwinter the plants.

The Conservatory, Gomshall Gallery, Gomshall, Surrey
GU5 9LB
Tel: 01483 203019 **Fax:** 01483 203282
Opening hours: 10.00–17.30 Monday to Saturday except Christmas, Easter and bank holidays. 14.00–17.00 Sunday from April to end September and bank holidays.
Visitors welcome: yes.
Catalogue: free.
Payment: cash, cheque, Visa, Mastercard, Switch, Delta.
Mail order: yes.
Post and packing: at cost (£7.50 to £15 for most orders).
Delivery: by arrangement. Next day if in stock.
Availability: most plants available all year round.
Refund/replacement: rarely occurs as plants leave in good condition.
Special services: free cultivation sheets for all plants.
Planting plans.

GARDENERS' RECOMMENDATIONS: ✿ *"Excellent."* Dr and Mrs R L Belsey.

See map page 392.

Green Farm Plants Loved by absolutely everybody, this nursery had no fewer than 33 recommendations from gardeners and is thus top of the favourite nurseries. The garden at Bury Court is designed with the assistance of the influential Dutch garden designer, Piet Oudolf, who uses bold drifts, carefully selected plants and especially grasses. "The design of the garden is as bold as it is surprising," say the owners, adding ominously that Oudolf's style "has erroneously been labelled as labour saving." The plants for sale follow this interest. The nursery's plants are always in excellent condition.

Green Farm Plants at Bury Court, Bentley, nr Farnham, Surrey
GU10 5LZ

Tel: 01420 23202 **Fax:** 01420 22382

Opening hours: 10.00–18.00 Thursday to Saturday.

Visitors welcome: yes.

Catalogue: send 3 first class stamps.

Payment: cash, cheque, Visa, Mastercard, Maestro, Visa Electron,
Switch, Solo, JCB.

Mail order: no.

Availability: most plants in the catalogue are produced in
quantities sufficient for the year but not all plants are available
all the time.

Refund/replacement: discretionary.

Special services: show garden, café, disabled facilities.

GARDENERS' RECOMMENDATIONS: ✾ *"All plants very well grown
and potted. Choice excellent – changes a bit each year. New garden
lovely. Assistance from Piet Oudolf."* Mr and Mrs M Conville.
✾ *"The absolute tops: always has the 'latest' plants, beautifully
presented. Stunning garden – even the cakes in the coffee shop are
delicious."* Mr and Mrs K H Wallis. ✾ *"I travel regularly to this well-
established nursery to add plants to my own collections …definitely
highly recommended by me."* Mr N Lucas, Knoll Gardens. ✾ *"There
is always something new to me, plants well grown and displayed by the
very dedicated owners."* Mrs Jessica Duncan. ✾ *"Wonderful plants,
well presented in clean pots at reasonable prices, also much expertise."*
✾ *"A wonderful nursery. They seem to be overstocked with unusual
and rare plants. Very helpful assistants and an interesting helpful
layout of plants in situ, especially their natural grass area. Good
restaurant, excellent food."* Mrs S White. ✾ *"Beautiful new garden in
old farmyard and oast house. Planted particularly for late summer and
autumn. Grasses and perennials. Small nursery next to it with excellent
quality plants. It is good that you can generally buy things you see in
the garden."* Mr and Mrs R V St John Wright. ✾ *Also recommended
by* Major and Mrs Arbuthnott, Stone House Cottage Gardens; Mrs
R Alexander, The English Gardening School at the Chelsea Physic
Garden; Mr John Carter, Rowden Gardens; Lady Scott, Rotherfield
Park and many others.

See map page 390.

Hill Park Nurseries These are rose specialists with an excellent list of everything from species roses like Rosa rubrifolia to hybrid teas and standard roses — though the species are very much in the minority. The firm has its own rose fields to visit between June and October where you can see the plants in bloom before choosing them for autumn planting.

> **Hill Park Nurseries**, Woodstock Lane, Kingston-by-Pass, Surbiton, Surrey KT6 5HN
>
> **Tel:** 020 8398 0022   **Fax:** 020 8339 0383
>
> **Opening hours:** 8.00–17.30 weekdays, 9.00–17.30 Saturday, 10.00–17.00 Sunday.
>
> **Visitors welcome:** yes.
>
> **Catalogue:** 50p.
>
> **Payment:** cash, cheque, major credit cards.
>
> **Mail order:** yes.
>
> **Post and packing:** at cost.
>
> **Delivery:** same day local delivery, 3-4 days by post.
>
> **Availability:** bare-rooted plants from October to end February, container plants from March to August/September.
>
> **Refund/replacement:** replacement.

GARDENERS' RECOMMENDATIONS: ☯ *"For roses."* Mrs P Seymour.

See map page 392.

V H Humphrey: The Iris Specialist A large list of nothing but irises from very classy hybrids to a good selection of species. The firm has been going for over three decades. When it started, only 85 irises were offered for sale — now there are over 500 with new ones turning up all the time. The catalogue helpfully lists height and year when the particular iris was registered but is a bit short on description for those not in the know.

> **V H Humphrey: The Iris Specialist**, Westlees Farm, Logmore Lane, Westcott, Dorking, Surrey RH4 3JN
>
> **Tel:** 01306 889827
> **Fax:** 01306 889371
>
> **Opening hours:** by appointment only during bloom season: May-July.
>
> **Visitors welcome:** by appointment during opening hours only.

Catalogue: send C5 sae or 3 first class stamps.

Payment: cheque.

Mail order: yes.

Post and packing: from about £2.50 for 5 plants.

Delivery: plants despatched at correct planting times.

Availability: supplies can be limited and some plants are available only at certain times of year.

Refund/replacement: yes.

Special services: open days during bloom season.

GARDENERS' RECOMMENDATIONS: ✾ *"Plants true to name. Can be small pieces and not cheap, but healthy. Replies to letters and willingly replaces the occasional failure. Excellent range."* Mr Duncan Skene.

See map page 392.

Hydon Nurseries

25 acres of grounds are naturalistically planted with rhododendrons, azaleas and camellias, both species and the more unusual hybrids along with acers, magnolias and prunus. Apart from small and dwarf plants, everything is grown in open ground. If you can't get to see them in flower, (and the nursery offers conducted tours) the catalogue is illustrated in full colour.

Hydon Nurseries, Clock Barn Lane, Hydon Heath, Godalming, Surrey GU8 4AZ

Tel: 01483 860252   **Fax:** 01483 419937

Opening hours: 8.00–12.45, 14.00–17.00 weekdays. Sunday by appointment during the flowering season.

Visitors welcome: yes.

Catalogue: £1.50.

Payment: cheque or credit transfer.

Mail order: yes.

Post and packing: at cost.

Delivery: orders despatched from October to April within 2-5 days of receipt depending on weather conditions.

Availability: personal callers may purchase plants throughout the year.

Refund/replacement: genuine complaints are dealt with sympathetically, and plant is usually replaced.

Special services: parties of rhododendron enthusiasts welcomed.

GARDENERS' RECOMMENDATIONS: ❀ *"Specialist and reliable."* Mr Bruce Archibold, former chairman RHS Rhododendron, Camellia and Magnolia Group. ❀*Also recommended by* Dr and Mrs Gallagher.

See map page 390.

Millais Nurseries
The nursery carries over 800 different varieties and species of rhododendron and azalea from dwarfs to very large specimens suitable for grandiose planting. Each list has new introductions from plant hunting trips along with new hybrids from the top breeders. The nursery and gardens are planted around with favoured varieties which can be seen in action.

Millais Nurseries, Crosswater Farm, Crosswater Lane, Churt, Farnham, Surrey GU10 2JN

Tel: 01252 792698 **Fax:** 01252 792526

E-mail: sales@rhododendrons.co.uk

Website: http://www.rhododendrons.co.uk

Opening hours: 10.00–13.00, 14.00–17.00 Monday to Friday, also Saturdays in spring and autumn. Daily during May.

Visitors welcome: yes.

Catalogue: send 4 first class stamps.

Payment: cash, cheque, Visa, Mastercard, Switch.

Mail order: yes. Minimum order £25.

Post and packing: £8.50 for orders up to £50, £12 for orders £50 to £100 in mainland UK.

Delivery: 48-hour service from November to March.

Availability: best from September to December.

Refund/replacement: rarely necessary.

GARDENERS' RECOMMENDATIONS: ❀ *"A long-established specialist rhododendron grower, with really fine display garden in the season."* Mr and Mrs T F Clarke. ❀ *"Specialist and reliable."* Mr Bruce Archibold, former chairman RHS Rhododendron, Camellia and Magnolia Group. ❀ *"The best rhododendron and azalea nursery in England. David Millais (third generation) is extremely knowledgeable and charming. Large choice. All is home produced, mostly on own roots and grown in open ground. Six-acre display garden."* Mr M J Jurgens. ❀ *"Very reliable for*

Himalayan rhododendrons and other ericaceae." The Marquess of Anglesey.

See map page 390.

Pantiles Plant and Garden Centre
The firm specialises in trees, especially ornamental ones. There's a huge list of acers, five different catalpas, 16 oaks, nine limes among others. Excellent list for those with large gardens, parks or picky habits.

> **Pantiles Plant and Garden Centre**, Almners Road, Lyne, Chertsey, Surrey KT16 0BJ
>
> **Tel:** 01932 872195 **Fax:** 01932 874030
>
> **E-mail:** pantiles@telinco.co.uk
>
> **Opening hours:** 9.00–18.00 (17.30 in winter) Monday to Saturday, 11.00–17.00 Sunday.
>
> **Visitors welcome:** yes.
>
> **Catalogue:** free.
>
> **Payment:** cash, cheque, Visa, Access.
>
> **Mail order:** no.
>
> **Delivery:** usually within 2 weeks.
>
> **Availability:** seasonal.
>
> **Refund/replacement:** yes.
>
> **Special services:** design and construction, aquatic centre.

GARDENERS' RECOMMENDATIONS: ✿ *"Very large and comprehensive, they have a particularly good selection of trees (we bought an Arbutus strawberry tree and Eucalyptus darympleana there). Plenty of space to park and walk around, close to M25 junction. Helpful for advice."* Frances and David Hopwood. ✿ *"For the research and supply of semi-mature shrubs and trees."* Mr and Mrs Hignett.

See map page 392.

Petersham Nurseries Ltd
A general all-rounder helpfully positioned just south of London. One speciality is bedding and patio plants, suitable for smaller or town gardens, along with hanging baskets and Christmas wreaths made to order.

> **Petersham Nurseries Ltd**, off Petersham Road, Petersham, Richmond, Surrey TW10 7AG

Tel/fax: 020 8940 5230

Opening hours: 9.00–17.30 Monday to Saturday, 10.00–16.00 Sunday.

Visitors welcome: yes.

Catalogue: none.

Payment: cash, cheque, major credit cards.

Mail order: no.

Refund/replacement: yes.

GARDENERS' RECOMMENDATIONS: *"We have dealt with this nursery for a number of years and found them unfailingly helpful in meeting our needs."* Mr and Mrs L A Darke.

See map page 392.

Planta Vera

The national collection of violas — over 400 varieties — is held here. The nursery also has violets and violettas. There is a difference between these, which the nursery will explain, but it is extremely complicated for what is basically a simple little plant. If you love them, of whatever name, as I do, this is the place to collect.

Planta Vera, Lyne Hill Nursery, Farm Close, Lyne Crossing Road, Chertsey, Surrey KT16 0AT

Tel/fax: 01932 563011

Opening hours: 10.00–16.00 daily from 3rd weekend in April to 2nd weekend in June or by appointment.

Visitors welcome: yes.

Catalogue: send 5 second class stamps.

Payment: cheque.

Mail order: yes. Minimum order £24.

Post and packing: £9 for orders up to £36, £4.50 for orders of £36 to £48, free thereafter.

Delivery: 24 hours.

Availability: violas mainly in spring, violets mainly in autumn.

Refund/replacement: yes.

GARDENERS' RECOMMENDATIONS: *"Excellent."*

See map page 392.

RHS Plant Centre at Wisley

As you would expect, a superb nursery with over 2,300 varieties of hardy perennials and 50 varieties of apple trees. Some specimens are propagated from the garden, especially fuchsias, hardy geraniums and ceanothus, there are numerous experts on hand and stock is guaranteed for two years. Plants can be potted up while you wait and there are specialist weekends where visiting experts give advice. And, of course, there are the gardens themselves and a splendid gardening book shop.

> **The Royal Horticultural Society's Garden**, Wisley, Woking, Surrey GU23 6QB
> **Tel:** 01483 211113 **Fax:** 01483 212372
> **Opening hours:** 10.00–18.00 Monday to Saturday in summer, 10.00–17.30 in winter. 11.00–17.00 Sunday in summer, 10.00–16.00 in winter.
> **Visitors welcome:** yes.
> **Catalogue:** none.
> **Payment:** cash, cheque, major credit/debit cards.
> **Mail order:** no.
> **Delivery:** locally within a week if possible.
> **Availability:** seasonal.
> **Refund/replacement:** yes, 2-year guarantee for hardy stock.

GARDENERS' RECOMMENDATIONS: ✤ *"Expensive but the best source of unusual, well-grown shrubs and now some rare trees. Herbaceous is less exciting and very expensive."* Mr and Mrs J D Sword. ✤ *"Outstanding and has new plant introductions to tempt you with."* Mrs G Wilson. ✤ *"Good but very expensive."* Mr and Mrs R V St John Wright. ✤ *Also recommended by* Mr and Mrs E G Millais, Millais Nursery *and* The Hon Mr and Mrs Robin Borwick, Neptune House Gardens.

See map page 392.

Seale Nursery

The May family have been nurserymen here since 1948 and currently David May specialises in rose growing, especially the old-fashioned scented varieties. There are also herbaceous perennials, over 150 varieties of both fuchsias and pelargoniums along with shrubs and hedging.

> **Seale Nurseries**, Seale Lane, Seale, nr Farnham, Surrey GU10 1LD
> **Tel:** 01252 782410

Website: http://www.sealenurseries.demon.co.uk

Opening hours: 9.00–17.00 daily. Closed from 25 December to 1 January.

Visitors welcome: yes.

Catalogue: none.

Payment: cash, cheque, Visa, Mastercard, Access, Switch, Connect, Delta.

Mail order: no.

Refund/replacement: yes.

Special services: if a customer wants to preserve a rose growing in their garden, but no longer available, the nursery offers a budding/grafting service.

GARDENERS' RECOMMENDATIONS: ✽ *"We have never been there but were impressed by their stall at the Autumn Apple Fair at the Museum of Garden History in Lambeth. They had some unusual, very healthy shrubs and they have grown well. The owners were there to talk to you and offer advice."* Frances and David Hopwood.

See map page 390.

Sylvatica Nursery
Specialists in sorbus such as rowans and whitebeams only recently established but with a comprehensive list including new introductions from China. These are generally most decorative trees, often colouring well in autumn. There is also a small perennial list.

Sylvatica Nursery, Crosswater Farm, Churt, Farnham, Surrey GU10 2JN

Tel: 01252 792775 **Fax:** 01252 792526

Opening hours: by appointment.

Visitors welcome: yes, by appointment.

Catalogue: send 4 first class stamps.

Payment: cash or cheque.

Mail order: yes.

Post and packing: 1-5 small perennials £5, £14 for up to 4 trees under 6ft, £14 each for larger trees.

Delivery: allow 3 days by Parcel Force. Overnight service available via Interlink.

Availability: supplies can be limited and some plants are available only at certain times of year.

Refund/replacement: yes.

GARDENERS' RECOMMENDATIONS: *"David Millais' brother has just started this nursery specialising in sorbus, rowans and whitebeams."* Mr M J Jurgens.

See map page 390.

The Vernon Geranium Nursery

"What can be better than sitting in the sun on a bright summer's day — comfy chair, good book and a glass of your favourite tipple! And how much nicer that experience is when surrounded by Vernon's fabulous geraniums and fuchsias!!" says this jolly catalogue. There is a huge list, nearly all illustrated, including pelargoniums.

The Vernon Geranium Nursery,
Cuddington Way, Cheam, Surrey
SM2 7JB

Tel: 020 8393 7616

Fax: 020 8786 7437

E-mail: mrgeranium@aol.com

Opening hours: 9.30–17.30 Monday to Saturday, 10.00–16.00 Sunday from March to July only.

Visitors welcome: yes.

Catalogue: £2.

Payment: cheque, Visa, Mastercard, Switch.

Mail order: yes.

Post and packing: from £2.05 for up to 5 plants to £6.45 for 40 in UK.

Delivery: 2-3 weeks or longer in spring.

Availability: mostly all year round. Regals, angels and fuchsias from October to April.

Refund/replacement: yes.

GARDENERS' RECOMMENDATIONS: *"Pelargoniums, fuchsias and some bedding plants. Very good catalogue with lots of pictures. I have visited the nursery several times."* Mrs Carol Lee. *Also recommended by* Mrs M Linklater.

See map page 392.

Sussex

Apuldram Roses   The nursery has a colourful rose field beside the picturesque Chichester Harbour which can be visited, as well as a garden, created from an orchard, in which all the roses in the catalogue are planted. There are more hybrid teas and floribundas than shrub roses.

Apuldram Roses, Apuldram Lane, Dell Quay, Chichester, West Sussex PO20 7EF

Tel: 01243 785769   **Fax:** 01243 536973

E-mail: d.sawday@virgin.net

Website: http://www.gardening-uk.com/apuldram/

Opening hours: 9.00–17.00 Monday to Saturday, 10.30–16.30 Sunday and bank holidays.

Visitors welcome: yes.

Catalogue: 50p.

Payment: cash, cheque, major credit cards.

Mail order: yes.

Post and packing: £4.55, or £8 by 48-hour service.

Delivery: orders received between June and November are posted before Christmas – mainly in November. In January and February plants are despatched every week.

Availability: only one crop grown each year so varieties can be sold out.

Refund/replacement: yes.

Special services: pruning demonstrations the first two weeks of March.

Gardeners' Recommendations: ✸ *"Excellent quality and very knowledgeable staff."* Mrs M Gayford. ✸ *"Good sturdy roses. Very organised."*

See map page 390.

Architectural Plants   One of my favourite nurseries for its combination of clear ideas, jokey advice and wonderful garden and plant area to visit. The plants, though not cheap, are impressively well grown. The catalogue is the most helpful I know. The choice is design-led and full of evergreens, spikes, giant leaves and wild oddities.

Architectural Plants, Cooks Farm, Nuthurst, Horsham, West Sussex
RH13 6LH

Tel: 01403 891772 **Fax:** 01403 891056

Also at Lidsey Road Nursery, Woodgate, Chichester, West Sussex
PO20 6SO

Tel: 01243 545008 **Fax:** 01243 545009

Opening hours: Horsham: 9.00–19.00 daily except Sundays.
Chichester: 10.00–16.00 daily except Saturdays.

Visitors welcome: yes.

Catalogue: free.

Payment: cheque, major credit cards.

Mail order: yes.

Post and packing: from £17.50 for 10kg by Interlink.

Delivery: 24 to 72 hours.

Availability: although the company endeavours to stock all
plants throughout the year, this is not always possible.

Refund/replacement: "complaints are always treated with the
utmost sympathy."

Special services: "bags of advice."

GARDENERS' RECOMMENDATIONS: ✻ *"Unusual plants. First class
help and advice."* Mr and Mrs R de Garston. ✻ *"A very unusual
nursery, beautifully laid out and landscaped, and a very impressive and
informative catalogue, written with a sense of humour. They specialise
in 'designer' plants – big, unusual leaves/colours/forms but have a
surprisingly large range. Helpful and well-informed staff. Definitely
worth a visit although it is quite a drive out into the country."* Frances
and David Hopwood. ✻ *"Great variety of standards, tree ferns, palms
and unusual shrubs. Immaculate nursery, handsome catalogue.
Expensive."* Mrs Carol Lee. ✻ *"Outstanding quality nursery both in
terms of plants, packing, delivery and knowledge. Worth a visit to see
how a nursery should be kept and presented."* ✻ *"Whatever trees we
have ordered have always been beautiful specimens and exactly in size
and growth etc as they have described."* ✻*Also recommended by* The
Hon Mr and Mrs Robin Borwick, Neptune House Gardens *and*
Lady Scott, Rotherfield Park.

See maps pages 392 and 390.

Berry Plants and Gardens Lucy Berry started her nursery in
1994 after studying landscape gardening and later working with

Architectural Plants (qv). Rather than follow their lead for bold exotics, her nursery aims to stock an entire garden with well-grown plants to her own liking. The list includes both well-loved varieties and others which are unusual. All are extremely well cared for.

Berry Plants and Gardens, Birchfold, Northchapel, West Sussex
GU28 9JZ

Tel/fax: 01428 708107

Opening hours: by appointment.

Visitors welcome: strictly by appointment.

Catalogue: send 4 first class stamps.

Payment: cash or cheque.

Mail order: no.

Availability: supplies can be limited and some plants are available only at certain times of year.

Refund/replacement: yes.

Special services: border design and plant positioning service, plants can be grown to order.

GARDENERS' RECOMMENDATIONS: ❀ *"Outstanding quality plants and vast horticultural knowledge. Run by Lucy Berry from her home. Open by appointment only but also offers a planting service and catalogue. She will happily grow plants to order from year to year for her customers and her plants are available at various fairs during the summer. Catalogue and lists of local fairs available by post."* Mr and Mrs P Warne.

See map page 390.

Bramber Nurseries A general nursery offering most plants the general gardener could want. These include many hybrid tea roses, dwarf conifers, fruit and ornamental trees. There are also garden ornaments, pots and garden furniture.

Bramber Nurseries, Chichester Road, West Wittering, West Sussex
PO20 8QA

Tel: 01243 512004 **Fax:** 01243 513851

Opening hours: 9.00–17.30 (16.30 in winter) daily. Closed Christmas to New Year.

Visitors welcome: yes.

Catalogue: £1.

Payment: cash, cheque, Visa, Access.

Mail order: no.

Availability: most stock available all year round.

Refund/replacement: where appropriate.

GARDENERS' RECOMMENDATIONS: *"This nursery has a good range of container grown shrubs, roses, bedding plants etc. I have found these people genuine, always helpful and willing to take trouble and give good advice."* Mr J Rank.

See map page 390.

Bramley Cottage Alpines

Bramley Cottage Alpines This is a nursery with a wide range of unusual and interesting hardy plants from alpines to shrubs and bulbs. Jane Anniss supplies a list of what is available and this ranges from acaenia to zygadenus; andromeda to spirea among the shrubs and alliums to tulip bulbs. Though she is keen to let visitors browse without hassle, she will also help on how to grow and site her plants. Long distance travellers get free tea or coffee and biscuits.

Bramley Cottage Alpines, Back Lane, Waldron, Heathfield, East Sussex TN21 0NH

Tel: 01435 866785

Opening hours: by appointment only between 10.00 and 17.00 daily from 1 March to 31 October. Details of open weekends available March.

Visitors welcome: yes.

Catalogue: free (send sae).

Payment: cash or cheque.

Mail order: no.

Availability: limited as the nursery grows small numbers of a wide range of plants. Bulbs not normally available after early May.

Refund/replacement: yes.

Special services: plants can be reserved for 24 hours or can be collected from plant fairs.

GARDENERS' RECOMMENDATIONS: *Recommended by* Sussex Clematis Nursery.

See map page 391.

Coghurst Nursery

Coghurst Nursery Specialists in camellias with dozens of species and varieties on an availability list. Camellias can be grown both outdoors in favoured places and are excellent in the conservatory as many are scented.

Coghurst Nursery, Ivy House Lane, nr Three Oaks, Hastings, East Sussex TN35 4NP

Tel: 01424 756228

Opening hours: 11.00–16.00 Sunday to Tuesday and Friday, or by appointment.

Visitors welcome: yes.

Catalogue: send 2 second class stamps.

Payment: cheque or postal order.

Mail order: yes, from 1 October to 31 March.

Post and packing: at cost.

Delivery: 2-3 weeks between October and March.

Availability: plants are available from the nursery at any time, but are only sent by mail order between October and March to avoid damage to tender new growth.

Refund/replacement: yes.

GARDENERS' RECOMMENDATIONS: *"Specialist and reliable."* Mr Bruce Archibold, former chairman RHS Rhododendron, Camellia and Magnolia Group.

See map page 391.

Courtlands Nurseries

Courtlands Nurseries This is an old-fashioned nursery on a 2-acre site: half is a display and vegetable garden. It sells herbaceous plants, shrubs, vegetable plants and bedding along with cut flowers, free-range eggs and vegetables. In season, you can also have tea here.

Courtlands Nurseries, Chilling Street, Sharpthorne, West Sussex RH19 4JF

Tel: 01342 810780

E-mail: SHURVELL@compuserve.com

Opening hours: 9.00–17.30. Coffee and teas from 10.30 am, from Easter to 31 October.

Visitors welcome: yes.

Catalogue: none.

Payment: cash or cheque.

Mail order: no.

Availability: limited to what can be grown at the nursery.

Refund/replacement: yes, in case of reasonable complaint.

Special services: display garden, advice on design/planting.

GARDENERS' RECOMMENDATIONS: *"This is a small nursery of excellent quality. Owner Lindsey Shurvell is the former head gardener of Gravetye Manor (of William Robinson fame)."* Mr and Mrs K Hill.

See map page 391.

Croftway Nursery

Croftway Nursery Specialists in bearded irises, hardy geraniums and other perennials. The irises are sensibly divided into colours and include those stunning colour combinations developed by the artist Sir Cedric Morris. Croftway runs special weekends to teach visitors about both irises and geraniums.

> **Croftway Nursery**, Yapton Road, Barnham, Bognor Regis, West Sussex PO22 0BH
>
> **Tel:** 01243 552121 **Fax:** 01243 552125
>
> **E-mail:** croftway@aol.com
>
> **Website:** http://www.members.aol.com/croftway/
>
> **Opening hours:** 9.00–17.00 Monday to Saturday, 10.00–16.00 Sunday from March to end November.
>
> **Visitors welcome:** yes.
>
> **Catalogue:** send 4 first class stamps.
>
> **Payment:** cash, cheque, Visa, Mastercard, American Express, Switch, in sterling or Euros.
>
> **Mail order:** yes.
>
> **Post and packing:** from £6.
>
> **Delivery:** allow 28 days.
>
> **Availability:** some plants are in limited supply. Bearded irises can be ordered at any time, but are despatched in August/September only.
>
> **Refund/replacement:** subject to standard terms. Any complaint is dealt with on its merits.
>
> **Special services:** hardy geranium weekend and iris picnic weekend in May.

GARDENERS' RECOMMENDATIONS: *"A specialist nursery with plants of very good quality."* *"Good size rhizomes. Lots of help when choosing."* *"A highly competent family firm, very courteous and knowledgeable about hardy geraniums and bearded irises in particular and many other perennials."* Mr and Mrs D Bingley.

See map page 391.

Great Dixter Nurseries Christopher Lloyd has made the garden a worldwide success and the nursery offers a constantly changing list in line with his views. It's also possible to find plants propagated from the garden such as Crocosmia masonorum Dixter Flame and his celandine, Brazen Hussy. The garden is a huge source of inspiration, backed up by the nursery.

Great Dixter Nurseries, Northiam, Rye, East Sussex TN31 6PH

Tel: 01797 253107 **Fax:** 01797 252879

E-mail: greatdixter@compuserve.com

Website: http://www.entertainnet.co.uk/attractions.htm

Opening hours: 9.00–12.30, 13.30–17.00 Monday to Friday. 9.00–12.00 Saturday in winter. All day Saturday and Sunday from April to October.

Visitors welcome: yes.

Catalogue: send 4 first class stamps.

Payment: cheque, Visa, Mastercard, Switch.

Mail order: yes. Minimum order £15.

Post and packing: £7 for orders from £15 to £60, £10 thereafter.

Delivery: allow 28 days if stock available.

Availability: orders are despatched from September to May. Limited supplies of certain popular plants. Stock failures are also possible.

Refund/replacement: yes, after review.

GARDENERS' RECOMMENDATIONS: ❀ *"Efficient and reliable mail order."* ❀ *Also recommended by* Mrs Jane Gladstone *and* Mrs R Alexander of The English Gardening School at the Chelsea Physic Garden.

See map page 391.

W E Th Ingwersen Will Ingwersen was a famous alpine gardener and grower and the nursery is a constant exhibitor at all the best shows. It still specialises in alpines with over 100 different sempervivums, and almost as many primulas and saxifrages. They encourage nursery visits and their advice on plants is well worth taking.

W E Th Ingwersen Ltd, Birch Farm Nursery, Gravetye, East Grinstead, West Sussex RH19 4LE

Tel: 01342 810236

E-mail: ingwersens@aol.com

Website: http://www.members.aol.com/ingwersens/index.htm

Opening hours: 9.00–13.00, 13.30–16.00 daily from March to September; weekdays only from October to February.

Visitors welcome: yes.

Catalogue: send 2 first class stamps.

Payment: cash or cheque.

Mail order: no.

Availability: seasonal.

Refund/replacement: yes.

GARDENERS' RECOMMENDATIONS: *"Gorgeous alpines."* ✿ *"Good for alpines."* Mr and Mrs A C O McGrath.

See map page 391.

Just Roses   They don't offer any special services, say the nursery owners "we are just very helpful." And that's what many people need in finding their way through the maze of rose growing. This catalogue offers a small, but choice, selection of the plants from weeping standards to ground cover.

Just Roses, Beales Lane, Northiam, Rye, East Sussex TN31 0QY

Tel: 01797 252355

Opening hours: 9.00–12.00, 13.00–17.00 Tuesday to Friday, 10.00–12.00, 13.00–16.00 at weekends.

Visitors welcome: yes.

Catalogue: free.

Payment: cash or cheque.

Mail order: yes (bare-root roses only).

Post and packing: £3.50.

Delivery: orders despatched every Monday from November to end February.

Availability: bare-root roses from November to March, then container plants available at the nursery until sold out.

Refund/replacement: yes.

GARDENERS' RECOMMENDATIONS: ✿ *"Excellent roses – best in this area."* Mr D G W Barham. ✿ *"A very personal, friendly service is supplied by John, owner and main worker in this small, but excellent,*

nursery. Roses sold from containers as well as field grown all year. Roses are attractively displayed in a well-designed, easy-to-view garden attached to the nursery, clearly labelled with John close at hand to answer questions. A large variety of both old and new roses available." Mrs Z Grant.

See map page 391.

Leonardslee Plants

Both Leonardslee and Loder (the owner of the nursery is Chris Loder) are extremely famous names in the annals of gardening. They have been growing rhododendrons for over a century. The list offered must be one of the most comprehensive in the world and there's also a consultancy service. A new sister nursery selling camellias is Tea Bush Nursery.

Leonardslee Plants, Market Garden, Cyder Farm, Lower Beeding, Horsham, West Sussex RH13 6PP

Tel: 01403 891412 **Fax:** 01403 891336

E-mail: loder@rhododendrons.com

Website: http://www.rhododendrons.com or http://www.rhododendron.co.uk

Opening hours: by appointment only.

Visitors welcome: yes, by appointment.

Catalogue: send 2 first class stamps.

Payment: cash, cheque, major credit cards.

Mail order: yes. Minimum order £5.

Post and packing: at cost, eg £16 for a box containing 5 plants by overnight service.

Delivery: 24 hours.

Availability: all year round.

Refund/replacement: yes.

Special services: consultancy service.

GARDENERS' RECOMMENDATIONS: ✿ *"Very good rhododendrons."* Dr and Mrs R L Belsey.

See map page 391.

Marchants Hardy Plants

Graham Gough is a nurseryman and lecturer whose nursery grows all its own plants and is therefore "able to offer genuine advice." He specialises in handsome herbaceous perennials, ornamental grasses, bulbs and distinctive shrubs. This is a new nursery with an elegant and fashionable selection.

> **Marchants Hardy Plants**, 2 Marchants Cottages, Ripe Road, Laughton, East Sussex BN8 6AJ
>
> **Tel:** 01323 811737 **Fax:** 01323 811737
>
> **Opening hours:** 9.30–17.30 Wednesday to Saturday from April to November.
>
> **Visitors welcome:** yes.
>
> **Catalogue:** send 4 first class stamps.
>
> **Payment:** cash or cheque.
>
> **Mail order:** no.
>
> **Availability:** supplies can be limited and some plants are available only at certain times of year.
>
> **Refund/replacement:** negotiable.

GARDENERS' RECOMMENDATIONS: ✿ *"New nursery. Has a fine range of herbaceous and perennial plants plus wonderful ornamental grasses. Imaginatively designed and planted garden by the nursery which displays many of the plants they sell. Good shrubs too and a newly planted small arboretum of choice trees combine to make this a nursery to watch."* Carolyn Pawson. ✿ *"A new nursery and garden being developed by a very knowledgeable and well-respected nurseryman. Potentially very exciting – it will however be necessary to check when the nursery is fully open."* Mr and Mrs K H Wallis. ✿ *"Graham Gough is late of Washfield Nursery, having been working with Elizabeth Strongman for many years. His new venture will flourish. New garden area now planted out showing great imagination and artistic flair."* Mr and Mrs J R McCutchan.

See map page 391.

Merriments Gardens   The gardens consist of eight acres with fine views over Sussex and Kent and have been going for over a decade. "We are not a specialist nursery but rather cater for the growing number of enthusiastic gardeners wishing to increase the range of plants in their garden." Since this is the vast majority of gardeners, the nursery has introductions in French, German and Dutch. There are good quantities of hostas, dicentra, geranium and salvias in an interesting general catalogue.

Merriments Gardens, Hawkhurst Road, Hurst Green, East Sussex, TN19 7RA

Tel: 01580 860666 **Fax:** 01580 860324

E-mail: info@merriments.co.uk

Website: http://www.merriments.co.uk

Opening hours: 9.30–17.30 Monday to Saturday, 10.30–17.30 Sunday. Closes at dusk in winter.

Visitors welcome: yes.

Catalogue: £1.

Payment: cheque, major credit cards.

Mail order: no.

Availability: seasonal.

Refund/replacement: yes, if justified.

GARDENERS' RECOMMENDATIONS: ✤*"A superb garden on a par with the best in the country."* Major and Mrs R H Blizard. ✤*"Very interesting garden specialising in herbaceous plants and shrubs with a particularly good collection of grasses."* Mr and Mrs R Esdale. ✤*"High standard with stunning demo garden."* Mr D G W Barham. ✤ *"Masses of unusual plants in well kept nursery area. Fabulous garden alongside. Worth a visit at every season."* Mr and Mrs B Jackson.

See map page 391.

Murrells Nursery A famous name among nurserymen, Murrells offers a good general list from alpines to vegetables. It is particularly strong on clematis, roses and fruit along with heathers, geraniums and fuchsias but can be used to create a garden from scratch with a planning service and home visits to offer advice.

Murrells Nursery, Broomers Hill Lane, Pulborough, West Sussex RH20 2DU

Tel: 01798 875508 **Fax:** 01798 872695

Opening hours: 9.00–17.30 (17.00 in winter) Monday to Saturday, 10.00–16.00 Sunday.

Visitors welcome: yes.

Catalogue: send 3 first class stamps.

Payment: cash, cheque, Visa, Mastercard, Switch, HTA gift tokens.

Mail order: no.

Delivery: same day delivery locally.

Availability: large quantities should be ordered in advance. Certain plants are seasonal.

Refund/replacement: yes.

Special services: garden planning service. Home visits offering advice.

GARDENERS' RECOMMENDATIONS: ✿ *"The plants are not forced to meet the demands of the market, they are weathered and therefore more reliable. The service is always helpful and friendly and they deal with only proper garden requirements, without competing with others for the side issues of large garden centres."* Mr and Mrs D Bowerman. ✿ *"A proper nursery, not just a garden centre."*

See map page 391.

Oakdene Alpine Nursery   David Sampson, who specialises in alpines, bulbs and dwarf shrubs, is keen to help customers with his own experience of growing the plants and he has also planted landscaped gardens with many rare trees and shrubs to demonstrate their virtues. Further, all his stock is home-produced. He offers a smallish list of extremely choice varieties some of which have a waiting list.

Oakdene Alpine Nursery, Street End Lane, Broad Oak, Heathfield, East Sussex TN21 8TU

Tel: 01435 864382

Opening hours: 9.00–17.00 Wednesday to Saturday, by appointment on Monday and Tuesday.

Visitors welcome: yes.

Catalogue: send 3 first class stamps.

Payment: cash or cheque.

Mail order: yes. Minimum order £10.

Post and packing: at cost.

Delivery: within 10 days of receipt of order, weather permitting.

Availability: certain rare items are in short supply and a waiting list operates for these.

Refund/replacement: yes, within reason.

GARDENERS' RECOMMENDATIONS: ✿ *"I obtain alpines from many specialists. David Sampson's material is nearly always the best."* Ernst and Janet Sondheimer. ✿ *"Wonderful plants, well-grown, unusual."* Dr and Mrs D W Eyre-Walker

See map page 391.

Perryhill Nurseries The firm has been established since 1972 and deliberately avoids mail order because the owner, Susan Gemmell, likes people to visit (though you can order in advance and collect.) It is, however, a big list of interesting plants — trees, shrubs, climbers, perennials and roses.

> **Perryhill Nurseries**, Hartfield, East Sussex TN7 4JP
> **Tel:** 01892 770377 **Fax:** 01892 770929
> **Opening hours:** March to October 9.00–17.00. November to February 9.00–16.30, 7 days a week.
> **Visitors welcome:** yes.
> **Catalogue:** £1.65.
> **Payment:** cheque, Visa, Mastercard, Switch, Delta.
> **Mail order:** no, but plants can be reserved for collection.
> **Post and packing:** not applicable. Delivery can sometimes be arranged.
> **Delivery:** normally within a week, but can vary according to the time of year.
> **Availability:** full range normally available all year round, but some plants are seasonal eg bare-root plants, alpines and herbs.
> **Refund/replacement:** yes.

GARDENERS' RECOMMENDATIONS: ❀ *"High standard, very extensive – one of the best."* Mr D G W Barham. ❀ *"Knowledgeable and friendly service."* Mr and Mrs D Jolley, Maycotts. ❀ *"Wide variety of plants available – not of uniformly high quality but have always found them ready to take back anything found to be inferior."* ❀ *"Perryhill has a wide range of plants of excellent quality."* ❀ *"Very wide stock with friendly, highly professional service."* Mr and Mrs C Lindsay.

See map page 391.

Rapkyns Nursery Steven and Fiona Moore (motto 'moore and moore plants') have a good range of rhododendrons and azaleas, along with clematis and other climbers and lots of penstemons and salvias, phygelius, malva and spheralceas. It's a good general nursery but, if we can take their motto, moore than just that. Situated down a long country lane, it is quite hard to find.

> **Rapkyns Nursery**, Scotsford Farm, Street End Lane, Broad Oak, Heathfield, East Sussex TN21 8UB

Tel/fax: 01892 652071, mobile: 07771 916933

Opening hours: 10.00–17.00 Tuesday and Friday from March to October inlcusive or by appointment.

Visitors welcome: yes.

Catalogue: free.

Payment: cash or cheque.

Mail order: no.

Delivery: free delivery within 20-mile radius for customers spending over £50.

Availability: supplies of certain rare varieties are limited.

Refund/replacement: yes.

Special services: will try to obtain plants not normally grown on the nursery.

GARDENERS' RECOMMENDATIONS: ✤ *"Produces good plants."* Mr and Mrs A C O McGrath. ✤ *"Helpful. and friendly."*

See map page 391.

Usual and Unusual Plants

Well, the name says it all — but most are perennials in a densely packed catalogue. Jennie Maillard is working on a show garden and is keen to advise on the plants she sells.

Usual and Unusual Plants, Onslow House, Magham Down, nr Hailsham, East Sussex BN27 1PL

Tel: 01323 840967 **Fax:** 01323 844725

E-mail: jennie@onslow.clara.net

Opening hours: 9.30–17.30 Wednesday to Saturday and bank holiday Mondays from 1 March to 31 July and from 1 September to 31 October. By appointment at other times.

Visitors welcome: yes.

Catalogue: 50p plus sae.

Payment: cash or cheque.

Mail order: no.

Availability: 1 March to 31 October only.

Refund/replacement: yes.

GARDENERS' RECOMMENDATIONS: ✤ *"A small nursery, but good stock of mainly rock plants."* Major and Mrs R H Blizard. ✤ *"A friendly and expert proprietor: the nursery lives up to its name."* Mr and Mrs K H Wallis. ✤ *"You always get a warm welcome from Jennie*

Maillard, who offers exactly what the nursery is called and her prices are really keen." W D Witherick and M Wilkinson. ❀ *"A beautifully kept small specialist nursery. Show garden being developed. Mouth-watering plants. Owner very helpful."* Mr and Mrs B Jackson. ❀ *"Jennie Maillard has a very extensive range of mainly herbaceous plants. She does not sell plants to customers if their soil is not suitable. She is making attractive stock beds for customers to see the plants growing."* Mr and Mrs J R McCutchan.

See map page 391.

Warrenorth Fuchsia and Pelargonium (Geranium) Nursery

Peter, Marion and Andrew Simmons send out two catalogues devoted to pelargoniums and fuchsias. Both are comprehensive with brief descriptions. Both, too, offer new introductions each year. These are lists for enthusiasts rather than beginners.

Warrenorth Fuchsia and Pelargonium (Geranium) Nursery,
East Grinstead Road, North Chailey, Lewes, East Sussex BN8 4JD

Tel: 01825 723266

Opening hours: 9.30–17.00 daily except Monday. Open bank holidays.

Visitors welcome: yes.

Catalogue: 50p.

Payment: cash or cheque.

Mail order: yes. Minimum order 6 plants.

Post and packing: £2.50 for 6 plants.

Delivery: 4-6 weeks. Rooted to order.

Availability: some plants are available only at certain times of year.

Refund/replacement: yes.

GARDENERS' RECOMMENDATIONS: ❀ *"Wide variety of less commonly known geraniums and fuchsias. Exceptionally clean and tidy glasshouse. Friendly young man proprietor assisted by his parents. Quality plants."* Mr and Mrs F Leocadi. ❀ *Also recommended by* Mr and Mrs Goodman.

See map page 391.

Wych Cross Nurseries   They hold more than 600 varieties of roses from hybrid tea (and, hoho, a Hybrid Tea Room) to ancient species. There are also many ornamental trees, shrubs and herbaceous perennials along with a good selection of garden furniture.

> **Wych Cross Nurseries**, Forest Row, East Sussex RH18 5JW
> **Tel:** 01342 822705 **Fax:** 01342 825329
> **E-mail:** roses@wychcross.co.uk
> **Website:** http://www.wychcross.co.uk
> **Opening hours:** 9.00–17.30 Monday to Saturday.
> **Visitors welcome:** absolutely.
> **Catalogue:** free.
> **Payment:** cash, cheque, Visa, Mastercard.
> **Mail order:** no.
> **Delivery:** by arrangement locally.
> **Availability:** widest rose selection in January gradually diminishing through the year. Other plants available seasonally.
> **Refund/replacement:** yes.
> **Special services:** advice, tea room, disabled access and toilet, wheelchair available.

GARDENERS' RECOMMENDATIONS: ❀ *"Vast selection of roses and well displayed – the tops."* Mr D G W Barham. ❀ *"Always very helpful and have time to discuss problems. Very good selection of shrubs and plants etc. Very good roses."* Mr and Mrs P Wright. ❀ *"They have the biggest selection of roses south of the Thames and some unusual shrubs and tender plants, and a tea room."* W D Witherick and M Wilkinson. ❀ *"Delightful people. Best roses in the S.E. Always very friendly and helpful. Huge selection of unusual plants and will do utmost to get anything not in stock."* Mr and Mrs K Hill.

See map page 391.

See also: Hellyer's Garden Plants, page 355; **The Lodge Nursery,** page 357.

Tyne & Wear

Birkheads Cottage Garden Nursery   The nursery prides itself on selling thousands of varieties — but without a catalogue. They specialise in unusual hardy perennials and have a three-acre garden to demonstrate the plants' qualities.

Birkheads Cottage Garden Nursery, nr Causey Arch, Sunniside, Newcastle-upon-Tyne, Tyne & Wear NE16 5EL

Tel: 01207 232262, mobile: 0378 447920 **Fax:** 01207 232262

E-mail: birkheads@breathemail.net

Opening hours: 10.00–17.00 daily from March to October. Please telephone first in winter.

Visitors welcome: yes.

Catalogue: none.

Payment: cash or cheque.

Mail order: no.

Availability: all year round.

Refund/replacement: yes.

Special services: 3-acre garden open to visitors. Garden design service.

GARDENERS' RECOMMENDATIONS: ✿ *"I visited this nursery on a horrible wet day last July. My friend and I received a warm welcome from Christine Liddle, the proprietor who, even though it was now late in the season, had a good selection of unusual plants, all home propagated. She has a delightful garden which she has designed and planted herself, where many of her 4,000 different hardy plants can be seen growing. I intend to return this spring/early summer."* ✿ *Also recommended by* Mrs I Bonas, county organiser for the National Gardens Scheme for 23 years.

See map page 397.

WARWICKSHIRE

Avondale Nursery   A good list of herbaceous perennials, bulbs, grasses and rushes ideal for co-ordinating a new border or garden. Brian Ellis and his wife, Stephanie, will also give advice on design and talks to local gardening clubs.

> **Avondale Nursery** at Smith's Nursery, 3 Stoneleigh Road, Baginton, Coventry; office: 3 Avondale Road, Earlsdon, Coventry CV5 6DZ
>
> **Tel/fax:** 024 7667 3662
>
> **Opening hours:** 10.00–12.30, 14.00–17.00 daily from March to October (closed Sunday afternoons in July and August). By appointment at other times.
>
> **Visitors welcome:** yes.
>
> **Catalogue:** £1 or 4 first class stamps.
>
> **Payment:** cash or cheque.
>
> **Mail order:** no.
>
> **Availability:** sometimes limited. Telephone before visiting if a particular plant is required.
>
> **Refund/replacement:** yes, if the nursery is at fault.
>
> **Special services:** design and landscaping consultancy.

GARDENERS' RECOMMENDATIONS: ✿ *"New nursery – young, keen collector of rare plants."* Mr and Mrs T Chalk. ✿ *"The nurseryman is Brian Ellis – a young man with a young nursery. He is a member of the Hardy Plant Society. The plants are sturdy and of great variety and the knowledge and courtesy extended is exceptional. Personally we have nothing but the highest praise for this young grower who deserves encouragement."* Mr and Mrs J Brown. ✿ *"A small one-man nursery specialising in perennials and new introductions."* Mr and Mrs K Hackett. ✿ *"A nice newish little nursery."* Major and Mrs Arbuthnott, Stone House Cottage Gardens.

See map page 393.

Bridge Nursery   Specialist growers of ornamental grasses, bamboos, unusual perennials and shrubs, with the nursery garden open to the public (it's always interesting to see the professionals at work). The list is interesting and many of the plants suitable for modern styles of gardening.

Bridge Nursery, Tomlow Road, Napton on the Hill, nr Rugby, Warwickshire CV23 8HX

Tel: 01926 812737

Opening hours: 10.00–16.00 each weekend from April to October and bank holidays. By appointment at other times.

Visitors welcome: yes.

Catalogue: send 4 first class stamps.

Payment: cash or cheque.

Mail order: no.

Availability: supplies can be limited and some plants are available only at certain times of year.

Refund/replacement: by arrangement.

GARDENERS' RECOMMENDATIONS: ✿ *Recommended by* Ms Campbell and Mr Crowley.

See map page 393.

Charlecote Plants and Flowers

The nursery is next to the National Trust's Charlecote Park and shares a car park with the house. Visitors can therefore take in both in a day, looking at the full range of plants, climbers and bedding plants for sale.

Charlecote Plants and Flowers, Dog Kennel Close, Charlecote, nr Stratford-on-Avon, Warwickshire CV35 9ER

Tel: nursery 01789 842674, office 01789 470947 **Fax:** 01789 842588

Opening hours: 9.30–17.30 from March to October.

Visitors welcome: yes.

Catalogue: 50p.

Payment: cash, cheque, credit/debit cards shortly.

Mail order: yes.

Post and packing: at cost.

Delivery: by arrangement.

Availability: generally throughout the year. Best range available in April and October.

Refund/replacement: yes.

GARDENERS' RECOMMENDATIONS: ✿ *"Visited by keen gardeners looking for something special. Very well stocked, healthy clean plants."* Mr and Mrs T Chalk. ✿ *"Large stock, healthy plants of many varieties. Helpful advice."* Mr and Mrs R S Smith. *"Very good quality plants, trees, shrubs etc. Well laid out."* Mrs C W Dodd. *"Wonderful selection of shrubs, perennials and bedding plants – often some fairly unusual plants. All very well looked after and displayed. Prices middle of range. Staff very pleasant and helpful."* Mrs E Butterworth.

See map page 393.

Collector's Corner Plants

The nursery now regularly updates its large, print-out catalogue whenever there are enough new varieties to warrant it — so the list is as up-to-date as can be. It is big and quite hard to work through but includes tree ferns (which come with growing instructions) and ordinary ferns along with rare and unusual trees, shrubs and herbaceous plants which justify the firm's name.

> **Collector's Corner Plants**, 33 Rugby Road, Clifton-upon-Dunsmore, Rugby, Warwickshire CV23 0DE
> **Tel:** 01788 571881
> **Opening hours:** by appointment.
> **Visitors welcome:** yes, by appointment.
> **Catalogue:** £1.50 or 6 first class stamps.
> **Payment:** cash, cheque, postal order.
> **Mail order:** yes.
> **Post and packing:** £4.50 to £8.
> **Delivery:** 3-4 days. Next day delivery available.
> **Availability:** generally all year round.
> **Refund/replacement:** yes.

GARDENERS' RECOMMENDATIONS: *Recommended by* Ms Campbell and Mr Crowley.

See map page 393.

Fibrex Nurseries

This is the firm I use both for ivies, ferns and pelargoniums. It is a family firm which takes great pride in its plants and can offer a huge variety within its specialities. They offer special collections of ferns and ivies for different places. Their plants are excellent and thrive.

Fibrex Nursery Ltd, Honeybourne Road, Pebworth, nr Stratford-upon-Avon, Warwickshire CV37 8XT

Tel: 01789 720788 **Fax:** 01789 721162

Opening hours: 12.00–17.00 Monday to Friday from January to March and September to December. 12.00–17.00 Tuesday to Sunday from April to August.

Visitors welcome: yes.

Catalogue: send 2 second class stamps.

Payment: cash, cheque, Visa, Mastercard.

Mail order: yes. Minimum order £10 plus p&p.

Post and packing: £4 for up to 5 plants, £5 for 6–10, £.6.50 for 11–15, £7.50 for 16-20.

Delivery: by first class post.

Availability: supplies can be limited and some plants are available only at certain times of year.

Refund/replacement: yes, if not received in good condition.

GARDENERS' RECOMMENDATIONS: ✦ *"National collection of pelargoniums, huge range of hederas, ferns."* Mr and Mrs R Paice. ✦ *"I bought ferns by post. All good."* Mrs A Conville. ✦ *"Excellent for hardy ferns and ivies."* Mrs Carol Lee.

See map page 394.

Sherbourne Nursery

The nursery sells common and uncommon shrubs along with clematis and other climbers, shrub and rambler roses, some vegetable plants and those for hanging baskets and bedding. The firm was started because the gardens of Sherbourne Park were opened under the NGS scheme and people asked for plants which they had seen. The greenhouses are in the old walled vegetable garden but demand has been so great that another open field has been taken over and expanded to create another display garden. The family-run nursery adds that it doesn't produce a catalogue because it can't keep the plants for long enough.

Sherbourne Nursery, Westham Lane, Barford, nr Warwick, Warwickshire CV35 8DP

Opening hours: 10.00–13.00, 14.00–16.00 daily.

Visitors welcome: yes.

Catalogue: none.

Payment: cash or cheque.

Mail order: no.
Availability: limited to what can be grown at the nursery.
Refund/replacement: never needed to date.

GARDENERS' RECOMMENDATIONS: ✿ *"Family-run local nursery, limited range but everything beautifully grown."*

See map page 393.

———————————————— ❧ ————————————————

See also: Coughton Court, page 352.

WEST MIDLANDS

Ashwood Nurseries The nursery concentrates on four genera: cyclamen, auricula, hellebores and lewisias and, as a result, have an excellent selection along with their own hybrids. All four are extremely popular at present and hugely collected by plantsmen. The nursery holds the national collections for lewisia and hardy cyclamen.

Ashwood Nurseries Ltd, Greensforge, Kingswinford, West Midlands DY6 0AE
Tel: 01384 401996 **Fax:** 01384 401108
Opening hours: 9.00–18.00 Monday to Saturday, 9.30–18.00 Sunday.
Visitors welcome: yes.
Catalogue: send 4 first class stamps.
Payment: cheque, Visa, Mastercard.
Mail order: seeds only.
Post and packing: seeds 95p in UK.
Delivery: varies according to crop and time of order (by return or several months).
Availability: supplies can be limited and some plants are available only at certain times of year.
Refund/replacement: yes.
Special services: garden club, open weekends for hellebores in February, tea room open 10.00–17.00 daily.

GARDENERS' RECOMMENDATIONS: ✿ *"The only 'garden centre' worth including for its unbelievable range of hellebores bred on the premises and cyclamen, lewisias and auriculas (ditto). I have just returned from a specialist hellebore day there held under the auspices of the Hardy Plant Society. There were 45 people attending and to get there we had to enter a ballot as the meeting was three times oversubscribed."* Rob Hubble. ✿ *"Immaculate presentation of a wide variety of herbaceous perennials and shrubs of exceptional quality. Inspired planting of display garden to include water feature, shade plantings and areas in full sun. Excellent restaurant serving all home-cooked food and home-made ice cream. Seating areas outside for warm days. Garden sundries shop and gift shop. Large areas of glasshouse given over breeding programmes with the previously mentioned plants. A good day out!"* Mr and Mrs B Wilson. ✿ *"Nirvana for hellebore fetishists – also autumn and spring cyclamen, hepaticas, Anemone pulsatilla, lewisias. Very well grown shrubs – especially good for unusual magnolias at reasonable prices, also viburnums."* Mr and Mrs J D Sword. ✿ *"A very large selection of excellent plants with clear labelling. Assistants with advice more elusive! Good restaurant and facilities."* ✿ *"Extremely knowledgeable staff who will, given advance warning, arrange tours for visitors re their specialist interests."* Mr and Mrs A S Rankine. ✿ *"A commercial garden centre, but the cleanest we have ever seen. Excellent plants, all neatly presented."* Mr and Mrs E W Dyer. ✿ *"Probably the best breeders of helleborus in the country."* Mr D J Wood.

See map page 394.

David Austin Roses

One of the best rose growers in the country producing constant introductions and holding a huge range of roses from ancient species to new arrivals. The catalogue is brilliant with profuse, well-photographed illustrations and advice so helpful that it works as a reference book.

> **David Austin Roses**, Bowling Green Lane, Albrighton, Wolverhampton, West Midlands WV7 3HB
>
> **Tel:** catalogue request line 01902 376376; orders 01902 376377; enquiries 01902 376300 **Fax:** 01902 372142
>
> **Opening hours:** 9.00–17.00 weekdays, 10.00–18.00 (dusk in winter) at weekends .

Visitors welcome: yes.

Catalogue: free.

Payment: cheque, Visa, Access.

Mail order: yes.

Post and packing: £4.25 for up to 3 roses, £5.25 for 4 or more.

Delivery: orders despatched in rotation during planting season (November to early April).

Availability: occasionally a variety may be sold out.

Refund/replacement: replacement.

GARDENERS' RECOMMENDATIONS: ✿ *"Wonderful collection of roses —I have always been pleased with their quality. Also very interesting collection of perennials."* Mrs Susan Beck. ✿ *"Most helpful and obliging."* ✿ *"Very efficient and good assortment of plants."* Mr and Mrs Dru Montagu. ✿ *"Very wide selection of roses. Very good mail order. All roses grew brilliantly plus good advice on planting."* Ms Venner and Mr Glassborow. ✿ *"Roses — excellent plants, service, delivery. Not herbaceous department — not good."* Mrs Craig.

See map page 394.

WILTSHIRE

Belmont House Nursery   Hellebores are on the up — which is good news because they are very easy plants. The nursery has a large number of hellebore hybrids along with true species collected from seed in the wild. There are also some other hardy perennials such as pulmonaria and primulas.

Belmont House Nursery, Little Horton, Devizes, Wiltshire SN10 3LJ

Tel: 01380 860510

Opening hours: by appointment.

Visitors welcome: yes, by appointment only.

Catalogue: send 2 second class stamps.

Payment: cash or cheque.

Mail order: no.

Availability: supplies can be limited and some plants are available only at certain times of year.

Refund/replacement: yes.

GARDENERS' RECOMMENDATIONS: *"Specialises in hellebores, also named varieties of snowdrop and pulmonarias. Very small (but very good plants)."*

See map page 390.

Connoisseur Plants at West Kington Nurseries
The firm has been a wholesale nursery for 19 years but has, very recently, branched out into retail sales with a list of plants not normally available at garden centres. For example, they have three unusual wisterias, topiary in box and yew, tender plants for tubs and terraces such as datura and plumbago and quantities of roses, alpines and herbaceous plants.

Connoisseur Plants at West Kington Nurseries, Pound Hill, West Kington, Chippenhall, Wiltshire SN14 7JG

Tel: 01249 782822 **Fax:** 01249 782953

E-mail: connoisseur.plants@virgin.net

Opening hours: 10.00–17.00 daily. Closed from Christmas Day to 1 February.

Visitors welcome: yes.

Catalogue: free.

Payment: cash, cheque, major credit cards.

Mail order: no.

Availability: some plants are seasonal.

Refund/replacement: yes.

Special services: demonstration garden (open from 14.00–17.00), design service, group visits, gift vouchers, teas and home-made cakes.

GARDENERS' RECOMMENDATIONS: *"Basically a wholesale nursery with a small retail side. Herbaceous plants – a broad selection of good plants."* Mr and Mrs A D Gill. *"Excellent plants, good staff and a good ambience, tasteful pots etc. Not the usual garish garden centre!"*

See map page 390.

Heale Gardens and Plant Centre

The garden was the first ever winner of Christie's/HHA garden of the year, is ever growing (a millennium garden is underway) and the list of plants is wide but interesting. The rose list is especially good.

Heale Plant Centre, Middle Woodford. nr Salisbury. Wiltshire SP4 6NT
Tel: 01722 782504
Opening hours: 10.00–17.00 daily all year.
Visitors welcome: yes.
Catalogue: 50p.
Payment: cheque, Visa, Access.
Mail order: no.
Refund/replacement: yes.
Special services: garden design.

GARDENERS' RECOMMENDATIONS: ✿ *"Heale House Gardens are lovely with the historic Heale House (Jacobean) as the centrepiece. The Plant Centre is the best we know, excellent range of common and rare species and varieties – all well grown (many from their own gardens) and very reasonable prices." ✿ "Small but attractive nursery in beautiful surroundings. Good range of interesting plants."* Miss Freya Watkinson.

See map page 390.

Longhall Nursery

A small but select list of herbaceous perennials, many with Awards of Garden Merit. Two different Eryngium x zabelii are among a good selection and there are some nice oriental poppies.

Longhall Nursery, Stockton, nr Warminster, Wiltshire BA12 0SE
Tel/fax: 01985 850914
Website: http://www.designbywire.com
Opening hours: 9.30–17.00 Friday and Saturday only.
Visitors welcome: yes.
Catalogue: send 3 first class stamps.
Payment: cash or cheque.
Mail order: yes. Minimum order 10 plants.
Post and packing: £10 for 10-20 plants, by quotation thereafter.
Delivery: within 21 days.
Availability: best selection April/May or September.

Refund/replacement: if notified within 7 days of receipt.

Special services: border and garden design.

GARDENERS' RECOMMENDATIONS: ✣ *"Excellent range of perennials, though very small."* ✣ *"Very many unusual plants, mainly herbaceous."* Miss Freya Watkinson.

See map page 389.

The Mead Nursery

A fine collection of hardy perennials but especial praise goes to the way the catalogue is laid out and the information in it. Though there are no illustrations, each plant is clearly described, diagrams show its preferences and its type, the height is given as is the price. Others please copy.

The Mead Nursery, Brokerswood, nr Westbury, Wiltshire BA13 4EG

Tel: 01373 859990

Opening hours: 9.00–17.00 Wednesday to Saturday and bank holidays, 13.00–17.00 Sunday from 1 February to 10 October.

Visitors welcome: yes, during opening hours.

Catalogue: send 5 first class stamps.

Payment: cash or cheque.

Mail order: no.

Availability: supplies of some varieties can be limited as only small quantities are grown.

Refund/replacement: yes.

GARDENERS' RECOMMENDATIONS: ✣ *"Ten out of ten rating on all fronts, run by a lovely, friendly and extremely knowledgeable couple, Steve and Emma Lewis-Dale. Not only do they offer an extremely good range of pot-grown bulbs, alpines and herbaceous perennials, including many recent introductions, but they're all tended to a remarkably high standard, grown in peat-free compost with biological pest controls rather than chemicals, and, best of all, they're cheap – well, very reasonably priced. I recommend them to all of my garden visitors and have never heard a complaint."* Mr Duncan Skene. ✣ *"The plants …are always extremely healthy and flourish when planted in the garden. The stock for sale is well-labelled and beautifully laid out on the very attractive site. There are display beds and many attractively planted sinks. The owners are most helpful to all customers with their advice and expertise. It is for these reasons a most delightful nursery to* *visit.*" ✤ *"A delightful couple who propagate all their plants (bar bulbs) from scratch and have lovingly developed and nurtured their nursery from an open field, with their home beside. They have had a plant stall in our garden on our NGS days and never fail to attract a lot of custom. Both are highly qualified, print an excellent catalogue with amusing descriptions and plants are very reasonable. Any customer can feel the personal touch. They have made a garden to show off many of their plants. Also open for NGS."* Major and Mrs J Oliphant. ✤ *Also recommended by* Mr and Mrs R Hubbard, Hill House Nursery.

See map page 389.

Rowde Mill Nursery   Just the place for tyro gardeners or those who don't want to be forever on their knees praying for a bit of growth. The nursery tells us it specialises in "good doers — nothing too demanding." These are generally hardy perennials, not necessarily common, which are all grown at the nursery.

> **Rowde Mill Nursery**, Rowde, Devizes, Wiltshire SN10 1SZ
> **Tel/fax:** 01380 723016
> **Opening hours:** 10.00–17.00 Thursday to Sunday and bank holiday Mondays from April to September.
> **Visitors welcome:** very much so.
> **Catalogue:** none.
> **Payment:** cash or cheque.
> **Mail order:** no.
> **Availability:** limited stock of a wide range of hardy perennials sold in their season. Particular emphasis on late summer perennials.
> **Refund/replacement:** yes.

GARDENERS' RECOMMENDATIONS: ✤ *"Specialises in hardy perennials, all grown on the nursery. A relatively new nursery (opened 1998) in exceptionally attractive stream-side setting, with large newly-planted display borders (which should be very attractive once established – perhaps even next year). More expensive …but larger plants, so one can often divide them!"*

See map page 390.

Sherston Parva Nursery A good selection of plants which like growing against walls — not just climbers (though the selection of clematis is good) but others which enjoy a bit of protection from behind.

> **Sherston Parva Nursery**, Malmesbury Road, Sherston, Wiltshire SN16 0NX
>
> **Tel:** 01666 841066 **Fax:** 01666 841132
>
> **E-mail:** clematis@sherson-parva.prestel.co.uk
>
> **Opening hours:** 10.00–17.00 daily.
>
> **Visitors welcome:** yes.
>
> **Catalogue:** £2 refundable against first mail order.
>
> **Payment:** cash, cheque, major credit cards.
>
> **Mail order:** yes, including Europe.
>
> **Post and packing:** from £6.50 for 2 plants to £16 for 10, £1 per plant thereafter.
>
> **Delivery:** allow 28 days.
>
> **Availability:** most plants available all year round.
>
> **Refund/replacement:** yes.

GARDENERS' RECOMMENDATIONS: ✿ *"Very good clematis."* Mr and Mrs J D Sword.

See map page 394.

Westdale Nurseries The place to go for plants for the conservatory: it has collections of pelargoniums and fuchsia but especially bougainvilleas. The nursery offers over a hundred varieties which can be grown as standards, climbers, pot plants or even bonsai. It is, they add, the world's most versatile and colourful plant.

> **Westdale Nurseries**, Holt Road, Bradford-on-Avon, Wiltshire BA15 1TS
>
> **Tel/fax:** 01225 863258
>
> **Opening hours:** 9.00–18.00 daily.
>
> **Visitors welcome:** yes.
>
> **Catalogue:** 50p. £1 for new catalogue.
>
> **Payment:** cash, cheque, Visa.
>
> **Mail order:** yes. Minimum order £10.
>
> **Post and packing:** £2.50 to £4.95.
>
> **Delivery:** allow up to 28 days.
>
> **Availability:** all year round.

Refund/replacement: yes, replacement if notified in writing within 7 days.

Special services: wheelchair access to bougainvilleas. Talks, coach parties and large groups by appointment.

GARDENERS' RECOMMENDATIONS: *"Conservatory plants, specialist bouganvillea."*

See map page 390.

Whitehall Garden Centre

Whitehall Garden Centre A fairly general garden centre with an encouraging interest in real plants. They have herbaceous, climbers, shrubs, ground cover, herbs, bedding roses plus fruit bushes, aquatic plants and a new area with specimen plants. There's also a restaurant.

Whitehall Garden Centre Ltd, Lacock, Chippenham, Wiltshire SN15 2LZ
Tel: 01249 730204 **Fax:** 01249 730755
E-mail: sales@whitehall-gardencentre.co.uk
Website: http://www.whitehall-gardencentre.co.uk
Opening hours: 9.00–18.00 in summer, 9.00–17.30 in winter.
Visitors welcome: yes.
Catalogue: none.
Payment: cash, cheque, major credit cards.
Mail order: no.
Refund/replacement: yes.

GARDENERS' RECOMMENDATIONS: *"Good healthy plants – offer guarantees – always find something 'different'."* Dr and Mrs S Jevons

See map page 390.

Sonia Wright Plants

Sonia Wright Plants A joy to visit this nursery alongside a large house up a country lane. Though it specialises in Barnhaven primulas, polyanthus and auriculas, it offers what it calls "a wide and somewhat eccentric collection" personal to Sonia Wright.

Sonia Wright Plants, Grove Farm, Stitchcombe, Marlborough, Wiltshire SN8 2NG
Tel: 01672 514003 **Fax:** 01672 541047

Opening hours: 10.00 until dusk.

Visitors welcome: yes.

Catalogue: £1.

Payment: cash, cheque, credit card service soon.

Mail order: yes, on certain items. Minimum order £15 plus p&p.

Post and packing: £3 for 6 plants.

Delivery: depends when the order is received.

Availability: supplies can be limited and plants may be available at certain times of year only.

Refund/replacement: yes.

Special services: landscaping advice.

GARDENERS' RECOMMENDATIONS: ❀ *Recommended by* Mrs Caroline Todhunter.

See map page 390.

WORCESTERSHIRE

Acton Beauchamp Roses A list which accords well with my own prejudices being full of the species and old fashioned varieties of rose with few of the more modern introductions. Each is given a selection of useful symbols — conditions the roses like, how scented, when to prune etc — which makes the choice extremely easy.

Acton Beauchamp Nurseries, The Tynings, Acton Beauchamp, Worcester, Worcestershire WR6 5AE

Tel: 01531 640433 **Fax:** 01531 640802

Opening hours: 10.00–17.00 Tuesday to Saturday, also bank holidays and Sundays in June and July.

Visitors welcome: yes.

Catalogue: send 3 first class stamps.

Payment: cheque, Visa, Mastercard.

Mail order: yes.

Post and packing: £4.50.

Delivery: allow between 21 days and 3 months.

Availability: orders despatched between November and March.

Refund/replacement: yes.

Special services: Gift cards can be enclosed with orders.

GARDENERS' RECOMMENDATIONS: ❀ *"Top quality old-fashioned and specie roses, field grown, with a very knowledgeable and enthusiastic owner – mail order too! A very good list with some rare and unusual plants, very healthy and well grown."* Mr and Mrs H Moore. ❀ *"Lindsay Bousfield only grows the most select roses and only sells first-class plants. Choice and quality you can trust absolutely and her catalogue (as does her little Paragon book) briefly covers the classification and pruning of roses better than any other publication I know."* Mr R S Edwards. ❀ *"Good, big, well-grown bare-root mail order roses and questions are answered."*

See map page 394.

Birlingham Nurseries

Paul Haydon and Nick Martin run a good general nursery with roses, fruit bushes, roses and alpines among others. They also offer cut chrysanthemums in the autumn.

Birlingham Nurseries, Birlingham, Pershore, Worcestershire WR10 3AB

Tel: 01386 750668

Opening hours: 9.30–17.30 daily from April to July, 9.3–17.00 daily from August to March.

Visitors welcome: yes.

Catalogue: none.

Payment: cash, cheque, Visa, Mastercard.

Mail order: no.

Delivery: 7 days locally.

Availability: supplies can be limited and some plants are available only at certain times of year.

Refund/replacement: yes.

Special services: asparagus grown and sold from March to June.

GARDENERS' RECOMMENDATIONS: ❀ *"Family owned, where quality is paramount. Apart from their own produce they distribute plants grown at the nearby Pershore Horticultural College."* Mr Clive Jennings.

See map page 394.

Cotswold Garden Flowers   The catalogue of this nursery gives plants a score — how easy they are to grow, how they look. Marks of five are OK, six are nice, eight is very good. Plants with no score are awaiting a verdict. Predictably, this owner was once a teacher. The nursery specialises in easy and unusual perennials and I can tell you Alstroemeria aurea Cally Fire got a sensational 9.5; Dahlia Bishop of Llandaff 7.5 but Polygonatum biflorum dwarf form managed only a mark of 4.

Cotswold Garden Flowers, Sands Lane, Badsey, Evesham, Worcestershire WR11 5EZ

Tel/fax: 01386 47337

E-mail: cgf@star.co.uk

Website: http://www.cgf.net

Opening hours: 9.00–17.00 weekdays, 10.00–18.00 weekends from mid-March to mid-October.

Visitors welcome: yes.

Catalogue: £1 (cheque or stamps).

Payment: cheque.

Mail order: yes.

Post and packing: at cost.

Delivery: allow 4 weeks in busy season.

Availability: supplies can be limited and some plants are available only at certain times of year.

Refund/replacement: yes.

Special services: lectures.

GARDENERS' RECOMMENDATIONS: ❀ *"Unusual perennials, reasonable prices, helpful staff, garden alongside."* ❀ *"Everyone's favourite, both for Bob Brown's personality and unusual plants."* Mr and Mrs M R Everett. ❀ *"Bob Brown's knowledge and beautifully thought out catalogue and interesting plant collection are well known. A key element of a visit to a good nursery must be one of thrill and excitement and a stimulant for new ideas and healthy plants. His fulfils all those."* Lucy Abel Smith. ❀ *"Large field crammed full of plants, many unusual. Lovely to see flowers growing naturally. Plants for sale in greenhouses and tunnels."* Mr and Mrs Wadey. ❀ *"Excellent selection of hardy perennials and many rare ones – Bob Brown great character."* Mr and Mrs P Short. ❀ *"Interesting plants. Personal (and amusing) comments."* Mrs A Conville.

See map page 394.

Eastgrove Cottage Garden Nursery   You'll often find famous garden photographers here, say the owners, snapping rare plants in peak condition for their photo libraries. Malcolm and Carol Skinner have been here over 30 years but all the plants for sale are still propagated by them. The range of hardy plants is huge and there are regular additions: new, for example, are Eryngium x zabelii, Kniphofia Fiery Fred and Rubus cockburnianus, the white stemmed blackberry. They have a fine selection of sempervivums — a special favourite of mine. The garden is outstanding.

Eastgrove Cottage Garden, Sankyns Green, nr Shrawley, Little Witley, Worcestershire WR6 6LQ

Tel: 01299 896389

Website: http://www.hughesmedia.co.uk/eastgrove/

Opening hours: 14.00–17.00 Thursday to Monday from 1 April to 31 July and 14.00–17.00 Thursday to Saturday from 2 September to 9 October.

Visitors welcome: yes, very enthusiastically.

Catalogue: send 5 second class stamps.

Payment: cash or cheque.

Mail order: no.

Availability: of the 1,000 varieties in the range not all will be available at any one time.

Refund/replacement: yes.

Special services: Outstanding cottage garden and developing arboretum. The owners are always in attendance to answer queries and offer constructive gardening advice.

GARDENERS' RECOMMENDATIONS: ✵ *"Not to be missed. Delightful black and white cottage, gorgeous garden. Specialises in unusual and interesting herbaceous plants and tender perennials."* Mrs N Bitschi. ✵ *"Good plants and lots of unusual ones."* Mr and Mrs D Williams-Thomas. ✵ *"A specialist nursery selling perennial and half hardy plants propagated from their own garden. The nursery is situated in a large beautifully laid out garden which also includes a small arboretum and surrounds the owners' black and white yeoman's cottage. Carol and Malcolm Skinner are both knowledgeable and friendly."* Mr and Mrs B Dudley. ✵ *"Has small garden of great interest attached with unusual plants.* " Mr and Mrs P Nicholls.

See map page 394.

Grange Farm Nursery   Asked if they provide any special services, Carol Nicholls says simply "No, we just provide good plants at a reasonable price." This includes architectural statement plants such as phormiums, cordylines and bamboos, cottage garden poppies, foxgloves and herbs, climbers, winter flowering shrubs, plants for wildlife and those which are easy to grow. The nursery is among farm buildings in what was once a small dairy farm.

> **Grange Farm Nursery**, Guarlford, Malvern, Worcestershire WR13 6NY
>
> **Tel:** 01684 562544
>
> **Opening hours:** 9.00–17.30 Monday to Saturday, 10.00–17.00 Sunday in summer. 9.00-dusk Monday to Saturday in winter. Closed Christmas to New Year.
>
> **Visitors welcome:** yes.
>
> **Catalogue:** none.
>
> **Payment:** cash, cheque, major credit cards, Switch.
>
> **Mail order:** no.
>
> **Delivery:** free delivery in Malvern area. Allow 2-3 days.
>
> **Availability:** changes weekly.
>
> **Refund/replacement:** yes.

GARDENERS' RECOMMENDATIONS: *"Carol, the owner of Grange Farm Nursery, is an excellent, keen and knowledgeable gardener. The nursery is immaculately kept, the plants of the highest quality and the displays mouthwatering. Other nurseries should take a leaf out of her book."* The Hon Lady Morrison.

See map page 394.

———————————————   ———————————————

Hayloft Plants   If you want to make a splash of colour in your garden, Hayloft Plants sell some of the gaudiest — but, after having been looked down on by grand gardeners, wild colour combinations are now in vogue again. The firm prides itself on mail order and offers gazania, osteospermum and wild coloured euphorbia.

> **Hayloft Plants**, Little Court, Rous Lench, Evesham, Worcestershire WR11 4UL
>
> **Tel:** 01386 793361   **Fax:** 01386 793761
>
> **Opening hours:** 9.00–17.00 daily at Knowle Hill, Badsey, Evesham.
>
> **Visitors welcome:** yes at Knowle Hill, Badsey, Evesham.
>
> **Catalogue:** free.

Payment: cheque, major credit cards.
Mail order: yes.
Post and packing: £2.
Delivery: allow 28 days between March and May. By arrangement at other times.
Availability: March to July.
Refund/replacement: yes

GARDENERS' RECOMMENDATIONS: *"Excellent young plants, well packed, mainly perennials."* Mr and Mrs G Davies. *"Mail order plantlets – excellent delivery conditions."* Professor and Mrs B Hibbard. *Also recommended by* Lady Barbirolli.

See map page 394.

Hills Nurseries

The firm sells an extremely wide range of plants, from conifers and ornamental trees to alpine, herbaceous and bedding plants along with services such as creating hanging baskets and tubs. "We try to supply a very wide range of garden plants for the beginner, specialist and even professional landscapers," they say.

Hills Nurseries, Pitchers Hill, Wickhamford, Evesham, Worcestershire WR11 6RT
Tel/fax: 01386 831199
Opening hours: 9.00–17.00 Monday to Saturday, 10.00–17.00 Sunday.
Visitors welcome: yes.
Catalogue: none.
Payment: cash, cheque, Visa, Mastercard.
Mail order: no, although plants can occasionally be posted.
Availability: full range of potted stock throughout the year. bare-root plants during winter only, bedding plants in spring, early summer and autumn.
Refund/replacement: yes.

GARDENERS' RECOMMENDATIONS: *"Good range of strong healthy general stock – knowledgeable and helpful."* Mr and Mrs W Boddington.

See map page 394.

Old Court Nurseries Paul Picton not only holds the national collection of michaelmas daisies, he has written a book on the subject, *The Gardeners' Guide to Growing Asters*. His catalogue answers a great many questions and offers a large variety, but Mr. Picton, who opens his gardens under the NGS scheme, will also advise you personally.

Old Court Nurseries, Colwall, Malvern, Worcestershire WR13 6QE
Tel: 01684 540416 **Fax:** 01684 565314
E-mail: picton@dircon.co.uk
Website: http://www.autumnasters.co.uk
Opening hours: 11.00–17.30 Wednesday to Sunday from April to October.
Visitors welcome: yes.
Catalogue: free (asters only).
Payment: cash or cheque.
Mail order: yes, in May.
Post and packing: from £7.
Delivery: despatched in May.
Availability: April to October for plants collected from the nursery. Mail order May only.
Refund/replacement: usually replacement.
Special services: Picton garden open from August to October. Colour guide to asters grown by Old Court Nurseries £2.

GARDENERS' RECOMMENDATIONS: ❀ *"Wonderful michaelmas daisies – but so frustrating often to be told 'Not available till next year'."* Mr and Mrs E W Dyer. ❀ *"Run by the owners, the nursery has a garden and largely produces the plants they offer."* Mr and Mrs J M Skinner, Eastgrove Cottage Garden Nursery. ❀ *"Has small garden of great interest attached with unusual plants."* Mr and Mrs P Nicholls. ❀ *"Staff pleasant and helpful."*

See map page 394.

Perhill Plants The family-run business has been going over 10 years and specialises in rare and unusual border perennials, alpines and herbs — not your run-of-the-mill garden centre stuff. All the plants are grown on site. They include a good selection of alliums, campanulas, house leeks in abundance along with foxgloves and cardoons. They love horticultural societies to visit and offer advice on everything they grow.

Perhill Plants, Worcester Road, Great Witley, Worcestershire WR6 6JT

Tel: 01299 896329 **Fax:** 01299 896990

Opening hours: 9.00–17.00 Monday to Saturday, 10.00–16.00 Sunday.

Visitors welcome: yes.

Catalogue: send 6 second class stamps.

Payment: cash, cheque, major credit cards, Switch.

Mail order: yes.

Post and packing: from £1 for orders under £2 to £25 for orders up to £200, 15% of order value thereafter.

Delivery: 7 days.

Availability: the majority of plants are available all year round.

Refund/replacement: yes.

Special services: talks given.

GARDENERS' RECOMMENDATIONS: ✾ *"One of my favourite nurseries – no garden but unusual well-priced plants."* Mr and Mrs D Williams-Thomas. ✾ *"Very helpful – excellent for penstemons."* Col and Mrs J G T Polley. ✾ *"Enormous range of perennials and alpines at very reasonable prices."* Tessa King-Farlow.

See map page 394.

Red House Farm Garden and Nursery

Maureen Weaver says her nursery is very small but she also has a cottage garden for customers to wander in. Her list, however, is full of interest with herbs, honeysuckles, irises and phlox among many other cottage garden plants.

Red House Farm Garden and Nursery, Flying Horse Lane, Bradley Green, Worcestershire B96 6QT

Tel: 01527 821269 **Fax:** 01527 821674

Opening hours: 9.00–17.00 Monday to Saturday, 10.00–17.00 Sunday and bank holidays.

Visitors welcome: yes.

Catalogue: send 2 first class stamps.

Payment: cash or cheque.

Mail order: no.

Availability: small numbers of a wide range of plants available in season.

Refund/replacement: yes.

GARDENERS' RECOMMENDATIONS: ❀ *"Interesting stock of cottage garden and other perennials with some shrubs. Demonstration garden open to public."*

See map page 394.

Rickards Hardy Ferns The owner has grown ferns for 30 years, sold them for nine and, most recently, gone as far as New Zealand to get a better understanding of their tree ferns, which are sold here. The nursery has won gold medals all over the place, including five at Chelsea. Ferns are pretty different from other plants, so there is specialist advice on how to grow and propagate them. They well repay the care they get.

> **Rickards Hardy Ferns**, Kyre Park, Kyre, Tenbury Wells, Worcestershire WR15 8RP
>
> **Tel:** 01885 410282/410729 **Fax:** 01885 410729
>
> **Opening hours:** 9.00–13.00, 14.00–17.00 Wednesday to Monday (closed Tuesday) from April to October and by appointment.
>
> **Visitors welcome:** yes.
>
> **Catalogue:** send 5 first class stamps for list.
>
> **Payment:** cash or cheque.
>
> **Mail order:** yes. Minimum order £20 in UK, £50 EC.
>
> **Post and packing:** 20% of order value in UK, 30-40% in EC.
>
> **Delivery:** 2-3 weeks, longer after Chelsea.
>
> **Availability:** certain items are inevitably out of stock during winter.
>
> **Refund/replacement:** yes.

GARDENERS' RECOMMENDATIONS: ❀ *"The best fern specialist in the country. Not all his ferns are 'hardy' either. He offers quite a few ferns on or beyond the edge of ordinary hardiness. Martin Rickard himself is expert and enthusiastic. And there's the bonus of Kyre Park itself, a magnificent Georgian landscape park which the Rickards are restoring (with tree ferns in the woods!) Not to be missed is the 'fern house', sunk into a hillside, in which grow his specimen plants of the really tender tree ferns."* Mr Tim Longville. ❀ *"Martin Rickard is lovely on the phone and talks one into buying exotica when one had initially enquired for a variety that will actually stand up to the rigours of the garden. Wins gold medals at the most important shows and writes very knowledgeably. Every imaginable fern from tiny* *delicate numbers to whopping New Zealand tree ferns. I can understand the Victorians' love of ferns and sense a renewed interest."* Diana Yakeley. ✿ *"We collect ferns. They are grown by him – not bought in."* Mr and Mrs J Southwell, Sherborne Garden.

See map page 394.

⌖

 Stone House Cottage Nurseries A three-quarter acre walled garden is the inspiration for the plants grown by this firm, which grows and displays virtually everything on sale. "It is probably one of the best collections of climbers and wall shrubs in the country," say the Arbuthnotts, adding firmly "we are not a garden centre." I spotted the strong blue of Ceanothus Pugets Blue, a good collection of viticella clematis and the very fashionable Muehlenbeckia complexa.

> **Stone House Cottage Nurseries**, Stone (A448), nr Kidderminster, Worcestershire DY10 4BG
>
> **Tel:** 01562 69902 **Fax:** 01562 69960
>
> **Opening hours:** 10.00–17.30 Wednesday to Saturday from March to mid-October.
>
> **Visitors welcome:** yes.
>
> **Catalogue:** send sae.
>
> **Payment:** cash or cheque.
>
> **Mail order:** no.
>
> **Availability:** March to mid-October.
>
> **Refund/replacement:** yes.

GARDENERS' RECOMMENDATIONS: ✿ *"Interesting plants, fascinating garden. Lots of ideas. Wall shrubs and climbing plants."* Mr and Mrs N R Wilson. ✿ *"Good range of unusual shrubs. Staff pleasant and helpful."* ✿ *"Different and unusual plants – changing stock all the time – wonderful for browsing and spending too much money."* Mr and Mrs J. Major. ✿ *"Specialising in wall plants and climbers this nursery is in James and Louisa Arbuthnott's own old walled garden. Their knowledge is very broad and everyone is made very welcome."* Mr M J Jurgens.

See map page 394.

⌖

Treasures of Tenbury

Treasures of Tenbury   The national collection of clematis is housed here by a charming riverside. The catalogue manages to cram in a great deal of information about how to grow these often tricky plants as well as helpful descriptions. On the same site is Mulu Nurseries, specialising in exotics and Jungle Giants who love bamboos.

Treasures of Tenbury, Burford House Gardens, Tenbury Wells, Worcestershire WR15 8HQ

Tel: 01584 810777   **Fax:** 01584 810673

E-mail: treasures@burford.co.uk

Opening hours: 10.00–18.00 daily except Christmas.

Visitors welcome: yes.

Catalogue: £1.

Payment: cheque, major credit cards.

Mail order: yes.

Post and packing: from £6.55 for 1-2 plants to £17.75 for 9–10.

Delivery: 48 hours.

Availability: mail order normally from September to March.

Refund/replacement: yes.

GARDENERS' RECOMMENDATIONS: ✸ *"Wonderful selection of clematis and fair selection of other plants."* Mr and Mrs S Smith.

See map page 394.

Martin Tustin Lavenders

Martin Tustin Lavenders   What it says — a selection of over 80 lavenders including at least one exclusive to the nursery. Lavenders can be tricky and Martin Tustin offers advice on how to plant and care for them.

Martin Tustin Lavenders, Bowers Hill Nursery, Willersey Road, Badsey, nr Evesham, Worcestershire WR11 5HG

Tel: 01386 832124   **Fax:** 01386 832124

Opening hours: by appointment daily except during Christmas week.

Visitors welcome: yes, by appointment.

Catalogue: send 2 first class stamps.

Payment: cash or cheque.

Mail order: no.

Refund/replacement: yes.

GARDENERS' RECOMMENDATIONS: *Recommended by* Mrs Caroline Todhunter.

See map page 394.

Wintergreen Nurseries   This small retail nursery grows all its own plants in peat-based compost and most can be seen in its own display border. The list is wide and full of hard-to-find varieties.

> **Wintergreen Nurseries**, Bringsty Common, Worcester, Worcestershire WR6 5UJ
> **Tel:** 01886 821858
> **Opening hours:** 10.00–17.30 Wednesday to Sunday from 1 March to 31 October and by appointment.
> **Visitors welcome:** yes.
> **Catalogue:** send 2 second class stamps.
> **Payment:** cash or cheque.
> **Mail order:** no.
> **Availability:** 70-80% of plants in stock throughout the year.
> **Refund/replacement:** yes.

GARDENERS' RECOMMENDATIONS: *"Good range of unusual plants, alpines and shrubs – they all seem to grow. Staff pleasant and helpful."*

See map page 394.

See also: Caves Folly Nursery, page 350; **Cranesbill Nursery,** page 353.

YORKSHIRE

Ashfield Hellebores   Anne Watson has a huge selection of hellebores which, promiscuous breeders as they are, are always on the move. She can offer up to 1,000 orientalis hybrids when they are in bloom and asks that customers come to the nursery to see them. "I do not send plants by post and do not accept orders or reservations."

People should ring to make an appointment and to check she actually has the plant.

Ashfield Hellebores, Rarer Plants, Ashfield House, Austfield Lane, Monk Fryston, Leeds, North Yorkshire LS25 5EH

Tel: 01977 682263

Opening hours: 10.00–16.00 at weekends from 1 February to 1 May.

Visitors welcome: yes.

Catalogue: send sae for list.

Payment: cash or cheque.

Mail order: no.

Availability: from 1 February to 1 May only.

Refund/replacement: no (never needed to!)

GARDENERS' RECOMMENDATIONS: ✽ *"Only open for a short time for hellebores and unusual plants."*

See map page 396.

Bishop Burton College Commercial Nursery The nursery offers "quality plants at sensible prices" including a wide range of shrubs, climbers, perennials, trees, conifers, grasses and bamboos. The selection is sensible though there are few surprises.

Bishop Burton College Commercial Nursery, Bishop Burton, nr Beverley, East Yorkshire HU17 8QG

Tel: 01964 553055/0411 112972 **Fax:** 01964 553101

E-mail: bishopb-college.ac.uk

Opening hours: 8.30–16.00 Monday to Friday, and at weekends by appointment.

Visitors welcome: yes.

Catalogue: free.

Payment: cash, cheque, account.

Mail order: no.

Availability: all year round.

Refund/replacement: if appropriate.

GARDENERS' RECOMMENDATIONS: ✽ *"This nursery caters mostly for the trade but welcomes the public during the week. The College gardens, especially the old walled garden, are also well worth a visit and many of the shrubs raised at the nursery come from cuttings taken from shrubs around the grounds. They also have a very good range of climbing plants and wall shrubs. It is sometimes difficult to find the staff but a walk through the glasshouses and round the nursery is always a pleasure and puts plenty of temptation in one's way. Guy Chapman, the nursery manager, is extremely knowledgeable and recently won the 'National Young Horticulturalist of the Year' run by the RHS. His travelling bursary took him to New Zealand and consequently he is developing a range of plants whose origins are from that part of the world."* Chris Powell.

See map page 396.

Cutting Edge Nursery This is a small nursery which sells mainly herbaceous perennials and shrubs for the garden. They try to stock as many varieties as possible and the two catalogues offer plenty of choice.

> **Cutting Edge Nursery**, Knowle Road, Barnsley, South Yorkshire
> S70 4AW
> **Tel:** 01226 730292
> **Opening hours:** 9.00–17.00 daily. Closed from Christmas to the first working Monday of the new year.
> **Visitors welcome:** yes.
> **Catalogue:** 50p or 2 first class stamps.
> **Payment:** cash or cheque.
> **Mail order:** no.
> **Availability:** not all plants are available at any one time.
> **Refund/replacement:** by arrangement.

GARDENERS' RECOMMENDATIONS: ✿ *"Our current favourite as a source of excellent plants at exceptional prices."*

See map page 396.

Daleside Nurseries Ltd The nursery offers a good range of trees, shrubs, climbers, including clematis along with fruit trees, seasonal bedding, alpines and, of course, herbaceous perennials.

> **Daleside Nurseries**, Ripon Road, Killinghall, Harrogate,
> North Yorkshire HG3 2AY
> **Tel:** 01423 506450 **Fax:** 01423 527872
> **Opening hours:** 9.00–17.00 Monday to Saturday, 10.00–12.00, 13.30–16.30 Sunday.

Visitors welcome: yes.

Catalogue: lists in season.

Mail order: no.

Availability: supplies of certain items are limited.

Refund/replacement: depending on circumstances.

GARDENERS' RECOMMENDATIONS: *"Have provided me with well grown material of AGM quality."* Mr R E J Compton, Newby Hall. ❀ *"Has good stock, well-grown plants. Courteous and helpful staff."* Mr J Muirhead. ❀ *"I can't omit our really excellent garden centre near here. It is family run and everyone working there is pleasant and helpful. They grow quite a lot of their trees and shrubs for sale and can sometimes provide a larger field-grown specimen if that is required. They are excellent for garden sundries and although nothing is particularly cheap, their service is aimed at pleasing enthusiastic gardeners rather than attracting family outings."* ❀ *"Excellent shrubs, indoor and out, plus climbers."* Dr and Mrs R L Belsey.

See map page 396.

Deanswood Plants This nursery has the delightful features of a 100-yard natural stream and three ponds all within a two-acre garden. Jacky Barber obviously concentrates on water-loving plants for streams or water margins — she has floaters and oxygenators, rushes, iris and marsh marigold along with arum lilies and polygonum for the water and a big list including hosta, primula and gunnera for the edges. Other plants are for sale but not listed. Visitors to the garden are asked to make a contribution to the NGS.

Deanswood Plants, Potteries Lane, Littlethorpe, Ripon, North Yorkshire HG4 3LS

Tel: 01765 603441

Opening hours: 10.00–17.00 Tuesday to Sunday from 1 April to 30 September or by appointment.

Visitors welcome: yes.

Catalogue: send 50p in stamps.

Payment: cash or cheque.

Mail order: no.

Availability: limited stock of some unusual plants.

Refund/replacement: yes, if justified.

Special services: group visits can be arranged.

GARDENERS' RECOMMENDATIONS: *"Very good small nursery run by Mrs Jacky Barber. Specialises in water and bog plants but also fair collection of herbaceous plants including those favoured by flower arrangers. Excellent garden with stream and ponds open under NGS. Advice good, freely forthcoming, propagates from own stock so you can see it growing. Customers sometimes need to hunt for plants (beds uneven and plants can get out of alphabetical order)."* *"Small but good."* Mr and Mrs J Ramsden.

See map page 396.

Dove Cottage Plants

The nursery specialises in choice and unusual herbaceous perennials with particular attention to hellebores, hostas, hardy geraniums, epimediums, pulmonarias and bamboos. All these are very much used in modern planting schemes. The owners will give advice on what to choose and how to display.

> **Dove Cottage Plants**, 23 Shibden Hall Road, Halifax, West Yorkshire HX3 9XA
> **Tel:** 01422 203553
> **Opening hours:** 10.00–18.00 Tuesday to Sunday from February to November.
> **Visitors welcome:** yes.
> **Catalogue:** none.
> **Payment:** cash, cheque, credit cards shortly..
> **Mail order:** no.
> **Availability:** seasonal.
> **Refund/replacement:** yes.
> **Special services:** display garden featuring grasses mixed with perennials.

GARDENERS' RECOMMENDATIONS: *"Last year's find of the season. A wonderful nursery run by a young couple. They grow marvellous plants, are very interested in what you are choosing and are most helpful with advice, also very reasonable prices."* Mrs P Clarke.

See map page 395.

Flaxton House Nursery

Specialists in shrubs, herbaceous perennials and alpines with a garden alongside to show off the plants and also advice on garden and border design. Among the shrubs there's a good list of cornus, hydrangea and a selection of roses.

Flaxton House Nursery, Flaxton, York, North Yorkshire YO60 7RJ
Tel: 01904 468753
Opening hours: 10.00–17.00 Tuesday to Sunday.
Visitors welcome: yes.
Catalogue: send 3 first class stamps.
Payment: cheque on receipt of pro-forma invoice.
Mail order: yes, although principally a retail nursery. Minimum order £3.50.
Post and packing: postage at cost plus 50p for packing.
Delivery: allow 7 days.
Availability: plants despatched by mail order during autumn and winter only.
Refund/replacement: yes.

GARDENERS' RECOMMENDATIONS: ❀ *"For herbaceous perennial plants – small operation, growing their own plants, very good value."* Caroline Peacock.

See map page 396.

Mires Beck Nursery

There are two catalogues to this nursery. The more ordinary is for herbaceous perennials which is good but not especially unusual. The other is for wild flowers "of Yorkshire provenance" which will surprise anyone who doesn't know the county with its diversity. There's a wild thyme, a wild basil, wild strawberry and the bright blue flowering chicory. Yellow flags, common rockroses and honeysuckle translate well in the garden. Interest in such natives is growing, not necessarily for wild-flower meadows but in gardens proper, as the Chelsea Flower Show annually indicates.

Mires Beck Nursery, Low Mill Lane, North Cave, Brough, East Yorkshire HU15 2NR
Tel: 01430 421543
Opening hours: 10.00–16.00 Thursday to Saturday from March to July, Thursday and Friday only from August to February.
Visitors welcome: yes.
Catalogue: 3 first class stamps appreciated.
Payment: cash or cheque.

Mail order: wild flowers only.
Post and packing: from £4.
Delivery: allow 2 weeks.
Availability: some varieties may be sold out until more plants are propagated.
Refund/replacement: yes.

GARDENERS' RECOMMENDATIONS: *"As you will see it is a rather special place but its horticultural speciality is 'wild flowers of Yorkshire provenance' and surprisingly they send parcels of 'root-trainer' plugs throughout the British Isles. Stephen Anderton recommended them in his* Times *article recently. They also supply retail outlets with a wide range of perennials."* Chris Powell.

See map page 396.

Oland Plants

There are normally over 2,000 different garden plants at this North Yorkshire nursery which has been going on the site for almost 20 years. Stock includes perennials, shrubs, trees, heathers, alpines and herbs. Leslie and Jane Oland run two other plant centres, one at Newby Hall — the best garden in the north, they say, and at Harlow Carr botanical garden near Harrogate.

Oland Plants, Sawley Nursery, Risplith, Ripon, North Yorkshire HG4 3EW
Tel: 01765 620622 **Fax:** 01765 620487
E-mail: plants@oland.softnet.co.uk
Opening hours: 9.00–17.00 daily. Closed at weekends from November to January.
Visitors welcome: yes.
Catalogue: none.
Payment: cash, cheque, Visa, Mastercard, Switch.
Mail order: no.
Availability: supplies of some plants are limited.
Refund/replacement: each case considered individually.

GARDENERS' RECOMMENDATIONS: *"Have provided me with well grown material."* Mr R E J Compton, Newby Hall. *"Very good – supplies Newby Hall and Harlow Carr."* Mr and Mrs J Ramsden.

See map page 396.

Oxtoby's Nursery Mike Oxtoby only sells fuchsias — those for baskets, upright varieties, triphylla hybrids, hardy fuchsias and what he delightfully calls "Odds and Ends." He also has his own introductions most years.

> **Oxtoby's Nursery**, 74 Westgate, North Cave, Brough,
> East Yorkshire HU15 2NJ
>
> **Tel:** 01430 423049
>
> **Opening hours:** 10.00–18.00 Tuesday to Sunday from November to July.
>
> **Visitors welcome:** yes.
>
> **Catalogue:** send 3 first class stamps.
>
> **Payment:** cash or cheque.
>
> **Mail order:** limited.
>
> **Post and packing:** £3 for up to 5 plants, 60p for each additional plant.
>
> **Delivery:** by arrangement.
>
> **Availability:** supplies can be limited.
>
> **Refund/replacement:** replacement if the nursery was at fault.

GARDENERS' RECOMMENDATIONS: ❀*Recommended by* Mr and Mrs G Davies.

See map page 396.

Perry's Plants This small nursery likes unusual and old-fashioned plants — anything from Brown Turkey fig to oregano and philadelphus. It's a characterful catalogue of plants which the owners clearly enjoy themselves. They also sell pond plants, aquatics and water features. The nursery is in the charming Yorkshire fishing village of Sleights.

> **Perry's Plants**, The River Gardens, Sleights, Whitby, North Yorkshire YO21 1RR
>
> **Tel:** 01947 810329 **Fax:** 01947 810940
>
> **Opening hours:** 10.00–17.00 daily from March to October.
>
> **Visitors welcome:** yes.
>
> **Catalogue:** send A4 sae for list.
>
> **Payment:** cash or cheque.
>
> **Mail order:** no.
>
> **Availability:** supplies can be limited and some plants are available only at certain times of year.
>
> **Refund/replacement:** yes.

Special services: licensed riverside café with home baking. 18-hole putting lawn, garden gift shop.

GARDENERS' RECOMMENDATIONS: *Recommended by* Chris Powell.

See map page 396.

Ravensworth Nurseries

This is a wholesale nursery which is also open to the public. They sell a wide variety of bedding plants, pot plants, shrubs, trees and perennials and offer planted arrangements for presents.

Ravensworth Nurseries, Richmond, North Yorkshire DL11 7HA
Tel: 01325 718370 **Fax:** 01325 718011
Opening hours: 8.00–16.30 daily.
Visitors welcome: yes.
Catalogue: none.
Payment: cash, cheque, Visa, Mastercard, Switch, Delta.
Mail order: no.
Availability: seasonal.
Refund/replacement: yes.

GARDENERS' RECOMMENDATIONS: *"For bedding plants."* Mr C Wyvill.

See map page 396.

R.V. Roger Ltd

Nurserymen since 1913, the firm boasts "one of the largest ranges of plant material available anywhere" so it's quite an effort working your way through the catalogue plus its many additions. The firm isn't idle in offering new ideas: they have grass trees (Xanthorrhoea johnsonii) and tree ferns (Dicksonia antarctica), separate tulip, narcissus and bulb lists, another for Alliaceae, lilies, and spring bulbs. Then you get to the main catalogue with roses, shrubs, climbers, hedging, and fruit, including a new banana passion fruit from Australia. Working its way through figs, nuts and strawberries, the catalogue ends with annuals. Phew.

R V Roger Ltd, The Nurseries, Pickering, North Yorkshire YO18 7HG
Tel: 01751 472226 **Fax:** 01751 476749

E-mail: ian@clivia.demon.co.uk

Opening hours: 9.00–17.00 Monday to Saturday, 13.00–17.00 Sunday. Closed 25 December to 2 January.

Visitors welcome: yes.

Catalogue: £1.50.

Payment: cash, cheque, postal order, Visa, Mastercard, Switch.

Mail order: yes.

Post and packing: from £4.50 for bulbs to £10 for trees.

Delivery: seasonal.

Availability: supplies can be limited and some plants are available only at certain times of year.

Refund/replacement: yes.

See map page 396.

Stillingfleet Lodge Nurseries

The garden of this nursery is open under the National Gardens Scheme and it holds the national collection of pulmonaria. Otherwise, it specialises in fragrant and grey foliage plants and unusual perennials. Grey leaved plants — salvia, rosemary and lavender, artemisia and helichrysum, for instance — are very tolerant of dry weather, so this is a place to plan a dry garden.

Stillingfleet Lodge Nurseries, Stillingfleet, North Yorkshire YO19 6HP

Tel/fax: 01904 728506

E-mail: vanessa.cook@still-lodge.freeserve.co.uk

Opening hours: 10.00–16.00 Tuesday, Wednesday, Friday and Saturday from 1 April to 18 October.

Visitors welcome: yes.

Catalogue: send 7 second class stamps.

Payment: cash or cheque.

Mail order: yes.

Post and packing: £5.50 for up to 5 plants to £8 for up to 15, then £1.50 for each additional 5 plants.

Delivery: plants despatched between mid-October and mid-March.

Availability: mid-October to mid-March.

Refund/replacement: yes, if notified within 2 weeks.

GARDENERS' RECOMMENDATIONS: ✤ *"This is a really good nursery with a very good catalogue and many plants you can't get anywhere else."* ✤ *"Small family run nursery. Wide selection of plants, many unusual. Mrs Cook is usually available for helpful advice. Plants are well grown and healthy. Catalogue available. Wonderful surrounding countryside and areas of interest can make a visit to Stillingfleet a lovely full day out too."* Mr and Mrs M Whitton. ❀ *"Owner-run nursery growing a wide selection of hardy plants really well. Some rarities all very well grown. Quite strict rules about mail order and opening times!"* ❀ *"This is a nursery well worth the visit. Setting is delightful and the nursery so well laid out – a pleasure to walk round and choose and choose. Recommend highly for design and good quality plants. Service excellent."* Mr and Mrs J Brown.

See map page 396.

Swanland Nurseries
Specialists since 1949 in plants for hanging baskets and tubs including regal and scented leaf pelargoniums, ivy leaf and cactus flowered pelargoniums. These are all in their catalogue along with good colour photographs. The nursery also sells trees, shrubs, alpines, herbs and herbaceous perennials — though not by mail order.

Swanland Nurseries, Beech Hill Road, Swanland, East Yorkshire HU14 3QY

Tel: 01482 633670 **Fax:** 01482 634064

E-mail: swanland@aol.com

Opening hours: 9.00–18.00 Monday to Saturday, 10.30–16.30 Sunday.

Visitors welcome: yes.

Catalogue: £1.

Payment: cheque, postal order, major credit cards, bank transfer.

Mail order: yes. Minimum order 6 plants.

Post and packing: £4 for 6 plants, £8 for 12, 80 per plant thereafter.

Delivery: usually within a week, maximum 6 weeks.

Availability: supplies of rarer varieties may be limited.

Refund/replacement: yes.

GARDENERS' RECOMMENDATIONS: ❀ *We have enjoyed lovely plants from this nursery."* Susan Bennett and Earl Hyde.

See map page 396.

Woodlands Cottage Nursery   Placed in the lush countryside of the dales, the nursery is small and attached to a garden open under the NGS and Red Cross schemes. Most plants — herbs, perennials, ferns, grasses and wild flowers among others — are propagated here (never in vast quantities but Jim Stark will try to produce what you want later). The list includes ferns and grasses, ground-cover plants and those which tolerate shade and, charmingly, a selection of wild flowers such as harebell, flag iris and devil's bit scabious. Strangely, it is our own native plants which are often hardest to find.

Woodlands Cottage Nursery,
Summerbridge, Harrogate,
North Yorkshire HG3 4BT

Tel: 01423 780765
Fax: 01423 781390

E-mail:
jim.stark@signetfbc.co.uk

Opening hours: 10.30–18.00
Monday, Wednesday, Friday
and Saturday from mid-
March to end September.

Visitors welcome: yes.

Catalogue: send 2 first class
stamps.

Payment: cash or cheque.

Mail order: no.

Availability: supplies of
some plants can be
limited depending on
their popularity.

Refund/replacement: yes.

Special services: garden
design service.

GARDENERS' RECOMMENDATIONS: ✪ *"Very good small nursery run by Mrs Ann Stark. Specialising in herbs, grey foliage plants and wild flowers. Plants all accurately named and checked in Plant Finder. Keen plants' collector has been on expeditions to China with Alpine Garden Society. Many unusual but good garden plants. nice garden also open under NGS."*

See map page 396.

NURSERIES IN
NORTHERN IRELAND

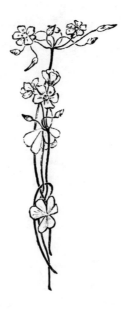

Ballyrogan Nurseries

Ballyrogan Nurseries "This is a small, part-time nursery," say the owners modestly. Maybe, but it holds three national collections — for celmisia, crocosmia and euphorbia. As well as this, there is a good collection of agapanthus, dierama, kniphofia and rogersia in a very interesting list.

> **Ballyrogan Nurseries**, The Grange, Ballyrogan, Newtownards, Northern Ireland BT23 4SD
>
> **Tel:** 028 9181 0451
>
> **Opening hours:** by appointment only.
>
> **Visitors welcome:** by appointment.
>
> **Catalogue:** send 2 first class stamps.
>
> **Payment:** cheque.
>
> **Mail order:** yes.
>
> **Post and packing:** at cost.
>
> **Delivery:** all plants are grown in open ground so are despatched in autumn or spring.
>
> **Availability:** very limited supplies of some rare and slow-growing plants.
>
> **Refund/replacement:** in case of genuine complaint.

GARDENERS' RECOMMENDATIONS: ❁ *"His catalogue is astonishing, his nursery almost beyond belief. Particularly since he also has a full-time day job and runs the nursery – and the attached three or four-acre garden – just in the evenings and at weekends. He holds three or four national collections and could easily hold ten or twelve more. The nursery's emphasis is on unusual semi-tender herbaceous plants but he also has quantities of unusual semi-tender shrubs. My vote for the country's most adventurous nursery on the largest scale. The sort of place where a plant-freak feels he's died and gone to heaven."* Mr Tim Longville.

See map page 397.

Seaforde Gardens

Seaforde Gardens The nursery is sited in a part of a five-acre walled garden which dates back at least to 1750 when the Forde family lived at Seaforde. The other half is a formal garden including a maze planted in 1975. The planting is exotic with Crinodendron patagua, Olearia x zennorensis, and avenues of eucryphias. The garden holds the national collection of 20 varieties of eucryphias and many are offered for sale as are camellias, rhododendrons and olearias. A most interesting and exotic list but many plants are semi-tender.

Seaforde Gardens, Seaforde, County Down, Northern Ireland BT30 8PG

Tel: 01396 811225 **Fax:** 01396 811370

Opening hours: 10.00–17.00 Monday to Saturday, 13.00–18.00 Sunday.

Visitors welcome: yes.

Catalogue: free.

Payment: cash or cheque.

Mail order: yes.

Post and packing: £10 per parcel.

Delivery: 2 days.

Availability: all year round.

Refund/replacement: yes, if genuine cause for complaint.

GARDENERS' RECOMMENDATIONS: *"Very reliable for Himalayan rhododendrons and other ericaceae."* The Marquess of Anglesey. *Also recommended* by Dr and Mrs R G Law.

See map page 397.

NURSERIES IN SCOTLAND

Ardfearn Nursery   Though this is a fairly general nursery for herbaceous perennials and shrubs, it seems to have a strong Scottish slant (not surprisingly). There are many heathers, primulas, rhododendrons and conifers.

Ardfearn Nursery, Bunchrew, Inverness, Inverness-shire IV3 6RH
Tel: 01463 243250 **Fax:** 01463 711713
Opening hours: 9.00–17.00 daily.
Visitors welcome: yes.
Catalogue: send 3 second class stamps.
Payment: cash or cheque.
Mail order: yes.
Post and packing: £5 for orders up to £50, free thereafter.
Delivery: orders despatched in rotation between October and March.
Availability: supplies can be limited and some plants are available only at certain times of year.
Refund/replacement: yes.

GARDENERS' RECOMMENDATIONS: ❀ *"Excellent small nursery with a variety of different plants, shrubs and trees."* Lady Spencer Nairn. ❀ *"Irresistible collection."* Simone Nelson. ❀ *"Excellent alpines."* Mr and Mrs P Cox, Glendoick Gardens.

See map page 398.

Ardkinglas Estate Nurseries   Based in Argyll, the nursery offers those plants which flourish in the warm, moist climate of the West Coast and like their soil acid rather than alkaline. There is a good list of azaleas and rhododendrons (some really interesting species like falconeri and lacteum) plus conifers, eucalyptus and acers.

Ardkinglas Estate Nurseries, Tree Shop, Clachan, Cairndow, Argyll PA26 8BH
Tel: 01499 600263 **Fax:** 01499 600348
E-mail: tree.shop@virgin.net
Opening hours: 9.30–17.00.
Visitors welcome: yes.
Catalogue: free.
Payment: cheque, Visa, Mastercard.
Mail order: yes.

Post and packing: £6.50 for 1-3 plants, £9 for 4-6, £11 for 7–10, £16 for 11–15.

Delivery: 28 days.

Availability: limited supplies, but mail order service all year round.

Refund/replacement: yes.

GARDENERS' RECOMMENDATIONS: *"Has a very wide range of trees grown locally and also unusual trees eg Selkova, Paulonia etc."* Mr and Mrs T Downie. *"A good selection of unusual trees and shrubs, good quality, also a woodland garden with some of the largest trees in Britain nearby."* Peter Cool, head gardener, Jura House Garden.

See map page 398.

Ardmaddy Castle Gardens Nursery

Sited on the mild West Coast of Scotland alongside the Gulf Stream and with a good acidic soil, the nursery obviously specialises in rhododendrons, azaleas and some camellias. Other plants include the lovely meconopsis, primulas and plants for damp places. There are some unusual shrubs, a few trees and vegetables in season.

Ardmaddy Castle Gardens Nursery, Ardmaddy Castle, Oban, Argyll, PA34 4QX

Tel/fax: 01852 300353

Opening hours: 9.00 to dusk daily.

Visitors welcome: telephone first to guarantee personal attention.

Catalogue: none.

Payment: cash or cheque.

Mail order: no.

Availability: ever-changing variety.

Refund/replacement: never been asked, but yes.

Special services: discount on bulk orders, plants acquired on request.

GARDENERS' RECOMMENDATIONS: *"Excellent choice of unusual plants not found in garden centres."* Mr and Mrs T Downie.

See map page 398.

Binny Plants   Run by Billy Carruthers in the grounds of a Sue Ryder home, the nursery recently won a silver-gilt at the RHS Strathclyde show. Carruthers has a nice list of herbaceous perennials along with excellent grasses and rushes, ferns and a few trees and shrubs.

> **Binny Plants**, West Lodge, Binny Estate, Ecclesmachen Road,
> nr Broxbourn, West Lothian EH52 6NL
> **Tel/fax:** 01506 858931
> **E-mail:** binnycrag@aol.com
> **Opening hours:** 10.00–17.00 Thursday to Monday.
> **Visitors welcome:** yes.
> **Catalogue:** send 3 first class stamps.
> **Payment:** cheque, Visa, Mastercard.
> **Mail order:** yes.
> **Post and packing:** £6.50.
> **Delivery:** 14-21 days.
> **Availability:** from October to March.
> **Refund/replacement:** yes.

GARDENERS' RECOMMENDATIONS: ❀ *"Billy Carruthers, the owner, is an extremely enthusiastic man and will spend hours showing you round his ever expanding nursery of unusual plants and has great plans for developing a large walled garden."* Lady Spencer Nairn. ❀ *"Very enthusiastic and helpful, especially for euphorbias, hostas and meconopsis."* The Hon Ranald and Mrs Noel-Paton. ❀ *"Produces a good catalogue with friendly personal service on site."* Mr and Mrs M Maxwell Stuart.

See map page 398.

Blairhoyle Nursery   A place to go for the more unusual varieties of heather, alpines, conifers, shrubs and hardy perennials. The nursery knows all about the plants it sells and will also undertake garden planning.

> **Blairhoyle Nursery**, East Lodge, Blairhoyle, Port of Menteith,
> Stirling FK8 3LF
> **Tel/fax:** 01877 385669 (ring first for fax).
> **Opening hours:** 13.00–17.30 Wednesday to Monday from March to October.
> **Visitors welcome:** yes.

Catalogue: none.

Payment: cash or cheque.

Mail order: no.

Availability: supplies can be limited and some plants are available only at certain times of year.

Refund/replacement: yes.

GARDENERS' RECOMMENDATIONS: *Recommended by* Mrs M Seymour.

See map page 398.

Bonhard Nurseries   A wide general nursery with alpines, heathers, shrubs, conifers, fruit and ornamental trees.

Bonhard Nurseries, Garden Cottage, Murrayshall Road, Scone, Perth, Tayside PH2 7PQ

Tel/fax: 01738 552791

Opening hours: 10.00–18.00 or dusk if earlier.

Visitors welcome: yes.

Catalogue: fruit tree and rose lists free.

Payment: cash, cheque, major credit cards.

Mail order: no.

Availability: all year round unless seasonal.

Refund/replacement: yes.

Special services: tea room.

GARDENERS' RECOMMENDATIONS: *"Family-run business of high quality. Both the Hinkmans and their staff are extremely helpful. Some unusual plants are from their own propagation, though, of course, a lot are bought in as their success increases. They do not advertise – word of mouth recommendation has seen their business grow."* *"Always helpful with ordering items not in stock."* The Hon Ranald and Mrs Noel-Paton.

See map page 398.

Buckland Plants   Sited 350 feet above sea level on the Galloway coast — which doesn't get much benefit from the Gulf Stream — the nursery specialises in plants which love moist and cool air, generally woodland plants, larger alpines and herbaceous perennials. It is rich

in dicentra, geraniums and primulas. Ideal for gardens with masses of damp shady areas.

Buckland Plants, Whinnieliggate, Kirkcudbright DG6 4XP
Tel/fax: 01557 331323
Opening hours: 10.00–17.00 Thursday to Sunday from 1 March to 1 November.
Visitors welcome: yes.
Payment: cheque or postal order.
Catalogue: send 4 first class stamps or £1.
Mail order: yes. Minimum order £15.
Post and packing: from £6 for orders up to £60.
Delivery: despatched in rotation from end March to October.
Availability: plants listed in catalogue are almost always available. Some rare plants not listed are in very limited supply.
Refund/replacement: yes.
Special services: planting advice.

GARDENERS' RECOMMENDATIONS: ❀ *"A tiny two-person nursery (basically just Rob Asbridge and his wife, Dina) run as much for love as lucre. He grows a wide range of interesting and often unusual plants, anyway, but he also and very commendably continues to grow and stock plants which he personally admires even though they don't actually sell very well. What's more, he's always got something new 'on the go' in the greenhouse which he's keen to show and proselytise for. In his 'spare time' he organises the Short Viability Seed Exchange for the Hardy Plant Society."* Mr Tim Longville. ❀ *"Unusual herbaceous plants."* Dr M R Paton. ❀ *Also recommended by* Dr and Mrs R G Law; Mr C James, Torosay Castle *and* Lady Barbirolli.

See map page 388.

Cally Gardens Michael Wickenden likes his herbaceous perennials as different as possible. He has about 3,500 varieties planted in 30 large borders within an 18th century walled garden. Many come from seed collected in the wild, from Slovakia to Tasmania, New Guinea to the Russian far east. His nursery opens new horizons.

Cally Gardens, Gatehouse of Fleet, Castle Douglas, Dumfries and Galloway DG7 2DJ
Fax and information tape: 01557 815029

Opening hours: 14.00–17.30 Tuesday to Friday, 10.00–17.30 at weekends.

Visitors welcome: yes, during opening hours.

Catalogue: send 3 first class stamps.

Payment: cash, cheque, postal order.

Mail order: yes. Minimum order £15 plus p&p.

Post and packing: from £5.50 for 10 plants to £9 for over 30.

Delivery: March to May for orders received between November and April.

Availability: supplies can be limited and some plants are available only at certain times of year.

Refund/replacement: yes, if notified promptly.

GARDENERS' RECOMMENDATIONS: ✿ *"New or difficult to obtain perennials – very good."* Mr P J Oliver-Smith. ✿ *"For interesting and unusual perennials this catalogue is usually hard to beat. Every year we say we haven't room for any more (or at least John does) but for the past 12 years we have always been tempted!"* Mrs Susan Beck. ✿ *"Handsome walled garden, stylishly planted (particularly impressive in late summer and autumn). Fascinating range of unusual plants, many half hardy, many brought back from his own seed-collecting expeditions.* Mr Tim Longville. ✿ *Also recommended by* Rosemarie Gray, Eggleston Hall *and* Major and Mrs Arbuthnott, Stone House Cottage Gardens.

See map page 397.

Candacraig Garden Nursery Within a walled garden built in 1820 to provide fruit and flowers for the big house adjoining (but now separately owned) is this three-acre nursery which stocks a good selection of meconopsis (including a pack of surplus seeds from the Himalayas for gamblers), Asiatic primulas and their top selling Scotch flame creeper. Most plants from the garden are available.

Candacraig Garden Nursery, Strathdon, Aberdeenshire AB36 8XT

Tel: 01975 651226 **Fax:** 01975 651391

E-mail: candacraig@buchanan.co.uk

Website: http://www.buchanan.co.uk/the_gardens

Opening hours: 10.00–18.00 from 1 May to 30 September. By appointment at other times.

Visitors welcome: yes.

Catalogue: free.

Payment: cheque.

Mail order: yes. Minimum order £15.

Post and packing: £5.85 for up to 5 plants, £7.50 for 6 or more. 10% of order value for orders over £75.

Delivery: 1 week.

Availability: from February to end April and September to end October.

Refund/replacement: yes.

GARDENERS' RECOMMENDATIONS: *"Good plants, lovely walled garden. Liz and Harry offer friendly, helpful advice when required."* Mr and Mrs R Avis. ❀ *"I believe in preserving old strains of cottage plants. The above nursery has done this and has a wonderful collection of meconopsis poppies."*

See map page 398.

Charter House

Charter House Specialists in hardy plants and especially astilbe, erodium, geraniums and hostas. The unfortunate owner had much of the nursery destroyed by winds reaching 120 mph on Boxing Day in 1998 and is trying to rebuild the collection of erodiums still. The nursery also stocks other hardy herbaceous plants.

Charter House Nursery, 2 Nunwood, nr Newbridge, Dumfries and Galloway DG2 0HX

Tel: 01387 720363

Opening hours: 9.00–17.00 Tuesday to Saturday from March to September or by appointment.

Visitors welcome: yes.

Catalogue: free to visitors, 3 first class stamps by mail.

Payment: cash or cheque.

Mail order: yes.

Post and packing: £5.50 for box up to 30kg, £3.50 for additional box.

Delivery: normally a few days.

Availability: quite often limited.

Refund/replacement: yes.

Special services: garden design and planting.

GARDENERS' RECOMMENDATIONS: *"Hardy geraniums – good selection, healthy stock."* Mr and Mrs R Gluckstein. *Also recommended by* Lady Barbirolli *and* Dr M R Paton.

See map page 397.

Christie's Nursery   Alpine specialists with the national collection of gentians along with meconopsis, trilliums and hardy orchids — generally plants which prefer acid soil, though some on the list tolerate lime. The nursery is keen to offer a personal service to callers.

> **Christie's Nursery**, Westmuir, Kirriemuir, Angus DD8 5LP
> **Tel/fax:** 01575 572977
> **E-mail:** christiealpines@btinternet.com
> **Website:** http://www.btinternet.com/~christiealpines
> **Opening hours:** 10.00–17.00 Monday and Wednesday to Saturday from March to October.
> **Visitors welcome:** yes.
> **Catalogue:** send 2 first class stamps.
> **Payment:** cash, cheque, major credit cards.
> **Mail order:** yes.
> **Post and packing:** £5.50 by courier.
> **Delivery:** 10 days.
> **Availability:** mail order in winter only.
> **Refund/replacement:** yes.

GARDENERS' RECOMMENDATIONS: *"Superb range of alpines from the normal to the rare. All well grown. Specialist in meconopsis, gentians, lewisias and many other genera."* Mr and Mrs Mattingley. *"Beautifully laid out display garden. Good selection of healthy plants – speciality is gentians – many varieties. Also alpines."* Mr and Mrs A Gardiner. *"Excellent and always helpful."* Mrs Farquhar Ogilvie. *"Masses of different gentians, meconopsis etc – all reasonably priced."* Mr and Mrs J Stansfeld.

See map page 398.

Crathes Castle Plant Centre   Some of the plants here are grown on site from old varieties found in the gardens of the Scottish National Trust's Crathes Castle. There are alpines and herbaceous perennials.

Crathes Castle Plant Centre, Banchory, Aberdeenshire AB31 5QJ
Tel: 01330 844525 **Fax:** 01330 844797
Opening hours: 1.30–17.30 daily from April to September.
Weekends only in October.
Visitors welcome: yes.
Catalogue: none.
Payment: cash or cheque.
Mail order: no.
Availability: April to October only.
Refund/replacement: yes.

GARDENERS' RECOMMENDATIONS: ✿ *"Very reasonably priced good plants."* Mrs M Seymour.

See map page 398.

Messrs Jack Drake
Helpful catalogue of rock garden plants with special attention to plants which like bogs or wild areas. There are regular new additions and a good seed list.

Messrs Jack Drake, Inshriach Alpine Nursery, Aviemore,
Inverness-shire PH22 1QS
Tel: 01540 651287 **Fax:** 01540 651656
Opening hours: 9.00–17.00 Monday to Friday, 9.00–16.00
Saturday. Closed on Sundays except bank holiday weekends.
Closed from mid-November to mid-February.
Visitors welcome: yes.
Payment: cheque, postal order, Visa, Switch.
Mail order: yes.
Post and packing: £5.20 in UK.
Delivery: 14 days.
Availability: certain varieties are only produced in small
quantities and orders are sent out in the spring, but adverse
weather conditions could lead to delays.
Refund/replacement: yes.

GARDENERS' RECOMMENDATIONS: ✿ *"Specialising in rock garden plants and also a good selection of plants for the woodland garden."* Lady Spencer Nairn. ✿ *"A marvellous specialist nursery which has just been bought by John Borrowman. He has some very exciting plans for new greenhouses etc and I came home with some red meconopsis plants, yellow hellebores and several kinds of fritillaries. I can highly recommend this nursery and emphasise that it will have an even greater variety of stock in a year or two's time."* Mrs W Steuart Fothringham. *"Efficient and reliable mail order."*

See map page 398.

Edrom Nurseries and Garden

The nursery has recently changed hands after being owned by Jim and Alison Jermyn for 20 years. The new owners are Cath Davis and Terry Hunt who are making some changes. The nursery's specialisation in alpine plants will, however, remain.

Edrom Nurseries, Coldingham, Eyemouth, Berwickshire TD14 5TZ
Tel/fax: 01890 771386
E-mail: terryhunt@dial.pipex.com
Opening hours: 9.00–16.30.
Visitors welcome: yes.
Catalogue: 50p if collected, or send 3 first class stamps.
Payment: cash or cheque.
Mail order: yes.
Post and packing: £6.50 for next-day delivery.
Delivery: usually within 2 weeks, but allow 28 days during busy periods.
Availability: supplies of some plants are limited because they are rare or very popular.
Refund/replacement: yes.

GARDENERS' RECOMMENDATIONS: *Recommended by* Mr C James, Torosay Castle.

See map page 398.

Garden Cottage Nursery

I spotted Arisarum proboscoideum on this list — the Mouse Plant — "a child's delight. ...the hidden flowers look exactly like mice running for cover." The whole catalogue has this delightful interest in its plants which are often for woodland, bog or maritime areas. The nursery is beside Inverewe Gardens beside a loch so it can grow quite tender plants.

Garden Cottage Nursery, Tournaig, Poolewe, Achnasheen, Wester Ross IV22 2LH
Tel: 01445 781777 **Fax:** 10445 781777

E-mail: rrushbrooke@easynet.co.uk
Website: http://easyweb.easynet.co.uk/rrushbrooke
Opening hours: 10.30–18.00 from mid-March to mid-October.
Visitors welcome: yes.
Catalogue: send 4 second class stamps.
Payment: cheque.
Mail order: yes. Minimum order £10.
Post and packing: between £5 and £10.
Delivery: orders are sent out between 31 October and 10 April.
Availability: the nursery offers a very wide range so supplies can be limited and some plants are available only at certain times of year.
Refund/replacement: yes.
Special services: horticultural consultancy.

GARDENERS' RECOMMENDATIONS: ❀ *"The knowledgeable owners, Mr and Mrs Rushbrooke, have a lovely collection of unusual herbaceous plants, particularly hardy geraniums, moisture loving plants and some very rare shrubs suitable for west coast gardens and warmer areas. Mr and Mrs Rushbrooke always find the time to offer helpful advice and suggestions. The nursery is set in idyllic west coast of Scotland scenery close to Inverewe Gardens, where many of the plants offered can be seen growing. There is a small garden in the nursery also, where plants can be seen growing in a natural setting."* Mr and Mrs R Vernon, Bluebell Nursery. ❀ *"Family-run nursery, good for many of the larger perennial plants."* Mr and Mrs Mattingley. ❀ *Also recommended by* Mr C James, Torosay Castle.

See map page 398.

Glendoick Gardens Limited I learnt everything I know about rhododendrons from this nursery which supplied me with excellent specimens able to cope with a windswept site on the Pennines. The selection tends more to the species than the cultivar with the rarest having waiting lists of over a year. The plants happily prove that some rhododendrons are beautiful, quite small and easy to grow without taking over.

Glendoick Gardens Ltd, Glencarse, Perth PH2 7NS
Tel: 01738 860205 **Fax:** 01738 860630
E-mail: sales@glendoick.com

Website: http://www.glendoick.com

Opening hours: garden centre 9.00–17.00 daily (carries a large range of nursery stock, nursery 9.00–17.00 Monday to Friday.

Visitors welcome: yes, by appointment.

Payment: cheque, major credit cards.

Mail order: yes.

Post and packing: from £7.50.

Delivery: usually during the month specified by the customer.

Availability: mail order service from 1 October to 1 April.

Refund/replacement: usually.

GARDENERS' RECOMMENDATIONS: ✻ *"The finest rhododendron and azalea nursery in the UK – one of the best in the world. Peter Cox is one of the world's leading authorities on species rhododendrons, having introduced many from the wild himself. Son, Kenneth, is also third generation rhodo nurseryman. Together they have written several outstanding books. Largest selection anywhere. Mail order plants are outstanding. Their Himalayan garden is magnificent. Peter's wife, Patricia, is a RHS award-winning painter."* Mr M J Jurgens. ✻ *"Although the garden centre is ruined by gift shops etc, etc, this is still a superlative propagator of rhododendrons and azaleas and some other trees and shrubs (as in their list). These can be ordered and collected bare-rooted in the dormant season, or they will send."* ✻ *"Slightly mass-production but very good for rhododendrons."* The Hon Ranald and Mrs Noel-Paton. ✻ *"Leave my Access card at home."* Simone Nelson. ✻ *Also recommended by* The Countess of Strathmore, Glamis Castle; The Marquess of Anglesey; Lady Anne Cowdray *and* Mr Bruce Archibold, former chairman RHS Rhododendron, Camellia and Magnolia Group.

See map page 398.

Glenwhan Gardens The plants are nearly all propagated from plants growing in the garden, which can be visited. You can see them as mature versions and evaluate their qualities. If you spot something not on sale, the owners will propagate it for you if they can. Specialities include rhododendron, azalea, primulas and olearias. The gardens themselves are spectacular.

Glenwhan Garden and Nursery, Dunragit, by Stanraer, Dumfries and Galloway DG9 8PH

Tel/fax: 01581 400222

E-mail: glenwha@glenluce.org.uk

Website: http://www.glenluce.org.uk/glenwhan.htm

Opening hours: 10.00–17.00 daily from mid-March to mid-October and by appointment at other times.

Visitors welcome: yes.

Catalogue: none.

Payment: cash or cheque.

Mail order: no.

Availability: mid-March to mid-October.

Refund/replacement: yes.

GARDENERS' RECOMMENDATIONS: ❀ *"Highly recommended."* Dr and Mrs R G Law.

See map page 397.

———————————— ✂ ————————————

Gowanbrae Nursery
This is a general retail nursery without a catalogue which sells a wide range of perennials, shrubs, rhododendrons and conifers. But what does make it different is that it stocks plants which don't mind coastal salt and winds and tries to stock unusual lines too.

Gowanbrae Nursery, Mainsriddle, by Dumfries, Dumfries and Galloway DG2 8AG

Tel: 01387 780273

Opening hours: 10.30–17.00 Tuesday to Friday, 10.00–16.00 Saturday, 11.00–17.00 Sunday. Closed on Monday.

Visitors welcome: yes.

Catalogue: none.

Payment: cash or cheque.

Mail order: no.

Availability: largest selection from March to June.

Refund/replacement: yes, shrubs replaced or refunded in case of failure within 6 months of purchase.

Special services: local garden advice service.

GARDENERS' RECOMMENDATIONS: ❀ *"Very knowledgeable."* Dr M R Paton. ❀ *"Very helpful chap and we have never had a 'failure' from him."* Captain and Mrs J B Blackett. ❀ *"All plants I have had from them have been excellent."* Mrs C H Thomas. *"Highly recommended."* Dr and Mrs R G Law.

See map page 397.

Highland Liliums   Calum and Nancy MacRitchie moved from Windsor to this Highland nursery in 1974. Now their son has joined them and they grow more than lilies. There are alpines and rock plants, herbaceous perennials, shrubs, herbs and climbers. There are lilies still but also a nice selection of wild flowers — dropwort, wild angelica, lady's smock and Bath asparagus — and primulas. This is a very big list, helpfully divided by different coloured papers.

> **Highland Liliums**, Kiltarlity, by Beauly, Inverness-shire IV4 7JQ
> **Tel:** 01463 741365   **Fax:** 01463 741272
> **E-mail:** neilhilil@aol.com
> **Opening hours:** 9.00–17.00 Monday to Saturday.
> **Visitors welcome:** yes.
> **Catalogue:** free.
> **Payment:** cheque, major credit cards.
> **Mail order:** yes. Minimum order £5.
> **Post and packing:** at cost.
> **Delivery:** 2 weeks.
> **Availability:** supplies can be limited and some plants are available only at certain times of year.
> **Refund/replacement:** yes.

Gardeners' Recommendations: *"They have a very large stock of everything and are always most helpful on the telephone."* The Countess of Sutherland. *"Very good plants."* Major Sir David and Lady Butter.

See map page 398.

Kirkdale Nursery   In bleak Aberdeenshire, the nursery manages to stock between 1,200 and 1,500 herbaceous plants along with a comprehensive range of both common and rare trees, plus shrubs, conifers, alpines and rhododendrons, also bare-rooted native and ornamental trees, apples, pears, plums and other fruits and hedging in winter.

Kirkdale Nursery, Daviot, Inverurie, Aberdeenshire AB51 0JL

Tel: 01467 671264 **Fax:** 01467 671282

Opening hours: 10.00–17.00 daily in summer, 10.00–16.00 daily in winter.

Visitors welcome: yes.

Catalogue: available shortly.

Payment: cash, cheque, major credit cards, Switch.

Mail order: no.

Availability: certain items are seasonal, but most are available all year round.

Refund/replacement: depending on circumstances.

GARDENERS' RECOMMENDATIONS: ✤ *"Specialises in plants which are hardy in NE Scotland."* Mr and Mrs C Millar. ✤ *"Knowledgeable nurseryman — many unusual plants, shrubs and especially trees."* Dr F McCance.

See map page 398.

Lilliesleaf Nursery   Though the firm has a good range of herbaceous plants, it really concentrates on epimediums (and holds the national collection of the plant), which can be mail-ordered. This comprises over 120 different varieties which will gradually come on sale. There is also a walled garden to visit.

Lilliesleaf Nursery, Garden Cottage, Linthill, Melrose, Roxburghshire TD6 9HU

Tel/fax: 01835 870415

Opening hours: 9.00–17.00 Monday to Saturday, 10.00–16.00 Sunday from 1 March to 15 December. Mail order all year round.

Visitors welcome: yes.

Catalogue: send 2 second class stamps for list.

Payment: cheque, plus cash or Visa at nursery.

Mail order: yes. Minimum order 3 plants. Epimediums only.

Post and packing: variable, quoted with order.

Delivery: allow 14 days.

Availability: no mail order service from March to May. Many young plants are too fragile for mail order.

Refund/replacement: yes.

Special services: NCCPG National Collection of epimediums at nursery.

Gardeners' Recommendations: *"A wonderful source of epimediums."* Mr and Mrs G Gough. *"Another walled garden but there's nothing stylish about this one: it's planted as a nursery, not as a garden. It's essentially a specialist collection of epimediums and the range is huge and the pricing impressively low — but there is also a continually changing cast of other rarities: you don't see arthropodium or billbergia in every nursery and you certainly don't expect to see them in the Scottish borders."* Mr Tim Longville.

See map page 398.

Logan Botanic Gardens

The stock here is based on the Southern hemisphere and offers many rare and unusual plants along with a range of half-hardy perennials. You can see them in situ in the adjoining gardens.

> **Logan Botanic Gardens**, Port Logan, by Stranraer, Dumfries and Galloway DG9 9ND
> **Tel:** 01776 860231 **Fax:** 01776 860333
> **Opening hours:** 9.30–18.00 daily from March to October.
> **Visitors welcome:** yes.
> **Catalogue:** none.
> **Payment:** cash, cheque, major credit cards.
> **Mail order:** no.
> **Refund/replacement:** by arrangement.
> **Special services:** plant sourcing.

Gardeners' Recommendations: *"Highly recommended."* Dr and Mrs R G Law.

See map page 397.

 Elizabeth MacGregor Perfect for the cottage garden, this nursery offers a wonderful selection of violas, Viola cornuta, odorata and violettas as well as loved perennials such as campanulas, penstemons and geraniums.

> **Elizabeth MacGregor**, Ellenbank, Tongland Road, Kirkcudbright, DG6 4UU
> **Tel/fax:** 01557 330620

Opening hours: 10.30–17.00 Friday and Saturday from May to September.

Visitors welcome: yes.

Catalogue: send 4 first class, or 5 second class stamps.

Payment: cheque.

Mail order: yes. Minimum order 6 plants.

Post and packing: £5.75 to £14.50.

Delivery: orders are sent out from March to May.

Availability: supplies can be limited and some plants are available only at certain times of year.

Refund/replacement: yes.

GARDENERS' RECOMMENDATIONS: ✪ *"Certainly the best mail order nursery we have come across and a lovely interesting catalogue."* Mr and Mrs G A Jones. ✪ *"A fascinating nursery …the violas in the greenhouse have to be smelt to be believed."* Mr and Mrs J H McBain. ✪ *"Viola specialist who also offers an interesting range of 'cottagey' perennials, many of them towards the tender end of the hardiness spectrum (lots of penstemons). Another nursery with walled garden attached – and another handsomely planted one: the huge formal 'squares' of violas are a particularly stunning sight."* Mr Tim Longville. ✪ *"She is a propagator of great ability. Her postal service could not be bettered."* Mr A B Measures. ✪ *"Friendly personal service on site."* Mr and Mrs M Maxwell Stuart. ✪ *Also recommended by* Mr C James, Torosay Castle *and* The Earl Haig.

See map page 397.

Macplants As you might expect, a Scottish nursery which grows all its plants in three nurseries in East Lothian. Most are herbaceous perennials and there is an excellent choice — herbaceous paeonies, crocosmia, cardoon — in just the varieties we like. There are also ferns, grasses, alpines and bamboos.

Macplants, Berrybanks Nursery, 5 Boggs Holdings, Pencaitland, EH34 5BA

Tel: 01875 341179 **Fax:** 01875 340842

E-mail: sales.macplants@virgin.net

Opening hours: 10.30 to 17.00 daily from mid-March to October.

Visitors welcome: yes.

Catalogue: send 3 first class stamps.

Payment: cash or cheque.

Mail order: no.

Availability: seasonal, but good range of stock available throughout the year.

Refund/replacement: in case of genuine complaint.

GARDENERS' RECOMMENDATIONS: ✿ *"Excellent choice of perennials and alpines. Very friendly and helpful service. Family run."* Sir Charles and Lady Fraser. ✿ *"Good and varied stock and the owners very helpful and friendly."* ✿ *"Excellent for herbaceous plants, ground cover – limited in shrubs but will obtain if requested."* Major Hon Colin and Mrs Dalrymple. ✿ *"This is an excellent nursery, run by the MacNaughton family who are tremendously knowledgeable and very helpful. They have a wide range of very healthy and unusual plants, including many which they have bred themselves. They specialise in herbaceous and alpine plants. Their own garden nearby, with an attractive riverside walk, is also open by arrangement."* Professor and Mrs D Rankin.

See map page 398.

Norc-Celt

Norc-Celt   Based about as far north as you can get, the nursery offers plants which cope with the worst of weathers including Chrysanthemum maximum Highland White Dream.

Norc-Celt, Skerray, Sutherland KW14 7TH

Tel/fax: 01641 521450/521445

Opening hours: 10.30–17.00 from May to October.

Visitors welcome: yes.

Catalogue: none.

Payment: cheque.

Mail order: yes.

Post and packing: by quotation.

Delivery: by arrangement according to stock levels.

Availability: early spring and October.

Refund/replacement: by arrangement.

GARDENERS' RECOMMENDATIONS: ✿ *"Highland White Dream is their speciality but they have shrubs and begonias and lots of other fill-*

ins. They are grown locally so we know they will flourish."
The Countess of Sutherland.

See map page 398.

Sheila Northway

Sheila Northway   A list of primulas and auriculas which are perfect little plants for most situations. Auriculas, especially, are good for windowsills, tiny town gardens or an outdoor room. The list is extremely helpful.

> **Sheila Northway**, Craig Lodge, Balmaclellan, Castle Douglas, Kirkcudbrightshire DG7 3QR
>
> **Tel:** 01644 420661
>
> **Opening hours:** by appointment only. Closed December and January.
>
> **Visitors welcome:** yes, by appointment.
>
> **Catalogue:** send sae.
>
> **Payment:** cheque.
>
> **Mail order:** yes. Minimum order £10.
>
> **Post and packing:** £4.50 for up to 6 plants, £6 for 6–15 plants, at cost thereafter. Express delivery at cost.
>
> **Delivery:** allow 21 days.
>
> **Availability:** most stock is home-raised therefore supplies can be limited.
>
> **Refund/replacement:** yes.

GARDENERS' RECOMMENDATIONS: ✿ *Recommended by* Mr Tim Longville.

See map page 397.

Orchardton Nursery

Orchardton Nursery   The family-run nursery is set in a fine 18th century walled garden beside Orchardton House. They have plenty of rare and unusual shrubs, bamboos, perennials and, of course, climbers.

> **Orchardton Nursery**, Orchardton House, Auchencairn, Castle Douglas, Kirkcudbrightshire DG7 1QL
>
> **Tel:** 01556 640366
>
> **Opening hours:** 12.00–18.00 Sunday to Tuesday from April to October.
>
> **Visitors welcome:** yes.

Catalogue: none.
Payment: cash or cheque.
Mail order: no.
Availability: April to October.
Refund/replacement: yes.

GARDENERS' RECOMMENDATIONS: *Recommended by* Dr M R Paton.

See map page 397.

Raemoir Garden Centre
This is a general garden centre which offers a wide range of stock designed for a wide range of customers.

Raemoir Garden Centre, Raemoir Road, Banchory, Aberdeenshire AB3 4ER
Tel: 01330 825059 **Fax:** 01330 825058
Opening hours: 9.00–17.30 daily.
Visitors welcome: yes.
Catalogue: none.
Payment: cash, cheque, major credit cards.
Mail order: no.
Delivery: free local delivery service.
Availability: seasonal stock.
Refund/replacement: yes.

GARDENERS' RECOMMENDATIONS: *"Good garden centre with good plants."*

See map page 398.

The Scottish Bamboo Nursery
In the last century, bamboos were brought back from their native lands by the far-flung traders, soldiers and adventurers of Scotland and lovingly tended in high-walled gardens there — especially the so-called bamboosalem of Inverewe. This fine catalogue shows bamboos surviving an Aberdeenshire winter which should convince beginners that the plant is very tough. The list is heavily illustrated and includes no fewer than four chusqueas (the hardest to find) culeou, breviglumis, montana and quila. Most impressive.

The Scottish Bamboo Nursery, Middlemuir Farm, Craigievar, Alford, Aberdeenshire AB33 8JS

Tel: 01975 581316 **Fax:** 01975 581316/563217

Opening hours: 10.00–18.00 Wednesday to Sunday and bank holidays.

Visitors welcome: yes.

Catalogue: £1.

Payment: cheque, major credit cards.

Mail order: yes.

Post and packing: £8.90 plus VAT for up to 5 plants.

Delivery: 5 working days.

Availability: all year round.

Refund/replacement: by arrangement.

GARDENERS' RECOMMENDATIONS: *"Hardy bamboos – a good selection."* Mr and Mrs A Gardiner.

See map page 398.

Tough Alpine Nursery

The nursery is situated in Tough, Aberdeenshire and the plants grown in this cold and windy spot have to perform. The list is big, with plenty of saxifrages, helianthemum and primulas with some excellent salix.

Tough Alpine Nursery, Westhaybogs, Tough, Alford, Aberdeenshire AB33 8DU

Tel: 01975 562783 **Fax:** 01975 563561

E-mail: fred@alpines.co.uk

Website: http://www.alpines.co.uk

Opening hours: 10.00–16.00 Monday to Friday.

Visitors welcome: yes.

Catalogue: send 3 second class stamps.

Payment: cash or cheque.

Mail order: yes. Minimum order £15.

Post and packing: from £5 for up to 10 plants to £20 for 70.

Delivery: 2 weeks, depending on weather conditions.

Availability: mail order from October to March only.

Refund/replacement: yes, if notified within 7 days.

GARDENERS' RECOMMENDATIONS: *"Excellent selection of alpines, well described and notes on cultivation. Many uncommon*

plants. Well laid out rock garden showing many plants hardy in exposed situation. Also alpine house." Mr and Mrs A Gardiner.

See map page 398.

See also: Kinlochlaich Gardens, page 356.

Nurseries in Wales

Aberconwy Nursery   The nursery is spectacularly sited in Conwy valley with wonderful views towards Snowdon. It has a windy climate ideal for alpines and woodland plants. It is especially well-known for Himalayan gentians, some of which it has introduced; also hellebores, meconopsis, primula and dwarf rhododendrons.

> **Aberconwy Nursery**, Graig, Glan Conwy, Conwy LL28 5TL
> **Tel:** 01492 580875
> **Opening hours:** 10.00–17.00 Tuesday to Sunday (closed Monday) from February to October.
> **Visitors welcome:** yes.
> **Catalogue:** send 2 second class stamps.
> **Payment:** cheque, Visa, Mastercard.
> **Mail order:** no.
> **Availability:** some plants sell out quickly.
> **Refund/replacement:** by arrangement.

GARDENERS' RECOMMENDATIONS: ✿ *"Small, helpful and really knowledgeable."* Mr and Mrs J. Major. ✿ *"Excellent general nursery with vast range of specialist alpines and small shrubs. Highly personal and helpful service, advice being freely given. Nursery is outstandingly well kept. Over a period of about 12 years we have had a highly satisfactory pleasureable customer relationship (ie the plants always do well). It stands out above the many other nurseries in the vicinity."* Drs J E and B E J Riding. ✿ *"A superb nursery with an adjacent magnificent garden. Keith Lever and his wife Rachel are in personal attendance and are always most helpful. Quite the best we know."* Mr and Mrs J S Buchanan. ✿ *"A wide range of interesting plants, welcoming personal attention and really knowledgeable staff."* Mr and Mrs M Thomas. ✿ *"Helpful and knowledgeable with a good stock of well maintained plants, home grown."* Jennifer Rickards.

See map page 395.

Aled Plants   Barbara and Jim Buchanan simply propagate the plants which are in their own garden — but, to their own surprise, discovered that they have more than 300 varieties for sale. These include alpines and perennials chosen because they are unusual. The garden is open under the NGS scheme.

Aled Plants, Tyn yr Odyn, Bryn rhyd yr Arian, Llannefydd, Denbigh
LL16 5HD

Tel: 01745 870394

Opening hours: most weekends and often during the week.
Ring first.

Visitors welcome: yes.

Catalogue: none.

Payment: cash or cheque.

Mail order: no.

Availability: March to October.

Refund/replacement: yes.

GARDENERS' RECOMMENDATIONS: ✹ *"This nursery is owned
by a dedicated and knowledgeable couple who have a beautiful
cottage-type garden. Mr Buchanan does all his own propagating,
running a small business from the house. He specialises in shrubs
and perennials with many unusual varieties."* Mr and Mrs
A Rumbold.

See map page 395.

Banwy Valley Nursery
A good general list of shrubs, trees and
perennials boosted with a nice choice of magnolias and
rhododendrons. You could stock a garden here without going
anywhere else.

Banwy Valley Nursery, Foel, Llangadfan, nr Welshpool, Powys
SY21 0PT

Tel: 01938 820281 **Fax:** 01938 820281

E-mail: syd@banwyvalley.swinternet.co.uk

Website: http://www.freespace.virgin.net/banwy.valley/

Opening hours: 10.00–17.00 (dusk in winter). Closed on Monday
except bank holidays.

Visitors welcome: yes.

Catalogue: send sae or can be downloaded from website.

Payment: cash, cheque or postal order.

Mail order: perennials only, September to March inclusive.

Post and packing: £4.

Delivery: 28 days.

Availability: supplies of some plants can be limited.

Refund/replacement: yes.

GARDENERS' RECOMMENDATIONS: ⊕ *"A small friendly nursery where Sid and Carol Luck always make time for customers. They told me that if customers had taken the trouble to find them then they wouldn't want to find the usual plants, but rather something special. I've been using them for years and always find a new treasure when I visit. Everything is in top condition and very realistically priced."* Mr and Mrs D Bennett.

See map page 394.

Bodnant Garden Nursery

Nurseries attached to famous gardens are always worth a visit and none more so than Bodnant. The plants in the garden were collected by such famous names as George Forrest, Ernest Wilson, Frank Kingdon-Ward and Frank Ludlow and the nursery is able to offer some of them exclusively. As well as this, because the plants come from the garden, you know you'll get the most meritorious varieties. The garden centre is owned by the Aberconway family, gardeners and stalwarts of the RHS for generations, but fully co-operates with the National Trust who own the gardens.

Bodnant Garden Nursery Ltd, Tal y Cafn, Colwyn Bay LL28 5RF
Tel: 01492 650731 **Fax:** 01492 650863
E-mail: sales@bodnant.co.uk
Website: http://www.bodnant.co.uk
Opening hours: 10.00–17.00 daily.
Visitors welcome: yes.
Catalogue: free or £2 refundable to plant centre visitors.
Payment: cash, cheque, major credit/debit cards.
Mail order: yes.
Post and packing: £12.50 for orders up to £30, 25% for orders from £30 to £75, 20% for orders £75 to £150, free thereafter.
Delivery: 7–10 days.
Availability: supplies of some plants may be limited.
Refund/replacement: in case of genuine complaint.
Special services: regular mailing of availability lists. Internet order facility.

GARDENERS' RECOMMENDATIONS: ⊕ *"I am usually tempted most autumns: their mail order is excellent."* ⊕ *"I like the way they sell seedlings as well as warranted species and hybrids and, although they have suffered yuppification to some degree and tend to open at hours to suit themselves rather than their customers, they do have some interesting plants and they do know how to look after those which they buy in. Rather expensive."* *"Very good."* Dr and Mrs R L Belsey. *"Good range with some unusual plants."* Mr and Mrs E W Dyer.

See map page 395.

Cefn Du Nurseries

Cefn Du Nurseries You can get trees up to 10 metres high here along with large specimens of evergreen shrubs and conifers, hedging and some perennials. They will help with planting the big trees, will create ponds and pools and advise on drainage.

Cefn Du Nurseries, Maesmawr, nr Welshpool, Powys SY22 6YF

Tel/fax: 01938 500208, mobile: 07967 021257/07977 078087

Opening hours: 10.00–18.00.

Visitors welcome: yes.

Catalogue: none.

Payment: cash or cheque.

Mail order: no.

Delivery: 1-2 weeks depending on season.

Availability: mature stock from September to April.

Refund/replacement: yes.

Special services: planting and delivery service.

GARDENERS' RECOMMENDATIONS:
 "A young couple rebuilding a 400 year-old black and white house and a lovely clean, spotless nursery." Ms Pritchard Evans.

See map page 394.

Paul Christian Rare Plants A list so abstruse that it's hard to find anything you know. Dr. Christian brings in plants from the wild and from what are known as Documented Nursery Salvage, a scheme run by the US to save plants from areas which are about to be destroyed. Though little is recognisable in the catalogue, it is extremely helpfully written and very, very tempting.

Paul Christian, P O Box 468, Wrexham LL13 9XR
Tel: 01978 366399 **Fax:** 01978 266466
E-mail: paul@rareplants.co.uk
Website: http://www.rareplants.co.uk
Opening hours: not open to the public.
Catalogue: £1 for 2 issues (summer and winter) in UK, £2 overseas.
Payment: cheque, major credit cards.
Mail order: yes.
Post and packing: £2 per order.
Delivery: varies according to season.
Availability: supplies of certain plants are limited and some are available in season only.
Refund/replacement: yes.
Special services: selection of collections, or gift collections.

GARDENERS' RECOMMENDATIONS: ✤ *"Specialist in rare bulbs, corms etc – expensive but no one else has such a range."* Mr P J Oliver-Smith. ✤ *"Good website, mail order prompt response, with some excellent rare bulbs stock."* Mr Mark Robson.

Crûg Farm Plants This nursery loves to introduce new plants to Britain collected in exotic places. It also stocks plants which like the shade. The list is full of unfamiliar names — without, it must be said, much help in describing them.

Crûg Farm Plants, Griffith's Crossing, Caerarfon, Gwynedd LL55 1TU
Tel/fax: 01248 670232
E-mail: bleddyn&sue@crug-farm.demon.co.uk
Website: http://www.crug-farm.demon.co.uk
Opening hours: 10.00–18.00 Thursday to Sunday from last Saturday in February to last Sunday in September, plus bank holidays.
Visitors welcome: yes.
Catalogue: send sae plus 2 second class stamps.
Payment: cash, cheque, major credit cards.
Mail order: no.
Availability: many plants may sell out as the season progresses.
Refund/replacement: by arrangement.

GARDENERS' RECOMMENDATIONS: *"This is an outstanding enthusiast's nursery."* Mr Tim Longville. *"Another fantastic find – too far away to visit often unfortunately. Very interesting selection of hardy geraniums, pulmonarias etc."* Mr and Mrs H Lock. *"Simply a treasure trove of hitherto (to me) unknown/unseen plants. My bank balance suffers a severe shortfall after an annual visit. Well known to serious plantaholics."* Mr and Mrs B P Kavanagh. *"Always good plants and excellent service. We pay several visits each year."* Mrs Wisden and Miss Hawkes. *"Would like to have recommended Crûg Farm Plants but their plants have become ridiculously expensive. Unusual stuff though."* Mr and Mrs M R Everett. *Also recommended by* Mrs R Alexander of The English Gardening School at the Chelsea Physic Garden.

See map page 395.

Dibley's Nurseries

This firm holds the national collection of streptocarpus and has won 10 consecutive gold medals at Chelsea, so you can see they know what's what. Other specialities are foliage begonias, coleus and gesneriads — all exotic looking plants.

Dibley's Nurseries, Llanelidan, Ruthin, Clwyd LL15 2LG
Tel: 01978 790677   **Fax:** 01978 790668
Opening hours: 10.00–17.00 daily from April to September.
Visitors welcome: yes.
Catalogue: free.
Payment: cash, cheque, Visa, Mastercard, Switch, Delta.
Mail order: yes.
Post and packing: £3.
Delivery: 28 days.
Availability: March to September.
Refund/replacement: 30-day guarantee.

GARDENERS' RECOMMENDATIONS: *Recommended by* Christopher Lloyd, Great Dixter.

See map page 395.

Dingle Nurseries Lots of gardeners are willing to drive miles to visit this nursery for its helpful and knowledgeable staff and beautiful rural setting. Apart from this, the list is wide-ranging and orders for trees, climbers, bare-rooted hedging, etc can be faxed in advance.

> **Dingle Nurseries**, Frochas, Welshpool, Powys SY21 9JD
> **Tel:** 01938 555145 **Fax:** 01938 555778
> **Website:** http://www.arik.co.uk/dinglenurseries
> **Opening hours:** 9.00–17.00 every day except Tuesday.
> **Visitors welcome:** yes.
> **Catalogue:** free.
> **Payment:** cash, cheque, major credit cards.
> **Mail order:** no.
> **Delivery:** allow a week or so depending on season.
> **Availability:** seasonal e.g. herbaceous.
> **Refund/replacement:** yes, depending on circumstances.
> **Special services:** 4-acre garden adjoining the nursery is open to the public on payment of a small fee to charity.

GARDENERS' RECOMMENDATIONS: ✪ *"They are not cheap but the plants are bigger and better with some unusual and rare plants, plus a wonderful garden to view."* Mrs P Longley. ✪ *"Owners are informative and very helpful. Prices not cheap but very worth the money. The Dingle is very peaceful and colour in the autumn is outstanding."* Col and Mrs J G T Polley. ✪ *"Amazing terraced garden. Good attached nursery – strengths are shrubs, trees and roses but one always finds some unusual and interesting plants. It's grown from a small individual concern to a quite large business but still very much 'hands on' by the family owners."* Mr and Mrs B P Kavanagh. ✪ *"Family business, excellent quality at reasonable prices, many unusual plants, lovely garden."* Mr and Mrs A S Rankine.

See map page 394.

Eastwick Plant Centre The nursery tries to grow new, unusual and rare varieties of plants and, because these can be difficult to assess, will offer free advice on how to grow them.

> **Eastwick Plant Centre**, Knolton, nr Overton-on-Dee, Wrexham, LL13 0LG

Tel: 01978 710848 **Fax:** 01978 710072
Opening hours: 9.00–18.00.
Visitors welcome: yes.
Catalogue: none.
Payment: cash, cheque, major credit cards.
Mail order: no.
Availability: supplies can be limited and some plants are available only at certain times of year.
Refund/replacement: yes.

GARDENERS' RECOMMENDATIONS: ❀ *"This is the nursery I use most and find it good with a wide variety of plants and shrubs."* ❀ *"There one deals with gardeners not merely a cashier."* Mr and Mrs Hollington.

See map page 395.

Eucalyptus Nurseries The eucalyptus and acacia specialists who send a most useful planting guide separately with their price list (others please follow.) Eucalyptus trees can be very trying to grow as they fall over all the time. Other than that, they have the most splendidly different barks, extraordinary leaf colour and shape and grow like anything. I am a fan.

Eucalyptus Nurseries, Carrog, Corwen, Denbighshire LL21 9LD
Tel/fax: 01490 430671
E-mail: info@eucalyptus.co.uk
Website: http://www.eucalyptus.co.uk
Opening hours: 9.00–16.15 Monday to Friday. Closed weekends and bank holidays.
Visitors welcome: yes.
Catalogue: send first class stamp.
Payment: cash, cheque, Visa, Mastercard, Switch, Delta.
Mail order: yes. Minimum order 3 plants.
Post and packing: included.
Delivery: 8–10 days.
Availability: all year round.
Refund/replacement: yes.

GARDENERS' RECOMMENDATIONS: ❀ *"Eucalyptus and acacia. Very wide range. Very helpful advice on cultivation and hardiness.*

Excellent quality and packaging and good value." Mr and Mrs P
Jackson. *Also recommended by* Dr and Mrs R G Law *and* Mr and
Mrs J Scott.

See map page 395.

Farmyard Nurseries   You can actually stay at this nursery in a
self-catering cottage; there are show gardens and a café too. They also
have over 3,000 varieties of plants grown in three acres 600 feet
above sea level with tricyrtis, hosta, hellebores, euphorbias, violas and
geraniums among their specialities. Expert advice is always available.

> **Farmyard Nurseries**, Llandysul, Carmarthenshire SA44 4RL
> **Tel:** 01559 363389   **Fax:** 01559 362200
> **E-mail:** farmyard.nurseries@btinternet.com
> **Website:** http://www.btinternet.com/~farmyard.nurseries
> **Opening hours:** 9.00–17.30 daily.
> **Visitors welcome:** yes.
> **Catalogue:** send 4 first class stamps.
> **Payment:** cheque, Visa, Switch.
> **Mail order:** yes.
> **Post and packing:** £10.
> **Delivery:** 2-3 weeks according to availability.
> **Availability:** all year round, except seasonal plants.
> **Refund/replacement:** yes.

GARDENERS' RECOMMENDATIONS: *"A very well stocked
nursery – reasonable prices – very knowledgeable. They specialise in
hellebores."* Mr and Mrs I Russell.

See map page 394.

Ladybird Nursery   A good general nursery offering a wide variety
of plants from ornamental trees and conifers, hedging, shrubs, roses,
fruit trees, annuals and perennials along with gardeners' sundries.

> **Ladybird Nursery**, Ciliau Aeron, Lampeter, Ceredigion SA48 7SG
> **Tel/fax:** 01570 470480
> **E-mail:** lbn@fsbdial.co.uk
> **Opening hours:** 9.00–18.00 (17.00 in winter) Monday and
> Wednesday to Saturday, 10.00–16.00 Sunday.

Visitors welcome: yes.

Catalogue: none.

Payment: cash or cheque.

Mail order: no.

Availability: supplies can be limited and some plants are available only at certain times of year.

Refund/replacement: yes.

GARDENERS' RECOMMENDATIONS: *"Small but well run. Personal attention – always helpful. No garden alongside."* Mr and Mrs I Callan.

See map page 394.

Little Rhyndaston Nurseries This is a small family-run nursery which was started in 1976 — husband, wife, daughter and son in law, propagate their own plants or sow them from seed . They also concentrate totally on their plants "preferring to put all our efforts into producing a plant which will grow in the customer's garden" which sounds a good idea. The list is large and comprehensive.

Little Rhyndaston Nursery, Haycastle, Haverfordwest, Pembrokeshire SA62 5PT

Tel: 01437 710656

Opening hours: 9.00–17.00 Monday to Saturday, 11.00–17.00 Sunday. Closed in August.

Visitors welcome: yes.

Catalogue: none.

Payment: cheque, Visa, Mastercard, Switch.

Mail order: no.

Availability: some items are seasonal, and others are grown in small batches and may sell quickly.

Refund/replacement: yes, within 7 days.

GARDENERS' RECOMMENDATIONS: *Recommended by* Mr and Mrs E Fitzwilliams.

See map page 394.

Jean Gomersall at Llwyn Nursery Problems with slugs? The nursery here is dedicated to growing plants which the beasts will

avoid. It has a wide selection of ferns, herbs, hebes, hardy geraniums and shrubs, generally in small quantities.

Jean Gomersall at Llwyn Nursery, Llwyn, Harlech, Gwynedd LL46 2PR

Tel: 01766 780474

Opening hours: 11.00–18.00 daily from mid-March to October, and occasionally in winter.

Visitors welcome: yes.

Catalogue: none.

Payment: cash or cheque.

Mail order: no.

Availability: 1,000 different plants are available at any time, but supplies can sometimes be limited.

Refund/replacement: yes.

Special services: Plants for sale are displayed in the nursery garden, situated in Snowdonia with magnificent views of sea and mountains.

GARDENERS' RECOMMENDATIONS: ✤ *"Mrs Gomersall is a keen and knowledgeable plantswoman who propagates from all her own garden material. She has thousands of plants for sale at the house. A point of interest is that she will not grow anything that is attacked by slugs."* Mr and Mrs A Rumbold.

See map page 395.

Rose Villa Nursery   Here you will get hardy garden plants and those for bedding, hanging baskets plus alpines, herbs, shrubs and trees. There's a garden shop too.

Rose Villa Nursery, Cwmrhydyceirw Road, Morriston, Swansea, West Glamorgan SA6 6LJ

Tel/fax: 01792 772602

E-mail: rvn@swig.online.co.uk

Opening hours: 10.00–18.00 Monday to Saturday in summer (BST); 10.00–17.00 Sundays, bank holidays and in winter.

Visitors welcome: yes.

Catalogue: none.

Payment: cash, cheque, major credit cards except American Express, Switch.

Mail order: no.

Delivery: local delivery only.

Availability: open ground stock, bedding plants and hanging baskets in season. Container grown stock generally available all year round.

Refund/replacement: yes.

Special services: garden design and landscape construction service. Hanging baskets refilled.

GARDENERS' RECOMMENDATIONS: *"Mr Bracewell is very knowledgeable, stocks a wide range of plants and is always very helpful. Off the beaten track, but well worth seeking out."* Mrs Anne Knatchbull-Hugessen, Cilwern Plants.

See map page 394.

Rosemary's Farmhouse Nursery   Rosemary Pryce has just opened her nursery — and has already been recommended, to her delight. The farmhouse, in beautiful mid-Wales, dates from 1680 and was bought in 1996. It allowed her to "realise a life-long ambition to run a nursery. We have 15 acres of land which includes areas of wetland." The nursery specialises in unusual perennials along with grasses. A collection of hardy geraniums is currently being built up.

Rosemary's Farmhouse Nursery, Llwyn-y-Moel-Gau, Llanfihangel, Llanfyllin, Powys SY22 5JE

Tel/fax: 01691 648196

Opening hours: 10.00–17.00 daily except Wednesday, by appointment only.

Visitors welcome: yes.

Catalogue: none at present, but a plant list should be available in the future.

Payment: cash or cheque.

Mail order: no.

Availability: seasonal.

Refund/replacement: yes.

Special services: customers may visit the garden to see plants in situ.

GARDENERS' RECOMMENDATIONS: *"New nursery in unspoilt countryside, offering a varied selection of hardy plants, shrubs and herbs all grown on site and sold along with advice on how to care for your purchases."* Mr and Mrs M Dearden.

See map page 394.

Waterwheel Nursery   A collection of trees, shrubs, climbers and perennials from a nursery in the splendidly named Bully Hole Bottom. Though the list is not huge, its spread is very wide, from five different oaks to 20 or more violas.

Waterwheel Nursery, Bully Hole Bottom, Usk Road, nr Shirenewton, Chepstow, Monmouthshire NP16 6SA

Tel: 01291 641577 **Fax:** 01291 641851

Opening hours: 9.00–18.00 Tuesday to Saturday plus bank holiday Mondays.

Visitors welcome: yes.

Catalogue: send 2 first class stamps.

Payment: cash or cheque.

Mail order: no.

Availability: most plants available all year.

Refund/replacement: replacement.

GARDENERS' RECOMMENDATIONS: ❋ *"This is run by a husband and wife team, it is a touch difficult to find without their map but is worth the effort. It is charming and carries a wide selection of plants, many of which are difficult to find. Prices are exceptionally low."* D S Taylor. ❋ *"Bully Hole Bottom is a magical place where, years ago, rare trees were dug up for us from some hidden part of the woodland, where rare shrubs are ordered for you by the friendly and knowledgeable owners who are able and willing to tell you everything you may wish to know about the many treasures in their nursery."* Mr R S Edwards. ❋ *"They offer an extremely wide range of unusual trees and shrubs chiefly and also good perennials. The advice given is always excellent with plenty of time given. The nursery itself if a bit haphazard which to me makes it more exciting as one always discovers a 'treasure' somewhere. The plants are very reasonable too."* Mrs G James.

"Excellent stock – wide selection – lovely nursery and garden. Owners take great interest in obtaining the plants I want and are knowledgeable and it is in lovely country and makes a super day out. I usually place an order well in advance and get useful information about what I have chosen." Miss J Loraine, Greencombe Garden Trust. ❀ *"Hidden away this is well worth a few wrong turns and doubts about one's wife's skills at map-reading. Charlotte Evans has a wide range of unusual plants. A planned hour took three!"* Mr E Harper. ❀ *Also recommended by* Derry Watkins, Special Plants.

See map page 394.

Woodland Services and Supplies Ltd Whatever its name, this nursery specialises in a good range of top and soft fruit and has over 150 varieties of roses. Less surprisingly, it offers forest trees, bare-root hedging and many unusual garden trees.

> **Woodland Services and Supplies Ltd**, Brooklands, Mardy, Abergavenny, Gwent NP7 6NU
>
> **Tel:** 01873 855431 **Fax:** 01873 858864
>
> **Opening hours:** 8.00–17.00 Monday to Friday, 10.30–17.30 Saturday, 11.00–17.00 Sunday.
>
> **Visitors welcome:** yes.
>
> **Catalogue:** none.
>
> **Payment:** cash, cheque, all credit cards except Diners.
>
> **Mail order:** no.
>
> **Availability:** bare-root hedging and trees during winter only.
>
> **Refund/replacement:** yes.
>
> **Special services:** free advice at the customer's garden when a reasonable number of plants are purchased.

GARDENERS' RECOMMENDATIONS: *Recommended by* Mrs J F Fox.

See map page 394.

See also: Cilwern Plants Nursery and Gardens, page 351; **Cottage Garden Perennials,** page 352.

GARDENERS WHO RECOMMEND THEIR OWN NURSERIES

Caves Folly Nursery

This is an organic nursery, one of only a handful in the country. They offer herbaceous perennials, grasses and alpines, all container grown.

Caves Folly Nursery, Evendine Lane, Colwall, nr Malvern, Worcestershire WR13 6DU

Tel: 01684 540631

E-mail: willeaper@cavesfolly.freeserve.co.uk

Opening hours: 10.00–17.00 Thursday to Saturday.

Visitors welcome: yes.

Catalogue: plant list free.

Payment: cash or cheque.

Mail order: no.

Availability: supplies of rare and unusual plants are limited.

Refund/replacement: yes.

See map page 394.

Sheila Chapman Clematis

It's almost impossible to have too many clematis. They can be grown everywhere and the many varieties flower over a long period. Sheila Chapman has an excellent list, offers advice on growing the trickier ones and holds lessons on pruning, which can also be difficult.

Sheila Chapman Clematis at Crowther Nurseries Ltd, Ongar Road, Abridge, Essex RM4 1AA

Tel: 01708 688090 **Fax:** 01708 688677

Opening hours: 9.30–17.00.

Visitors welcome: yes.

Catalogue: £1 or 4 first class stamps.

Payment: cash, cheque, Visa, Mastercard.

Mail order: no.

Availability: supplies of certain rare varieties are limited, but most are available all year round.

Refund/replacement: plants are guaranteed for 14 days from purchase.

Special services: tea shop with home-cooked food, group visits, pruning demonstrations.

See map page 392.

Cilwern Plants Nursery and Gardens Sited in the pretty Welsh countryside near Llandeilo, this small nursery run by Anne Knatchbull-Hugessen specialises in perennials, especially hardy geraniums, along with shrubs, grasses and a few trees. She is keen to offer customers advice and also creates fresh wreaths and other decorations for Christmas.

Cilwern Plants Nursery and Garden, Cilwern, Talley, Llandeilo, Carmarthenshire SA19 7YH

Tel: 01558 685526

Opening hours: 11.00–18.00 Tuesday to Sunday from March to October, 14.00–17.00 bank holiday Mondays. By appointment from November to February.

Visitors welcome: yes.

Catalogue: none.

Payment: cash or cheque.

Mail order: no.

Availability: all year round.

Refund/replacement: yes.

Special services: planting plans.

See map page 394.

Congham Hall Herb Gardens An unusual nursery in that it is alongside a country house hotel and restaurant (so gardeners can stay while they make up their minds.) They grow about 700 different herbs of which 300 are for sale according to season.

Congham Hall Herb Gardens, Congham Hall Country House Hotel, Grimston, Kings Lynn, Norfolk PE32 1AH

Tel: 01485 600250 **Fax:** 01485 601191

E-mail: reception@conghamhallhotel.demon.co.uk

Opening hours: 14.00–16.00 daily except Saturday from April to September.

Visitors welcome: yes.

Catalogue: none.

Payment: cash, cheque, major credit cards.

Mail order: no.

Availability: seasonal.

Refund/replacement: by arrangement.

See map page 393.

Cottage Garden Perennials

Cottage Garden Perennials The nursery sells what you would expect: the delightful Barnhaven primulas, hardy arum lilies, lobelias, grasses and campanulas — all grown without the use of pesticides.

> **Cottage Garden Perennials**, Brynsifi, Cwm Ifor Road, off Trimsaren Road, Llanelli, Carmarthenshire SA15 4RE
>
> **Tel/fax:** 01554 810294 (evenings)
>
> **Opening hours:** by appointment. Plants are also available at Llanelli open air market Thursday and Saturday from April to August.
>
> **Visitors welcome:** yes, by appointment.
>
> **Catalogue:** none.
>
> **Payment:** cheque.
>
> **Mail order:** yes. Minimum order £20 plus p&p.
>
> **Post and packing:** at cost.
>
> **Delivery:** 7–10 days.
>
> **Availability:** April to September.
>
> **Refund/replacement:** yes.
>
> **Special services:** hedge laying and tree maintenance from October to January.

See map page 394.

Coughton Court

Coughton Court The plant centre is attached to the wide-ranging gardens of Coughton Court itself and most of the herbaceous plants, shrubs, trees and climbers are propagated from the gardens. The whole makes a splendid day out with visits to the house, gardens, restaurant and plant centre.

> **Coughton Court**, Alcester, Warwickshire B49 5JA
>
> **Tel:** 01789 400777 **Fax:** 01789 765544
>
> **Website:** http://www.coughtoncourt.co.uk
>
> **Opening hours:** 11.00–17.30 when house is open. Ring for dates.
>
> **Visitors welcome:** yes.
>
> **Catalogue:** none.
>
> **Payment:** cash, cheque, Visa, Mastercard.
>
> **Mail order:** no.
>
> **Availability:** all year round.
>
> **Refund/replacement:** yes.

See map page 394.

Cranesbill Nursery

Good for hardy geraniums and other herbaceous plants which are grown in the garden alongside.

Cranesbill Nursery, White Cottage, Earls Common Road, Stock Green, Worcestershire B96 6SZ

Tel: 01386 792414

Opening hours: 10.00–17.00 Monday, Tuesday and Friday from mid-April to end July and in September. Ring for weekend opening hours.

Visitors welcome: yes.

Catalogue: send 4 first class stamps.

Payment: cheque.

Mail order: yes.

Post and packing: £8.45.

Delivery: usually 2 weeks.

Availability: mail order from end August to end November. Less common varieties are in limited supply.

Refund/replacement: yes, in case of genuine complaint.

Special services: group visits to the garden by arrangement.

See map page 394.

Dunge Valley Gardens

The nursery is attached to a beautiful garden in the Pennines which has been compared to a mini Bodnant. As a result it sells many rhododendrons, including new yellow varieties, olearias, old fashioned roses, tree paeonies as well as unusual bamboos, the handkerchief and Chilean fire trees and shiny-barked Prunus serrula.

Dunge Valley Hardy Plant Nursery, Windgather Rocks, Kettleshulme, nr Whaley Bridge, High Peak, SK23 7RF

Tel/fax: 01663 733787

Opening hours: 10.30–18.00 daily except Mondays (open on bank holiday Mondays) from April to August.

Visitors welcome: yes.

Catalogue: send A4 sae.

Payment: cash or cheque.

Mail order: no.

Availability: seasonal.

Refund/replacement: by arrangement.

See map page 395.

Edenbridge House The nursery is attached to the garden, where the plants on offer can be seen in their prime. As well as the expected alpines, hardy perennials and a few shrubs, there is a good selection of half-hardy perennials such as pelargoniums, canna lilies, fuchsias, dahlias and argyranthemums.

Edenbridge House, Crockham Hill Road, nr Marlpit Hill, Edenbridge, Kent TN8 6SJ

Tel: 01732 862122 **Fax:** 01732 867395

Opening hours: 14.00–17.00 Tuesday and Thursday from April to October and on NGS open days, or by appointment.

Visitors welcome: yes.

Catalogue: none.

Payment: cash or cheque.

Mail order: no.

Availability: from April to October.

Refund/replacement: yes.

See map page 391.

Geddington Gardens Along with bulbs, climbers, herbs, grasses and alpines, the nursery likes cottage garden plants, especially geraniums, penstemons and campanulas. The garden, with dry areas, a white walk and sunken garden, is open under the NGS scheme.

Geddington Gardens, The Spinney, Grafton Road, Geddington, Northamptonshire NN14 1AJ

Tel: 01536 461020

Opening hours: 10.00–17.00 Wednesday to Sunday.

Visitors welcome: yes.

Catalogue: yet to be finalised.

Payment: cash or cheque.

Mail order: no.

Availability: seasonal.

Refund/replacement: replacement.

Special services: Garden club discounts. Group evening visits with discount. 1-acre display garden.

See map page 393.

Sue Hartfree Specialises in unusual plants, hardy and half-hardy perennials, shrubs and a list of over 40 varieties of salvia. Her garden is open to the public and she also lectures on horticulture.

> **Sue Hartfree**, 25 Crouch Hill Court, Lower Halstow, nr Sittingbourne, Kent ME9 7EJ
>
> **Tel:** 01795 842426
>
> **Opening hours:** by appointment.
>
> **Visitors welcome:** yes, at any time by appointment.
>
> **Catalogue:** £1.
>
> **Payment:** cash or cheque.
>
> **Mail order:** yes. Minimum order £15 plus p&p.
>
> **Post and packing:** £10.50.
>
> **Delivery:** within 28 days.
>
> **Availability:** supplies can be limited and some plants are available only at certain times of year. Mail order service from October to March only.
>
> **Refund/replacement:** yes, if justified.
>
> **Special services:** garden design, lectures throughout the south east.

See map page 392.

Hellyer's Garden Plants The nursery is run by Penelope Hellyer, daughter of the late great garden writer, Arthur Hellyer, from his home at Orchards. As Mr. Hellyer got older, the garden fell into neglect from which his daughter and her husband recently rescued it. "We have both worked tremendously hard to clear, reclaim, restore, redesign and replant the garden." In 1992 she started the nursery for which she grows all the plants. "It covers a wide range of plants, particularly hardy perennials, my speciality and passion being hardy geraniums." The selection of these is excellent.

> **Hellyer's Garden Plants**, Orchards, off Wallage Lane, Rowfant, nr Crawley, West Sussex RH10 4NJ
>
> **Tel:** 01342 718280
>
> **Opening hours:** 10.00–17.00 Wednesday to Saturday from March to October.
>
> **Visitors welcome:** yes. Garden open from 12.00 to 16.00 for NGS, Wednesday to Saturday from March to October.
>
> **Catalogue:** send 1 first class stamp plus A5 sae.
>
> **Payment:** cash or cheque.
>
> **Mail order:** yes (UK mainland only).

Post and packing: included.

Delivery: by return if available.

Availability: small quantities available throughout the growing season. Waiting list and propagation service.

Refund/replacement: replacement.

Special services: garden open from 12.00–16.00 between March and October.

See map page 391.

Kinlochlaich Gardens
Helpfully sited on the Gulf Stream in the sheltered banks of a loch, the garden centre has one of the largest selection of plants in Scotland. This is in an old walled garden of the house, whose gardens regularly win awards. When I asked them to describe what they sold, they replied simply "Plants." As you might expect in that area, these tend towards the acid-loving.

Kinlochlaich Gardens, Appin, Argyll, PA38 4BD

Tel: 01631 730342 **Fax:** 01631 730482

E-mail: 101602.3101@compuserve.com

Website: http://www.robbins-associates.co.uk/kinlochlaich

Opening hours: 9.30–17.30 Monday to Saturday, 10.30–17.30 Sunday from April to mid-October. 9.30–17.00 Monday to Saturday only from mid-October to March.

Visitors welcome: yes.

Catalogue: none.

Payment: cash, cheque, Visa, Access, Eurocard.

Mail order: no.

Refund/replacement: depends on circumstances.

Special services: design, consultancy, planting.

See map page 398.

Lea Gardens
The gardens are sited in the remains of a medieval millstone quarry and cover about four acres of wooded and rocky hillside. The nursery specialises in rare rhododendrons, azaleas and alpines as well as encouraging wildlife.

Lea Gardens, Lea, nr Matlock, Derbyshire DE4 5GH

Tel: 01629 534380 **Fax:** 01629 534260

Opening hours: 10.00–17.00 daily from 20 March to 30 June. By appointment at other times.

Visitors welcome: yes.
Catalogue: 30p plus sae.
Payment: cash or cheque.
Mail order: yes. Minimum order £15.
Post and packing: at cost.
Delivery: 1 week.
Availability: all year round.
Refund/replacement: by arrangement.

See map page 396.

The Lodge Nursery

The nursery has only been going since 1995 but has developed hugely and now stocks well over 1,000 varieties, especially unusual perennials, grasses and hostas. The selection of salvias is excellent as are the crocosmias and geraniums.

The Lodge Nursery, Cottage Lane, Westfield, nr Hastings, East Sussex TN35 4RP

Tel: 01424 870186

Opening hours: 10.30–17.00 from Wednesday to Sunday from mid-March to end October and bank holidays.

Visitors welcome: yes.

Catalogue: 75p or 4 first class stamps.

Payment: cheque.

Mail order: yes.

Post and packing: £4 for 1-5 plants, £8 for 6–10, by quotation thereafter.

Delivery: 2-3 weeks for orders received from September to March.

Availability: most plants available all year round.

Refund/replacement: yes.

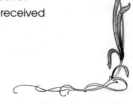

See map page 391.

Mr and Mrs D Jolley, Maycotts

Like many gardeners, the Jolleys became frustrated at not being able to get exactly the plants they wanted. "We have started our own small nursery specialising in unusual perennials …I'm propagating what I want here."

Mr and Mrs D Jolley, Maycotts, Matfield, nr Tonbridge, Kent
TN12 7JU
Tel: 01892 722203 **Fax:** 01892 723222
E-mail: debbie.jolley@dial.pipex.com
Opening hours: by appointment.
Visitors welcome: yes.
Catalogue: none at present.
Payment: cheque, Visa.
Mail order: yes.
Post and packing: by quotation.
Delivery: by arrangement.
Availability: supplies can be limited and some plants are available only at certain times of year.
Refund/replacement: by arrangement.

See map page 391.

Mrs Mitchell's Kitchen and Garden
Strangely, the plants here are not vegetables but cottage garden perennials such as geraniums, hellebores, pulmonarias, oriental poppies, salvias and hostas. Almost everything is grown in the garden (and there's also a range of chutneys and pickles made from the fruits.)

Mrs Mitchell's Kitchen and Garden, 2 Warren Farm Cottages,
West Tytherley, Hampshire SP5 1LU
Tel: 01980 863101
Opening hours: 10.00–18.00 every Friday and third Sunday and Monday of each month from May to October. At other times by appointment.
Visitors welcome: yes.
Catalogue: send 4 first class stamps for plant list.
Payment: cash or cheque.
Mail order: no.
Availability: most plants are seasonal.
Refund/replacement: yes.
Special services: almost all plants are propagated from the garden and can be seen in situ.

See map page 390.

Old Hall Plants Herb specialists who grow over 600 different species from around the world. Such as ashwagandha (Withania somnifera), buffalo currant (Ribes odorate) and the Cuban oregano. More normally, there's a big list of mint, lavender, sage and thyme and all the old favourites you might expect. You can see the rare herbs growing in their garden.

> **Old Hall Plants**, 1 The Old Hall, Barsham, nr Beccles, Suffolk NR34 8HB
> **Tel:** 01502 717475
> **Opening hours:** by appointment.
> **Visitors welcome:** yes.
> **Catalogue:** send 4 first class stamps.
> **Payment:** cash or cheque.
> **Mail order:** rare plants only.
> **Post and packing:** at cost, by first class post or express.
> **Delivery:** 1-2 weeks.
> **Availability:** small quantities only.
> **Refund/replacement:** yes.

See map page 393.

Overcourt Garden Nursery This is a new nursery growing by the minute and specialising in herbaceous perennials. The plants are grown in their own compost mix without heat or forcing. The owners are "always prepared to give visitors time to discuss their garden, help find the right plant for the right place and encourage them to see the garden for plant associations."

> **Overcourt Garden Nursery**, Overcourt, Sutton St Nicholas, Herefordshire HR1 3AY
> **Tel:** 01432 880845
> **E-mail:** harpover@wbsnet.co.uk
> **Opening hours:** 10.00–17.00 Wednesday to Saturday from 1 March to 31 October.
> **Visitors welcome:** yes.
> **Catalogue:** send 3 first class stamps.
> **Payment:** cash or cheque.
> **Mail order:** no.
> **Delivery:** can be arranged locally.
> **Availability:** although every effort is made to maintain stock throughout the year some popular plants can sell out.

Refund/replacement: yes.

Special services: garden open under NGS. Groups welcome by appointment.

See map page 394.

Pine Lodge Garden Nursery
This nursery holds the national collection of grevilleas and the other plants on sale are mostly grown from seed collected on plant expeditions which travel the world.

Pine Lodge Garden Nursery, Cuddra, St Austell, Cornwall PL25 3RQ

Tel/fax: 01726 73500

E-mail: pine@thin-end.co.uk

Website: http://www.thin-end.co.uk/pinehome.html

Opening hours: 14.00–17.00 Wednesday to Sunday from April to September plus bank holidays.

Visitors welcome: yes, during opening hours.

Catalogue: send 4 first class stamps.

Payment: cash or cheque.

Mail order: no.

Availability: April to September.

Refund/replacement: yes.

See map page 388.

Trevi Garden The garden opens under the NGS and is only open under that scheme (or by appointment.) It is gradually building up a good stock of epimediums plus pulmonarias, penstemons, hardy geraniums and a few shrubs such as azalea and clematis.

> **Trevi Garden,** Hartpury, Over Old Road, nr Gloucester Gloucestershire GL19 3BJ
> **Tel:** 01452 700370
> **Opening hours:** as shown in NGS yellow book.
> **Visitors welcome:** only by prior appointment.
> **Catalogue:** none.
> **Payment:** cash or cheque.
> **Mail order:** no.
> **Availability:** supplies can be limited.
> **Refund/replacement:** by arrangement.

See map page 394.

Westcountry Lupins You need an appointment to visit this lupin specialist, which has been on *Gardeners' World*, but they do offer a mail order service. As with many specialist nurseries, they also offer advice. Lupins are having a comeback and it's well worth while looking at the exciting range available.

> **Westcountry Lupins,** Ford Hill Forge, Hartland, Devon EX39 6EE
> **Tel/fax:** 01237 441208
> **E-mail:** sarahconibear@westcountrylupins.freeserve.co.uk
> **Opening hours:** not normally open to the public.
> **Visitors welcome:** by prior appointment for collections only.
> **Catalogue:** £1 or send 3 first class stamps.
> **Payment:** cheque, major credit cards.
> **Mail order:** yes.
> **Post and packing:** see catalogue.
> **Delivery:** see catalogue.
> **Availability:** orders taken from September for spring delivery.
> **Refund/replacement:** yes, if notified immediately.

See map page 388.

Specialist Nurseries

Acacias

Acers

Agapanthus

Alpines

Callistemons

Camellias

Campanulas

Celmisias

Cistus

Clematis

Conifers

Conservatory plants

Erodiums

Eryngiums

Eucalyptus

Eucryphias

Euphorbias

Exotic and tender plants

Grasses

Grevilleas

Heathers

Hebes

Hedging plants

Hellebores

Hemerocallis

Herbs

Hollies

Honeysuckles

Hostas

Hydrangeas

Iris

Nepetas

Orchids

Oriental poppies

Paeonies

Pelargoniums

Penstemons

Phlomis

Roses

MAPS

The following maps show the approximate location of the nurseries listed in the guide.

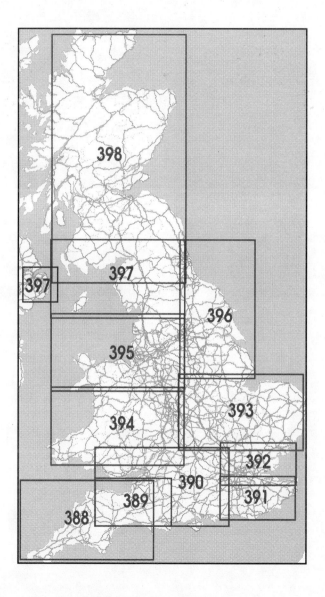

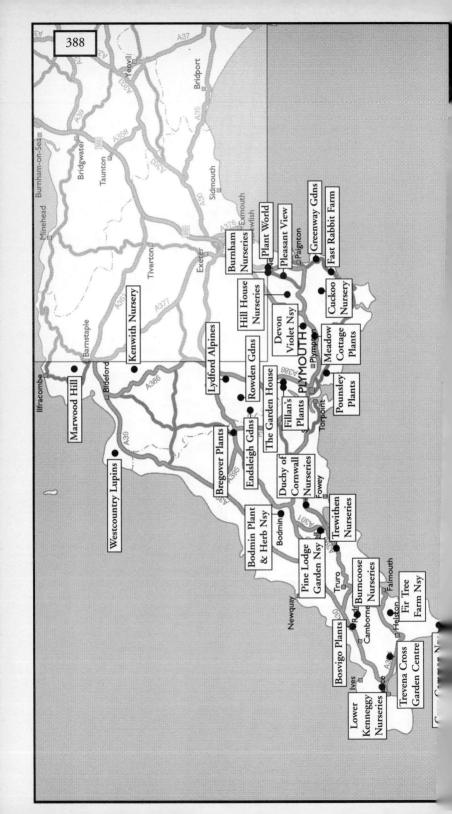

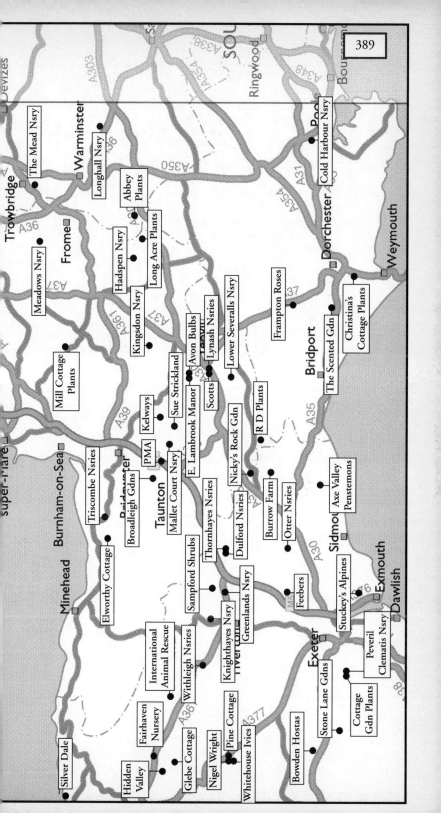

389

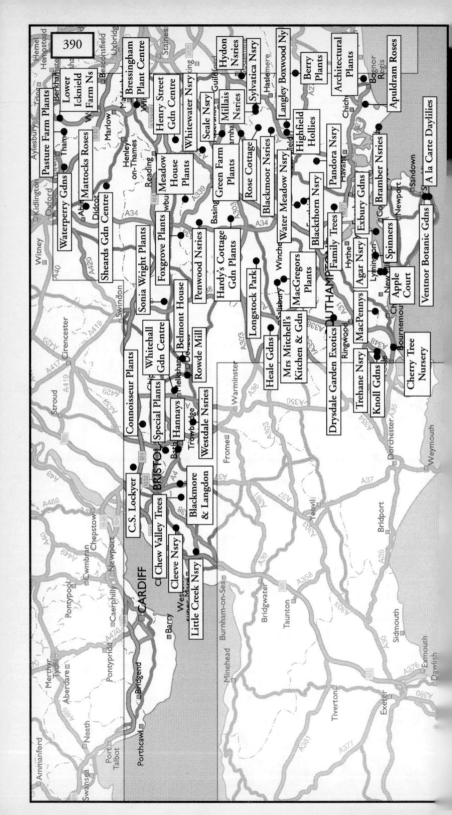

390

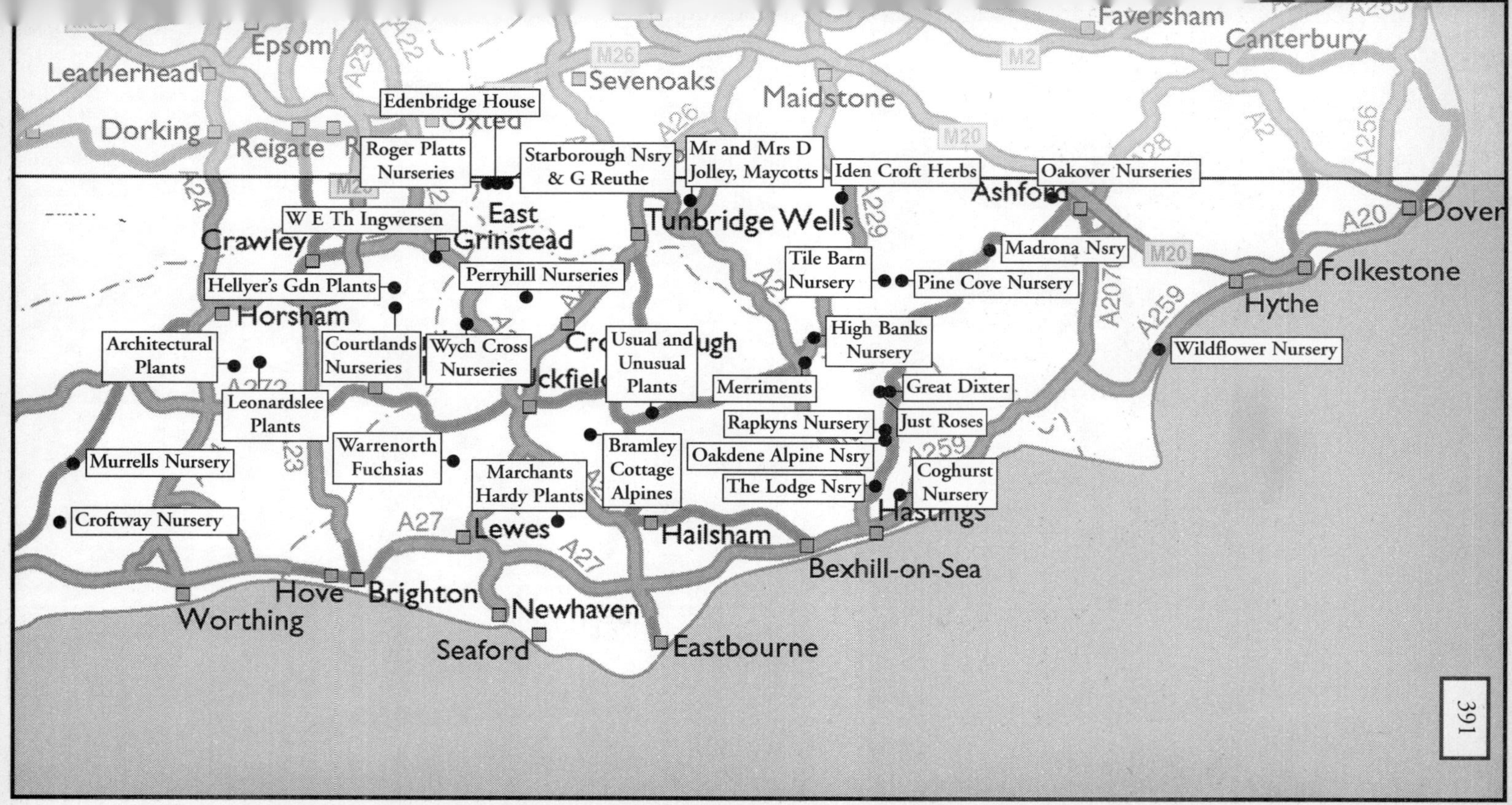

Faversham
Canterbury
Epsom
Leatherhead
Sevenoaks
Maidstone
Dorking
Reigate
Edenbridge House
Oxted
Roger Platts Nurseries
Starborough Nsry & G Reuthe
Mr and Mrs D Jolley, Maycotts
Iden Croft Herbs
Oakover Nurseries
Ashford
Dover
W E Th Ingwersen
East Grinstead
Tunbridge Wells
Crawley
Madrona Nsry
Folkestone
Hythe
Tile Barn Nursery
Pine Cove Nursery
Hellyer's Gdn Plants
Perryhill Nurseries
Horsham
Wildflower Nursery
High Banks Nursery
Architectural Plants
Courtlands Nurseries
Wych Cross Nurseries
Usual and Unusual Plants
Merriments
Great Dixter
Leonardslee Plants
Rapkyns Nursery
Just Roses
Warrenorth Fuchsias
Bramley Cottage Alpines
Oakdene Alpine Nsry
Murrells Nursery
Marchants Hardy Plants
The Lodge Nsry
Coghurst Nursery
Hastings
Croftway Nursery
Lewes
Hailsham
Bexhill-on-Sea
Hove
Brighton
Worthing
Newhaven
Seaford
Eastbourne
M26
M2
M20
M23
A22
A23
A24
A26
A2
A256
A28
A229
A21
A20
A2070
A259
A272
A27

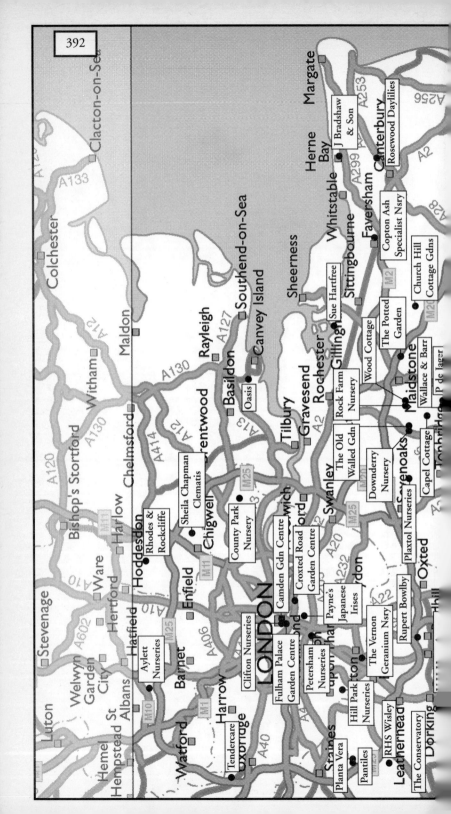

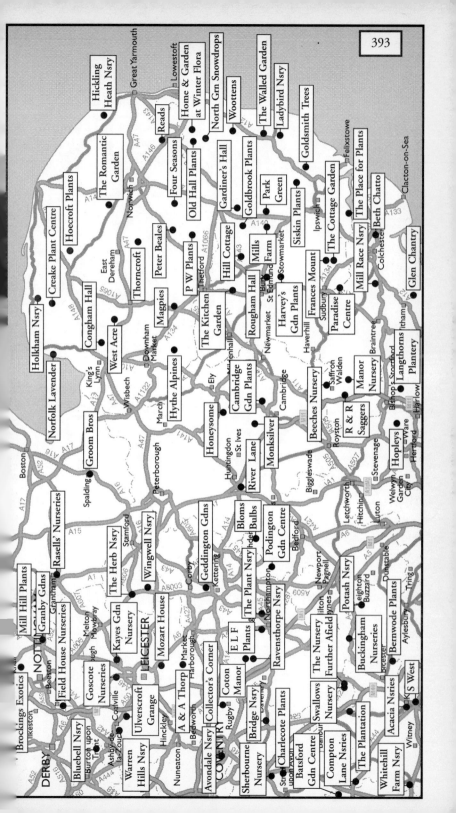

393

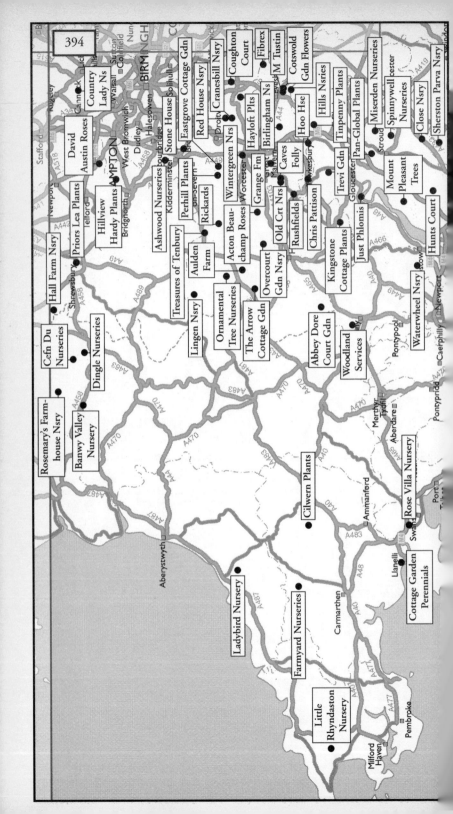

394

A59 Ilkley Yeadon Bingley Shipley
Keighley Shipley
A650 A6038
A59 Colne Nelson BRADFORD
Holden Clough Nsry
Clitheroe Burnley Accrington Ravenstall
Dove Cottage Plants
Huddersfield
Leeds A62 A616 A1(M)
Glossop
Dunge Valley Gdns Buxton A623 A515
Barker's Gdn Centre
Blackburn Rochdale Middleton Oldham
Bury Bolton Salford MANCHESTER Stockport Cheadle
The Firs Nsry A537 A523
Tissington Nursery
Uttoxeter A50 A52
Preston A6 Chorley Standish Wigan
Leyland
Stoney Leach Nsry
Skelmersdale Kirkby
Wilm Fryer's Roses
Altrincham Knutsford
Congleton Biddulph Kidsgrove Leek
STOKE-ON-TRENT
Stone Stafford A51
Blac Catforth Gdns
Fleetwood
The Hawthornes Nsry
Southport Formby
Lady Green Nsry
Crosby Bootle Wallasey Birkenhead LIVERPOOL
Caddick's Clematis Nsry
Bellhouse Nsry Runcorn
Arley Hall Northwich
Stonyford Cottage Nsry
Crewe Nantwich Newcastle-under-Lyme
Sandstones Cottage Garden Plants
A49 A41 A53
Widnes Ellesmere
Lodge Lane Nsry
F Morrey
Okells Nurseries
Wrexham
Eastwick Plant Centre
Oswestry A5 A495
Heysham Lancaster
Prestatyn Rhyl
Ness Gardens Flint
Aled Plants
Colwyn Bay Conwy Abergele
Dibley's Nurseries
Eucalyptus Nurseries
Llandudno
Aberconwy Nsry
Bodnant Garden
Llwyn Nursery
A470 A494 A5
Holyhead
Crûg Farm
A487 A5

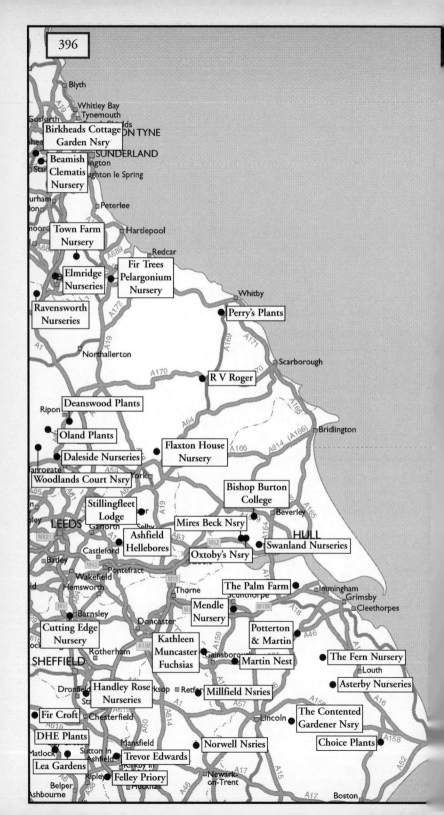

Blyth

Whitley Bay
Tynemouth

Gosforth

ON TYNE

Birkheads Cottage
Garden Nsry

SUNDERLAND

Beamish
Clematis
Nursery

ington

ughton le Spring

Peterlee

Hartlepool

Town Farm
Nursery

Redcar

Elmridge
Nurseries

Fir Trees
Pelargonium
Nursery

Whitby

Ravensworth
Nurseries

Perry's Plants

Northallerton

Scarborough

R V Roger

Deanswood Plants

Ripon

Bridlington

Oland Plants

Flaxton House
Nursery

Daleside Nurseries

York

Woodlands Court Nsry

Stillingfleet
Lodge

Bishop Burton
College

Beverley

LEEDS

Garforth

Mires Beck Nsry

HULL

Selby

Ashfield
Hellebores

Swanland Nurseries

Castleford

Oxtoby's Nsry

Batley

Pontefract

Wakefield
Hemsworth

The Palm Farm

Immingham
Grimsby

Thorne

Scunthorpe

Cleethorpes

Barnsley

Mendle
Nursery

Doncaster

Cutting Edge
Nursery

Potterton
& Martin

Kathleen
Muncaster
Fuchsias

Gainsborough

SHEFFIELD

Rotherham

Martin Nest

The Fern Nursery

Dronfield

Handley Rose
Nurseries

ksop

Retf

Millfield Nsries

Louth

Asterby Nurseries

Fir Croft

Chesterfield

A1

Lincoln

The Contented
Gardener Nsry

DHE Plants

Mansfield

Norwell Nsries

Choice Plants

Matlock

Sutton in
Ashfield

Trevor Edwards

Lea Gardens

Belper

Ripley

Kirkby in

Felley Priory

Hucknall

Newark-
on-Trent

Ashbourne

Boston

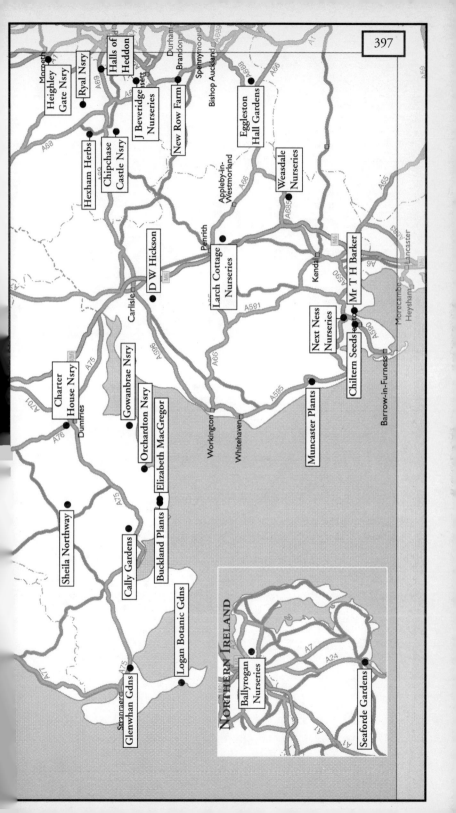

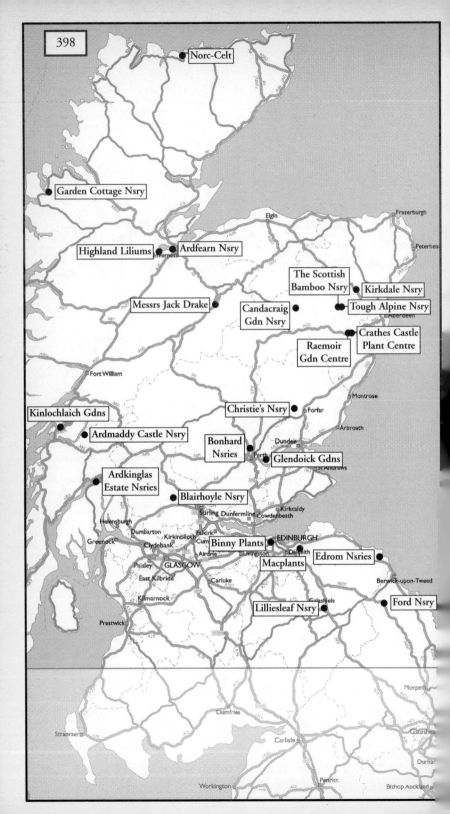

398

Norc-Celt

Garden Cottage Nsry

Fraserburgh

Elgin

Peterhead

Highland Liliums   Ardfearn Nsry
Inverness

The Scottish
Bamboo Nsry   Kirkdale Nsry

Messrs Jack Drake   Candacraig
Gdn Nsry   Tough Alpine Nsry

Aberdeen

Crathes Castle
Plant Centre

Raemoir
Gdn Centre

Fort William

Montrose

Kinlochlaich Gdns   Christie's Nsry   Forfar

Arbroath

Ardmaddy Castle Nsry

Bonhard
Nsries   Dundee

Perth   Glendoick Gdns

St Andrews

Ardkinglas
Estate Nsries   Blairhoyle Nsry

Kirkcaldy

Stirling Dunfermline Cowdenbeath

Helensburgh

Dumbarton   Kirkintilloch   Falkirk
Cum   Binny Plants   EDINBURGH
Clydebank   Airdrie   Livingston   Dalkeith   Edrom Nsries

Greenock

Paisley   GLASGOW   Macplants

East Kilbride   Carluke   Berwick-upon-Tweed

Kilmarnock   Galashiels   Ford Nsry

Prestwick   Lilliesleaf Nsry

Morpeth

Dumfries

Gateshea

Stranraer   Carlisle   Durhar

Workington   Penrith   Bishop Auckland

INDEX

Readers' Report Form

Future editions of this book will be improved if you write with your comments, letting us know (i) if any nurseries are not included which you think should be and (ii) if you have any comments on a nursery listed in the guide. Please print your name clearly.

Send your comments to:

**Columbine Press Ltd
42 Canonbury Square
London N1 2AW**
E-mail:dovebooks@aol.com

Gardeners' *Favourite* Nurseries

To the author
From my own experience the following nursery should/should not be included:

NURSERY'S NAME: ....

Address: ....

....

....Tel:...................................

Comments:...

....

....

YOUR NAME: ....

Address: ....

....

....

Readers' Report Form

Future editions of this book will be improved if you write with your comments, letting us know (i) if any nurseries are not included which you think should be and (ii) if you have any comments on a nursery listed in the guide. Please print your name clearly.

Send your comments to:

Columbine Press Ltd
42 Canonbury Square
London N1 2AW
E-mail:dovebooks@aol.com

Gardeners' *Favourite* Nurseries

To the author
From my own experience the following nursery should/should not be included:

NURSERY'S NAME: ....

Address: ....

....

....Tel:......................

Comments:...

....

....

YOUR NAME: ....

Address: ....

....

....

Readers' Report Form

Future editions of this book will be improved if you write with your comments, letting us know (i) if any nurseries are not included which you think should be and (ii) if you have any comments on a nursery listed in the guide. Please print your name clearly.

Send your comments to:

**Columbine Press Ltd
42 Canonbury Square
London N1 2AW**
E-mail:dovebooks@aol.com

Gardeners' *Favourite* Nurseries

To the author
From my own experience the following nursery should/should not be included:

NURSERY'S NAME: ....

Address: ....

....

....Tel:...........................

Comments:...

....

....

YOUR NAME: ....

Address: ....

....

....

Readers' Report Form

Future editions of this book will be improved if you write with your comments, letting us know (i) if any nurseries are not included which you think should be and (ii) if you have any comments on a nursery listed in the guide. Please print your name clearly.

Send your comments to:

Columbine Press Ltd
42 Canonbury Square
London N1 2AW
E-mail:dovebooks@aol.com

Gardeners' *Favourite* Nurseries

To the author
From my own experience the following nursery should/should not be included:

NURSERY'S NAME: ....

Address: ....

....

....Tel:.................................

Comments:..

....

....

YOUR NAME: ....

Address: ....

....

....